KU-329-223

Computer Integrated Production Systems and Organizations

The Human-Centred Approach

NATO ASI Series

Advanced Science Institutes Series

A series presenting the results of activities sponsored by the NATO Science Committee, which aims at the dissemination of advanced scientific and technological knowledge, with a view to strengthening links between scientific communities.

The Series is published by an international board of publishers in conjunction with the NATO Scientific Affairs Division

A Life Sciences B Physics	Plenum Publishing Corporation London and New York
C Mathematical and Physical Sciences D Behavioural and Social Sciences E Applied Sciences	Kluwer Academic Publishers Dordrecht, Boston and London
F Computer and Systems Sciences G Ecological Sciences H Cell Biology I Global Environmental Change	Springer-Verlag Berlin Heidelberg New York London Paris Tokyo Hong Kong Barcelona Budapest

NATO-PCO DATABASE

The electronic index to the NATO ASI Series provides full bibliographical references (with keywords and/or abstracts) to more than 30000 contributions from international scientists published in all sections of the NATO ASI Series. Access to the NATO-PCO DATABASE compiled by the NATO Publication Coordination Office is possible in two ways:

- via online FILE 128 (NATO-PCO DATABASE) hosted by ESRIN, Via Galileo Galilei, I-00044 Frascati, Italy.

- via CD-ROM "NATO Science & Technology Disk" with user-friendly retrieval software in English, French and German (© WTV GmbH and DATAWARE Technologies Inc. 1992).

The CD-ROM can be ordered through any member of the Board of Publishers or through NATO-PCO, Overijse, Belgium.

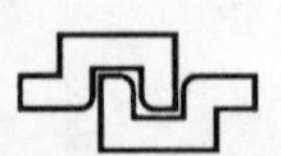

Series F: Computer and Systems Sciences, Vol. 134

Computer Integrated Production Systems and Organizations

The Human-Centred Approach

Edited by

Felix Schmid

Department of Manufacturing and Engineering Systems
Brunel University, Uxbridge, Middlesex UB8 3PH, UK

Stephen Evans

The CIM Institute, Cranfield University
Cranfield, Bedfordshire MK43 0AL, UK

Andrew W. S. Ainger

Human-Centred Systems Ltd
Hemel Hempstead, Hertfordshire HP2 4SE, UK

Robert J. Grieve

Department of Manufacturing and Engineering Systems
Brunel University, Uxbridge, Middlesex UB8 3PH, UK

Springer-Verlag
Berlin Heidelberg New York London Paris Tokyo
Hong Kong Barcelona Budapest
Published in cooperation with NATO Scientific Affairs Division

Proceedings of the NATO Advanced Study Institute on People and Computers – Applying an Anthropocentric Approach to Integrated Production Systems and Organisations, held at Loughborough University, UK, July 5–17, 1993

CR Subject Classification (1991): J.6, J.2, K.6

ISBN 3-540-58275-4 Springer-Verlag Berlin Heidelberg New York
ISBN 0-387-58275-4 Springer-Verlag New York Berlin Heidelberg

CIP data applied for

Printed in Germany

Typesetting: Camera ready by editors
SPIN 10130768 45/3140 - 5 4 3 2 1 0 - Printed on acid-free paper

Preface

The Background to the Institute

The NATO Advanced Study Institute (ASI) *'People and Computers — Applying an Anthropocentric Approach to Integrated Production Systems and Organisations'* came about after the distribution of a NATO fact sheet to Brunel University, which described the funding of ASIs. The 'embryonic' director of the ASI brought this opportunity to the attention of the group of people, (some at Brunel and some from outside), who were together responsible for the teaching and management of the course in Computer Integrated Manufacturing (CIM) in Brunel's Department of Manufacturing and Engineering Systems. This course had been conceived in 1986 and was envisaged as a vehicle for teaching manufacturing engineering students the technology of information integration through project work. While the original idea of the course had also included the organisational aspects of CIM, the human factors questions were not considered.

This shortcoming was recognised and the trial run of the course in 1988 contained some lectures on 'people' issues. The course team were therefore well prepared and keen to explore the People, Organisation and Technology (POT) aspects of computer integration, as applied to industrial production. A context was proposed which would allow the inclusion of people from many different backgrounds and which would open up time and space for reflection. The proposal to organise a NATO ASI was therefore welcomed by all concerned. The team, including members of faculty from Brunel University, Universität Stuttgart and the Dansk Tekniske Hojskole (Technical University of Copenhagen), drew up an idea for an ASI to be held in September 1992. The director started the task of seeking additional sponsorship for the event, so as to be able to fund participants from Eastern Europe. Fortunately BP Engineering had just moved to Uxbridge, the home town of Brunel University, and generously agreed to contribute a very substantial sum to the organisation of the event. British Gas North Thames, under the stewardship of Mr Jack Fallow and Ms Jill Grant, made a contribution in kind by seconding Mrs Irene Loader for one day per week to the University. It must be recorded here that without the help and encouragement of BP Engineering, represented by Mr Geoff Parker, and British Gas North Thames, the ASI would most probably not have happened.

As a result of the worldwide recession deepening in 1991 no further sponsors could be encouraged to support the event and this, together with less than ideal marketing, meant that the ASI had to be postponed to 1993. However, this was a blessing in disguise, since it allowed a complete rethink of the Institute. This was relaunched in September 1992, with a new management team:

Andrew Ainger:	Human Centred Systems Ltd
Robert Bear:	Brunel University
Steve Evans:	Cranfield Institute of Technology
Robert J Grieve:	Brunel University
Chris Hinde:	Loughborough University of Technology
Kate Laskowitz:	Purdue University
Anthony J Medland:	Brunel University
Geoff Parker:	BP Engineering
Carys Siemieniuch:	Loughborough University of Technology

The Design of the ASI

The core team, A. Ainger, S. Evans, K. Laskowitz, C. Hinde, C. Siemieniuch, R. Bear, G. Parker and F. Schmid, held several meetings which resulted in the new structure of the Institute, reflected in the present proceedings. Perhaps the key decision was the move to include a substantial element of group work into the Institute, a calculated risk. This move required a division of the event into three parts: a lecture block of three days' duration, a block of four days of managed group work and a period of three days devoted to testing the results of the preceding seven days. The SCANCO activity described in these pages took place in between the lecture block and the managed group work. It served to heighten the participants' awareness of the issues of POT and, perhaps even more so, to turn into strong teams groups of people, who had met for the first time on the first day of the Institute.

Interspersed with the managed and independent team activities were topical lectures from outside speakers. Also included in the programme was a half day of industrial visits, to establish a context for the Institute, as well as cultural and social activities which helped forge links among the participants that will continue to flourish.

The inclusion of team and group work in the ASI, instead of seminars and tutorials, brought benefits and drawbacks. In comparison with a 'standard' ASI, the participants had to take upon themselves a great deal of work and, resulting from this, real stress. They had to give up some of the precious free evenings to summarise the day's work and to prepare the next day's sessions. Some participants even volunteered to turn the group work into contributions for the Proceedings! However, the format also allowed much better opportunities for the exploration of particular issues and for self-motivated learning. Many participants from outside the Anglo-Saxon domain also experienced new forms of collaborative working, some for the first time.

Structure of the Proceedings

The ASI was in its essence a cross-disciplinary event covering a wide range of topics. A rigid classification of the written record has therefore proved impossible. All the same, the editors have attempted to organise the papers and other contributions in four sections, preceded by a keynote paper on social innovation by Prof. Karamjit Gill, introducing the concepts of human purpose, social and cultural richness and diversity. The author presents a thorough overview of the whole field of Human Centred System design and its history. The papers of the first section place Human Centred Systems (HCS) work in its industrial and economic contexts while the authors of the contributions in the second section deal with information and system requirements issues. Section three contains some of the more technical and practical results of the Institute whereas the fourth section is devoted to reporting the results of the team-work based second and third phases of the Institute.

The second phase of the Institute was strongly structured and dealt with key aspects of the system design process, namely, System Specification, Design and Build, Testing and Evaluation. Each aspect was introduced through a lecture or a set of lectures and then developed through several short group work sessions. The leaders of these blocks present their input and reflect on the outcomes of the group work.

The third phase of the Institute was devoted to group work which was designed to elicit different views of the overall systems design process. The results of this work have been summarised by members of the five working groups and are presented here in an edited form by the manager of the activity, Dr. Steve Evans.

Acknowledgements and Thanks

Thanking people is one of the enjoyable duties of a Director. I should like to use these last few lines to express my gratitude to British Petroleum and British Gas for their substantial and generous contributions. I would like to acknowledge in particular the services of Geoff Parker, Jill Grant and Irene Loader. Thanks are due to Robert Bear who helped organise the event on a negligible stipend and to Steve Evans, the member of the organising committee who cheerfully took on the management (and stress) related to the team work activities. I thank June Phillips for keeping me organised, Chris Ellis and Sibylle Bosshard for encouraging me to maintain an interest in sport, despite all the pressures, and Tania Hancke of ABB for many stimulating discussions on Human Factors and related issues. Prof Jim Alty of Loughborough University of Technology (LUT) provided a most entertaining and instructive opening address on multimedia issues to which the audience was most receptive. LUT's help, especially that of the team in the Department of Computer Studies in providing the venue and the logistics for the Institute must also be acknowledged here.

The present proceedings are therefore dedicated to NATO and all the people and organisations who made possible the Institute, to all those who helped in its running and all those who attended. You were all brilliant and wonderful!

Uxbridge, December 1993

Felix Schmid

Table of Contents

Keynote Paper

Business and Enterprise Context of Human Centred Systems

Information, Communication, Interfacing and their Requirements

Technology and its Usability

The Systems Development Process and Results from the Group Work Sessions

1. Human-Centred Shaping of Social Innovation

Karamjit S. Gill

SEAKE Centre, LIS Department, University of Brighton, Falmer, Brighton BN1 9PH, UK

Abstract. A major challenge of human centred shaping of technology and social innovation is how to design, use and diffuse science and technology, which supports social and economic development of peoples and regions, while sustaining diversity in an evolving interdependent world. The dominant techno-centric focus of innovation is rooted in the causal view of science, the notion of 'productive functionality' and the 'one best solution'. It continues to exclude human purpose from its concerns and considerations. A human centred vision of innovation provides an alternative approach to development which builds upon the social and cultural richness of people and societies. This vision of social innovation promotes notions of co-development, co-existence and valorization of diversity.

Keywords. Human Centred Systems, Social Innovation, Development, Technology, Sustainability, Human Skill, Knowledge Transfer, Learning Network

1.1 Human Centred Shaping of Technology

A major challenge of human centred shaping of technology is how to design, use and diffuse science and technology, which supports social and economic development of peoples and regions while sustaining diversity in an evolving interdependent world. Another challenge is how to transfer and exchange knowledge and expertise between and across nations, regions and cultures to sustain and develop social and economic life. Advanced technology has failed to make any substantial contribution to the social and economic prosperity of people in the developing regions of Europe or developing countries. This failure is mainly due to the belief that societal development can be achieved through technological and bureaucratic innovations only. Technological innovations are based on the causal view of science, and continue to exclude human purpose from their concerns and considerations. Bureaucratic innovations are based on the concept of 'productive functionality' and excludes those who do not fit neatly into the managerial definition of 'production'. These types of innovations are essentially located in the mechanistic world view, which promotes techno-centric notions such as the 'one best way', 'one culture', and 'sameness of scientific ideas'

This mechanistic world view also supports the principles of separation and exclusion, for example the social from the economic, tacit from the objective, mind from body, living from work, and individual from society. The notion of 'information society' has also played a central role in separating the world into two camps, 'information poor' and 'information rich', thus consolidating the mechanistic view of modernity of social innovation. 'Knowledge is power' view of innovation remains the dominant theme of information society. Knowledge is treated as a product that can be produced from human raw material, and as a commodity that can be marketed in the competitive economic world. Social and economic progress, from this 'knowledge = power' perspectives, focuses on the organisation and control of the flow, transfer and exchange of information. This view of knowledge separates knowledge from the social and cultural contexts in which it is constructed, interpreted and maintained through its practical use in context. This impoverished view of the information society rests on the notion of information as a traded commodity, supporting new sectors of activity within a simple market economy. This view defines the citizen in terms of economic relationship of production and consumption of information.

This world view creates dependency of nations on inappropriate technologies which consequently leads to the increasing instability of many societies and social vulnerability of people in the developing world, Eastern Europe, Africa, Asia and South America. The problems of social and economic development can no longer be treated as simply a matter of technological and bureaucratic innovations, they are essentially social and cultural. A human centred vision of innovation provides an alternative approach to development which builds upon the social and cultural richness of people and societies.

1.1.1 Human-Centredness: a new paradigm for social innovation of technology

Human centred shaping of technology is itself a tradition of social innovation within the wider socio-economic context of the industrial culture. This tradition places human need, skill, creativity and potentiality at the centre of the activities of technological systems. It is an emancipatory tradition which is rooted in the diversity of European cultural, scientific, and philosophical traditions. The tradition originated in Britain in the 1970s, it has influenced the development of culturally-oriented traditions in Europe, for example "humanisation of technology" in Germany, and "democracy in participation" in Scandinavia.

During the 1960s and 1970s, sociotechnical ideas became attractive to management, attempting to increase productivity and reduce turnover without any additional costs. The experiments of Volvo Kalmar in the 1970s and of Volvo Uddevalla in the 1980s are well known examples of work satisfaction and health and safety aspects of technical functionality and quality of products.

One of the most valuable principles of the sociotechnical approach is the centrality of participation. The human is perceived as a member of a group, and active and a responsible member doing "a good day's work". An informal communication network is considered just as important as the official one. There is, at least, some scope for end-user collaboration and democratic participation of the workforce. However, the approach has several conceptual limitations. The organisation is treated as two separate systems, technical and social, in equilibrium of some kind. This means that the technical system is, by and large, taken for granted, and the equilibrium is achieved through making the social relations adaptable to existing technical devices, or management dominated decisions. Thus the scope for radical changes in human-organisation relations was rather limited from the very beginning.

The human centred approach widens the socio-technical approach, and places human beings in direct personal communication before machines or technical-mediated communication. The shaping concept of the human centred approach is described as a perspective which intends to cross the borders between technical and social sciences as well as between theoretical and practical knowledge through an action-based dialogue [Corbett et al 1990]. Three main human-centred traditions which provide the central focus for the European research on human-centred systems, are the British tradition of "human-machine symbiosis", the Scandinavia tradition of "collective resource", and the German tradition of "humanisation of technology".

1.1.2 LUCAS PLAN: an Innovation in Socially Useful Technology

The origin of the human centred technological tradition in Britain lies in the LUCAS Plan, an innovation in socially useful technology, of the 1970s. The rapid development of microelectronics in the 1970s gave rise to a wave of rationalisation in the British aerospace industry. Workers at Lucas Aerospace put forward an action plan to use their expertise to develop socially useful products. The idea of human centredness and socially useful products was identified as follows:

- workers have a right to play a dual role, as producers and consumers;
- production should be compatible with social needs, and should be determined by use value rather than exchange value;
- the economy should be a mixture of market-oriented and socially useful.

The Lucas Plan has had a major impact on the British and international debates on alternative, socially compatible production. Highly skilled engineers, technicians and skilled workers, who lost their jobs due to rationalisation, turned their protest into constructive ideas for socially useful products, and "demonstrated in a practical and direct way the creative power of "ordinary people"...the audit of their own skills and abilities, and surveys in different factories and workshops analysing and assessing the production equipment, product ranges and skills, represented an enormous extension of consciousness." [7]

The Lucas Plan provided the basis of a large scale programme launched by the Greater London Council (GLC) to develop a regional technology policy for London towards socially useful and use-value-oriented product design. Under the leadership of Mike Cooley, the London Technology Network was founded. The aim was to put to community use the large scale capacity for innovation represented by the competence, skills, experience and expertise of researchers, workers, professionals and community groups. Human centredness was reflected through the design of technological systems which were aimed at shaping the future of London and meeting the needs, requirements and interests of people of London. The belief behind the London Technology Network was that collaboration between producers, and users would lead to the shaping of socially compatible technology.

Research into human systems at the university level was pioneered by Rosenbrock at UMIST [35]. In the 1970s Rosenbrock became concerned with the increasing automation of CAD systems based on Taylor's "Scientific Management", with its goal of eliminating skill and responsibility in the worker. The rapid change in technology in the 1970s offered scope for experimenting with alternative routes of development to Taylorist approaches. Rosenbrock's concept of alternative technological development rests on two basic ideas. The first of these he calls the "Lushi Hill effect" which basically signifies that there are many ways to reach the peak of Lushi Hill, and one cannot say which is the best, i.e. there is no one best way. The second idea encapsulates the dynamic development of productivity. According to this idea, the strategy of rationalisation and investment based on the further reduction of skilled workers is bound, in the long run, to prove economically inferior to the strategy designed to use the skill and potential of skilled workers.

The term "human-centred" in the UMIST research, concerns autonomy and the use of skill. The basis of the research was a recognition that Taylorism had been (or rather, is) about minimising autonomy and the use of skill on the part of operators, and the central focus of the design activity was in these two areas. However, that left two more: interaction with others and development through learning. Interaction with others and group aspects cannot be designed into a piece of equipment, they are a matter of how that equipment is then installed and used by the purchaser.

The British ideas and initiatives created a great deal of interest in Scandinavia and in collaboration between British, Danish and German research groups on human centred systems design. It was probably also the first European project to bring together three European traditions of human-centredness, British, Scandinavian and German, to develop a framework for future research into human centred systems, as well as to establish a basis for technological developments from the human-centred perspective. The project began in 1986 with the Danish partner concerned with the Computer Aided Design (CAD) work, the British partner concentrating on Computer-Aided Manufacturing (CAM) developments, and the German partners on the Computer Aided planning (CAP) work. The project was based on the premise that Computer Integrated Manufacturing (CIM) will be more efficient, more economical, more robust and more flexible if a person is directly in charge than a comparable unmanned system. The project highlighted some of the conflicts and problems for collaborative research in a new area which does not fit into the traditional research culture or challenges the dominant scientific and technological tradition. For example, Rosenbrock [35]:

- Attitudes embedded in the scientific and technological culture make it hard to acknowledge and accept human purpose, and the skill which represents a purpose accomplished in work. To the engineer and technological worker, a system which relies upon the existence of human skill, and particularly manual skill, will appear defective and incomplete. Only knowledge which is explicit and definable is accepted: knowledge which can be embodied in text-books, transmitted to a new generation, and used as a basis for further advance.
- To achieve a fruitful collaboration between social scientists and technologists, it is necessary for both disciplines to respect each other's point of view. For the technologists, the problem is to include in the decision making process of design a social dimension which is usually ignored. This also means the inclusion of the consideration whether the users will be subordinated to the technical means of the final system or will be able to use it as a tool to achieve their roles as a creative part of the production process. For the social scientists, on the other hand, converse problems arise. Generalities have to be made specific, and this has to be done in the face of very hard constraints. Here Japanese experience may be a valuable guide to show that an organisation which values and obtains and uses the initiative and ability of all those who work in it will be more effective, more flexible and more successful, other things being equal.

1.1.3 Benetton: a cultural innovation of a network organisation

Benetton exemplifies new forms of network models of technological and organisational innovations. They remain rooted in the social and cultural traditions of their regions, while successfully adapting to and learning from innovations emanating from other industrial cultures. Mitter [28] suggests that the most successful application of the principle of JIT on European soil has been in the "third Italy" (the central and north-eastern regions of Italy) in the form of creating network models of production and organisation. These network models, described either as "flexible specialisation" or as "models of productive decentralisation", consist of networks linking small factories (subcontractors) to large companies, whereby the small factories produce parts or whole of products for the big retailing companies. This organisation model is attractive to conservative planners because it strives to achieve labour flexibility, and is attractive to socialist planners because it offers the decentralisation of economic power and opportunities for self employment.

Benetton in Italy can be regarded as the most successful example of this network model of firms. Belussi [3] shows the unique way Benetton has used computer-aided technology to achieve an optimum combination of production and market strategies. A novel part of the Benetton's innovation network lies in achieving mass production through decentralisation of production while retaining central control of the market. In other words, the "geographical spread of the moving assembly line". Information technology is playing a crucial role in integrating the JIT strategy of production with the JIT strategy of distribution, and in the case of Benetton, the information system allows the linking up of a network of wholesalers and retailers with a large constellation of producers.

However, this "third Italy" network model is situated in the Italian regional economic cultures, and is based on the historical traditions of regions like the Veneto. Companies like Benetton are able to draw upon the tacit skills of women and men workers who are involved in the decentralised operations of assembling, ironing and finishing. Non-technological and entrepreneurial aspects linked to design, trademark and advertising have been just as important as computer-aided machines in accounting for the success of Italian clothing companies. The crucial entrepreneurial characteristics of the Italian network model reside in the family-like organisation structure of small Italian firms, providing a framework for distributed working, experience based learning, and the tacit dimension of entrepreneurial skills. Benetton itself is a family firm, and its networking with subcontracting firms can be regarded as part of the extended family structure, with the tacit understanding that all firms pull together for the good of the parent company. Companies like Benetton provide a model of how to use computer technology to not only improve the quality of management, control, coordination and production on the main factory floor, but also to facilitate the decentralisation of skilled work to smaller units in and around Veneto. The network model such as that of Benetton itself creates a paradox. The paradox is that whereas the decentralisation of production erodes the rights and privileges of workers, it also enhances the prospect of self-employment especially for women. Belussi questions the validity of replicating the "third Italy" model elsewhere in Europe and beyond. Decentralisation of production which is also not accompanied by the decentralisation of skill leads to the exploitation of home workers as well as workers of the small subcontracting firms.

She argues that the evolutionary growth of a "small firm network" into a "big firm" leads to the emergence of new organisational "concentrate regimes". The success of network models such as Benetton's lies also in the nature of the industry itself. One of the characteristics specific to the fashion industry is the domination of small firms, due mainly to the volatility of demand, low entry barriers and lack of economies of scale. The Benetton strategy has been aimed specifically at reducing the potential competitive advantage of small firms in expanding its market share. Benetton's dominance over the peripheral network of subcontracting firms thus comes through its technological leadership and its retailing power. The effects of Benetton's organisational revolution, matched with a high propensity to innovate, have deeply modified the pre-existing market structure.

Benetton signifies the essence of entrepreneurial innovation based upon the traditional family and social network cultures which still exist in many parts of

Europe and the developing world. The historical development of Benetton provides an insight into how informal social and cultural networks can be used to build and sustain new forms of production structures and working cultures. It is significant to note that in spite of the technological innovations and global competition, Benetton remains a family firm, consisting of one sister, Giuliana, and three brothers, Luciano, Gilberto and Carlo Benetton. The division of labour amongst the family remains clear-cut: Luciano deals with marketing, Giuliana with the design function, Gilberto with administration and finance and Carlo is in charge of production. The origin of Benetton's organisational structure lies with the ancient local putting-out system, which was never fully superseded by the factory mode of production. Benetton draws its network characteristics from the social system, and thus provides a creative industrial cultural model for innovations in new forms of working and living.

These developments have provided the foundation for the creation of a new European tradition of "Anthropocentric Production Systems" (APS), which build upon and extends the industrial and manufacturing contexts of human centred approaches to industrial cultures at an international level. Research into APS undertaken by the FAST (EC) concludes that: "reliance upon technology alone is an inadequate response to the challenges of world markets in the future; successful modernisation of European industry depends upon its most valuable resource — human skill and creativity" [45]. A hallmark of the APS research is the recognition that the notions of human centredness and anthropcentricty are rooted in social and cultural traditions. From this cultural perspective, different national interpretations of APS are regarded as a strength rather than as a weakness of European industrial cultures in the sense that European diversity allows for different trajectories for technological innovation and industrial production in response to challenges of global competition. This diversity has also provided a European network model of research into APS consisting of multidisciplinary research teams from different nations.

1.2 Human Centred Shaping of Work and Skill

Machine-centred focus of new technological innovations in recent times has not only removed the 'tool' from the hand of the skilled craftperson and inserted it into the machine, but it is separating human knowledge and experience from the head of the skilled operator and embodying it in the computer program, thereby controlling the process of design, planning and manufacture. On the one hand this has resulted in a higher level of technical knowledge and supportive computer power which is enabling effective intervention through the active redesign of alternative technical and organisational systems. On the other hand, there have been increases in the rate of product and process innovation along with changes in market demand. These are providing an economic incentive to encourage the creation of more flexible and adaptive technical and organisational structures.

A recent FAST (EC) research initiative on anthropocentric production systems is one of the most significant developments in shaping work, technology and organisational structures [6,8,32,45]. This shaping philosophy takes a holistic view of the production culture, including organisational forms, working practices and work-based learning strategies. From a human-centred perspective, APS takes an evolutionary approach, and emphasises that the enhancement of human skills in production will constitute the new core paradigm for industrial development into the next century, taking advantage of opportunities opened up by the microchip revolution. It is argues that within a European cultural dimension, it could harness the inherent cultural diversity of Europe to create a permanent wave of creativity and innovation which, culturally as well as economically, would yield a global competitive edge for European industry — somewhat analogous to the 'Japanese miracle' [8]. This European vision takes a historical view of evolution from the replacement of the tool to the machine, and recently the replacement of uniform Fordism by flexible post-Fordism impacted by the microelectronic revolution. The initial promise that new technologies of robotics and artificial intelligence would create an era of the automated factory is slowly fading away. The dream that technology is a solution to all problems and will give rise to a leisure society is now no longer sustainable.

It is now widely recognised that, while the Fordist approach may have been undermined by the new flexibility offered by microelectronics, replacing workers by sophisticated machines causes its own problems. The automated factory creates its own rigidity and inflexibility when it is implemented under the old technocentric conditions. For example it results in a misalignment between human skill and machine capacity, and in many cases automation is inadequate in duplicating the skilled processes, or replacing them or transcending them. Rosenbrock [35] points out this misalignment between new technology and human skill results from the rationalisation of human activities. This leads to the creation of a work force which is rendered more passive as technology becomes more active. The tendency is to design increasingly complex technologies which are capable of handling a wide variety of tasks belonging to the human domain. Humans are left to handle trivial and single tasks which will be too expensive to be handled by the machine. This situation gives rise to a 'misalignment' between human abilities and the demands of some tasks.

The process of eliminating the misalignment between technology and human skill gives rise to a paradox. To use a complex machine to perform a trivial task is too expensive and hence there is a need to design a simple machine to perform the task cost-effectively. Where the task is too complex, the solution is to decompose the task into simple tasks which are manageable by the machine. In both these cases the concern is to use the machine more economically and to make full use of its abilities. There seems to be, however, no such concern shown for human skills and abilities.

APS is offered as an alternative to the Fordist approach as a "search for ways of designing work and technology which combine unique human capabilities with the performance of machines". Here APS is represented as a way of exploiting both the available technological and human resources. The limitation of this notion of resource exploitation is that those human attributes and knowledge which are unique and irreproducable may not be deemed economic in the production process, and may therefore be excluded from any learning or organisational innovation. There is also a concern that wholesale automation would destroy the skill base of society, undermining its ability to innovate and reproduce itself [4].

To a certain extent, the APS approach does deal with these concerns by adopting various forms of group technologies and collaborative and integrative organisational structures and working practices. One way to achieve this is through the integration of the work structure and the institution of a flat management hierarchy. That is, through a high horizontal integration of skills, initiative and decision making, using concepts of team work combined with the vertical delegation of planning and executive tasks to the shop floor and the institution of new patterns of participation. Some innovations in this area are: extension of work cycles; modular production; integration of qualified indirect work (e.g maintenance into manufacture); cooperation of team work; and quality circles. These innovations draw on a number of new directions in flexible manufacturing such as the British concepts of human-machine symbiosis [7,35] and the Japanese concept of group work rather than individual work. The latter is based on high personnel flexibility, task integration, self regulation and use of workers' knowledge, e.g. through quality circles. These innovations also draw upon the German concepts of the humanisation of work-life as well as the Scandinavian models of semi-autonomous work groups, which are particularly developed in the automotive industry [11].

Within a broader vision of the industrial culture, The EC/FAST report [7] argues that since the European manufacturing base is largely composed of SMEs, and is characterised by highly skilled and flexible workforce, its future strength will depend upon the development of anthropocentric systems which build on skill, ingenuity and expertise of working people. It emphasises the need to develop infrastructures, educational forms, and means of production which accord with the cultural, geographical, economic and environmental realities of the European Community, and build upon the cultural richness and variety in Europe. The role of responsive education and life long learning is seen central to vision. It is also recognised that "developing the skill and competence necessary in the 21st Century will require nothing short of a cultural and industrial renaissance".

1.2.1 Industrial Culture, Technology and Skill

Technological innovation in the areas of flexible manufacturing systems, flexible specialisation and anthropocentric systems require a fundamental shift towards new forms of organisational and working structures. These in turn require new forms of skills, competences and knowledge to make effective uses of new technology. Central to these developments are new forms of education and training which transcend the current technical notions of skill and the elitist forms of university education. Recent developments in new forms of organisation such as team working, semi-autonomous work groups, quality circles, group technology, multi-skilling and organisational aspects of JIT, are associated with 'Japanisation' as well as the earlier QWL (Quality of Working Life) movement and humanisation of work programmes in Europe. In spite of the extensive discussion of new forms of organisation to reduce hierarchical levels, increase the transparency of decision making, and lessen the vertical and horizontal rigidities to increased integration, their application in Britain is limited and piecemeal. This is mainly due to the traditional managerial resistance to change, skill demarcation, and a general climate of 'low trust' industrial relations in the voluntaristic systems of British industrial relations. Employee involvement and authority, multi-skilling and group forms of work organisation form an important prerequisite for anthropocentric production systems and skill-based flexible production. Their implementation in Britain has been undercut by the combination of both institutional and cultural features of the employment systems, in particular low job security, and the system of industrial relations and narrow job related training.

This narrow view of job related training is rooted in the job related notion of skill used in Britain. As in any other country, the nature and level of skill in British industry reflects the nature and culture of the industrial culture in Britain. This is reflected by the managerial goal of using new technology to reduce the costs of direct labour, with just minimal interest in job design for the remaining workers. Since the managerial goal in British manufacturing has been to reduce costs, this has resulted in the reduction of jobs for unskilled workers, and the remaining jobs have been high skilled ones. This is possibly resulting in higher skill profiles for the remaining British manufacturing workforce.

The managerial concept of skill can be understood by considering the culture of British industry. British manufacturing is concentrated (by output and employment) in large organisations which are more likely to be bureaucratic with a rigid division of labour between departments and job categories. The 'low-trust' relationship between employees and employers, together with traditional rigid skill demarcations is a powerful inhibitor of flexible multi-skilling and work re-organisation. Charles et al comment that UK manufacturers are opting for 'numerical' rather than 'functional' flexibility via increased sub-contracting and casualization of labour — relying upon a part-time and temporary peripheral labour segment to increase enterprise flexibility. British manufacturing strategy appears to lack direction in terms of the new production concept. It is caught in the choice between the strategy of upgraded Fordism and variants of diversified quality production which rely heavily on employee involvement and high skilled human capital.

British employers have remained traditional in their concerns with short-term returns on investment. The departmental budgeting and accounting controls encourage short-termism and thereby inhibit long-term innovations in integrated manufacturing and organisation systems. Although computer-aided production management systems are now recognised as a vital feature of advanced manufacturing, for example, MRP (material requirement planning), and JIT (Just-in-Time), their implementation has not made a significant headway in Britain. It may be that the British management culture of control and short-termism is not amenable to fundamental organisational changes of integration and collaboration required by MRP and JIT [6].

From the APS study on Ireland [32], it is worth noting that the attitude of the Irish and British management towards life long learning is very similar and short-term. In the Irish industry as whole, firms are reluctant to provide training in more flexible and transferable skills because of a concern that employees so trained may leave, thereby taking benefits elsewhere. In these circumstances, industry as a whole losses out — since most firms recognise that they would benefit from a highly skilled workforce — although individual companies are each acting rationally in their own interests. Strict demarcation of employee tasks also acts as an impediment to broader training for more flexible production and employment. There is therefore a need to adopt a collective approach to further training at a strategic level in order to maximise industry and individual gain.

New forms of work and organisation require new forms of skills, a widening of technical task competencies, interpersonal skills for team working, the capacity to self-learn through experience, and the capacity to think holistically. Skills are developed through national systems of education and training provisions and also through the development of the abilities of the existing workforce. Responsive forms of education and training can contribute to: developing an initial competence for lifelong learning, that will facilitate in particular the horizontal mobility of persons between related areas of skill and areas at broadly similar levels; providing opportunities for adding new competences, both "horizontally" in related areas at the same level and "vertically"; and providing opportunities for those at the lower skill and education levels to gain access to higher levels [6].

It is worth noting that in both Ireland and Britain, being an apprentice and a technician is generally looked down upon. Vocational training has tended to be very directly related to perceived short-term needs of industry, leading to a narrow approach. An emphatic distinction between training and education is reflected both in training and education programmes. People with professional skills and those with practical skills follow different career paths within enterprises. There is very little mobility of semi-skilled craft workers to skilled craft workers, and from skilled craft workers to professional and management levels.

Charles et al note that the features of the British education system reflects the elitist legacy of academic education, the divorce between theory and practice, and the low status of non-university technical training. Social science and organisational studies are insufficiently incorporated into the curriculum of technical and engineering courses and post-school vocational training initiatives have been inadequate in the context of a voluntaristic system of provision.

Current education and training systems in Ireland are rigid, restrictive, class based and produce people with a narrow outlook and narrow skills. There is a need for an education system which produces a highly skilled, educated and flexible population, possessing a broad understanding of social, economic, and industrial systems, and capable of innovative, even radical approaches to their work and life. Such an education system needs to make ample opportunities available for further education and career changes. Because of the lack of an old industrial culture, Ireland now has an opportunity to promote an industrial culture based on human centred and anthropocentric concepts and practices [32].

New ideas and experiments in multi-skilling, learning organisations, and life long learning emphasise the development new flexible and adaptable production cultures and working practices. The discussion above illustrates that industrial cultures such as those of Britain and Ireland have not been enthusiastic in adopting Scandinavian or German production models, such as flexible manufacture or autonomous groups. It has been suggested that this may be due to wider social and cultural factors such as demarcation between education and training, hierarchical structures of social systems, elitist and exclusive practice of university education which form the foundation of the industrial culture.

1.3 Human Skill: Beyond Cognition

In seeking to define common training policies for Europe, there may be a temptation to define common core competences and skills which allow for the flow of workers and their skills within and across organisations. The need for common skills may also arise out of the policies of social and economic cohesion and consequent strategies of harmonisation of education and training. In addition to these social and economic factors, there may also be a strong information technology push to define education in terms of core competences and skills which can be transferred and exchanged within and across European regions without the physical flow of learners or teachers. In the case of SMEs, an even stronger case for the electronic transfer of skills may be made because of the lack of in-house training infrastructures and costs of external consultants and trainers. While the case for inter-cultural, inter-social, and language skills, as well as the case for common scientific, technological and managerial competences is overwhelming, the danger is that the technology push may lead to describing human performance in terms of common cognitive processes, specific dispositions and action and reaction strategies. This may then lead to describing learning firstly in terms of core competences, and then competences in terms of the forms and rules of cognitive science. Learning could then be described as an ordered and a rule based procedure which could be broken down into discrete steps and governed by a series of rules, a kind of managed learning process. This idea of managed learning however assumes that organisations function rationally and predictably, and that people can be regarded as cognitive agents, rather than as people socially situated and possessing knowledge and skills that are culturally conditioned and given value.

One of the emerging technological research areas which takes a broader view of skill than that of the narrow technical view of cognitive science, is the area of computer supported cooperative working [2]. Here the idea of distributed cognition is developed which regards technology as a cognitive artifact. Artifacts serve the purpose of coordination, communication, information representation, storage and retrieval i.e. core cognitive capabilities. Understanding these core capabilities is the key to user-centred design for co-operative working. The issue of human communication is turned into the issue of human-machine interaction, thereby shifting the idea of social mediation to the idea of mediation by the machine. This idea of interaction leads to seeing technology, for example, as providing the flexible inter-connectivity to extend the range of informal social encounters between people in work communities e.g. i) over distances; ii) a whole 'space' of 'new encounters' are possible, i.e. the laying out of a taxonomy of space of social interactions [2].

Although this radical shift from human mediation to technological mediation recognises the importance of social interaction, human social competences are, increasingly, seen in terms of cognitive skills. The crucial point here is that technology not only impacts upon the work and labour process, it also affects the description and role of skills. This trend tends to marginalise the crucial role of the tacit knowledge which people possess through its focus on their cognitive skills. It is therefore not sufficient to just study the emerging patterns of qualification and learning as a reaction to the integration of technology in the workplace, but it is also essential to study the processes of designing technology itself and taking a proactive stance to retain a balance between tacit competences and cognitive competences. From this perspective, the design of technological systems must be based upon participation with people who really know the work process that is to be redesigned, and upon the tacit skills that workers have acquired through their long and diverse experiences of learning-by-doing. This need is not only for democratic reasons but is also for strong epistemological reasons. One of the crucial epistemological issues for systems design is what Wittgenstein called "language-games". Language games in the context of design is the expression of the practices of both the users and the designers, where the users are experienced in the language games of their work or use situations, and the designers are experienced in the language games of design [25].

This cognitive science notion of skill not only separates learning from its social and cultural contexts, but also separates individual learning from learning with peers and within the community of learners. Cognitive science centres around the 'Representation hypothesis': that is, the assumption that cognition rests on the manipulation of symbolic representations that can be understood as referring to objects or properties in the world [44]. This representation view of cognition allows for human knowledge and skill to be separated from the social context, and thereby separate the objective knowledge from the tacit. This view of skill is deeply rooted in the three dreams of rationalism: the dream of the exact language, the rational method and the united science [42]. The 'exact language' seeks to define competences and skill in the same universal language so as to realise their transfer across language barriers; the rational method seeks to describe skill performance in individualistic and mechanistic terms; and the united science seeks to define skill in terms of the 'one best way'. Although these 'noble dreams' rooted in 17th and 18th century rationalism may continue to excite us for a long period of time, they may prove to be a dangerous legacy for an increasing interdependent world. Cognitive science, in building upon these 'dreams', continues to seek for the description of skill in explicit, certain and unambiguous forms. This scientific description of skill is regarded as infinitely more important than the process of learning by doing or by working with or gaining knowledge from people. Description is thereby overvalued and is taken as an absolute, instead being subjected to controlled use in particular circumstances. "Description will always be arbitrary and context bound, the kind and degree of arbitrariness depends upon the purposes, communicative, instructional etc., for which the description is being fashioned" [41]. Core competence are therefore as much to do with social and cultural skills as they are to do with cognitive skills.

It is therefore essential that the description of core skills and competences for differing working domains, professions and disciplines should also consider learning contexts which enable their transfer, exchange and sharing within and across these domains. Even within the same domain, practitioners find it impossible to fully describe skills and competences gained through long experiences. People use common sense and intuition to perform their skills effectively in different circumstances. It is the tacit dimension, i.e. knowing, common sense and intuition etc which makes for skills, and not well structured symbolic descriptions.

Traditionally, skills are associated with the recognised production of culturally defined artifacts and skilled action is determined as being by social and working life contexts. Skilled action or competence is part of the value system of the culture in which action takes place. Here action embodies wisdom, skill embodies practice, practice embodies knowledge, and they are all culturally situated. The action of a skilled performer (competence) cannot be understood simply in terms of a set of rational rules and a series of structured instructions. In other words, an understanding of what counts as skill cannot be reduced to descriptions of actions taken by the skilled performer.

In the modern working life, skill is a combination of traditional and technological skill, and is generally associated with a specific technology and production process. It is tempting to hypothesise that, since technology such as CAD is transferable over production processes, modern skill can also be transferred across production processes. This is based on an assumption that technological skills can be separated from the praxis in which skill is learnt and applied. This is very similar to the false assumption which has been prevalent in cognitive science that objective knowledge can be separated from the tacit knowledge, and hence knowledge (objective knowledge) can be transferred across application domains.

What is transferable is the content and explicit descriptions of the objective part of the describable knowledge, but not the objective knowledge itself. Knowledge belongs to the person or a group, and resides in the social context just as skill resides in a particular work context. The effective transfer of skill or knowledge can only take place when the person/group owning the skill or knowledge is also transferred to a similar working or social environment. That is why many organisations and companies rely on specialist knowledge and high tech skill transfer, upon their consultants, and hire specialists, recruit graduates and postgraduates from different universities and disciplines (Senker,1993). This enables the companies not only to gain new knowledge and skill but also create a working environment in which the transfer of tacit skill and tacit knowledge takes place through participation and human communication. This brings us to a human centred framework of learning which enshrines participation within the group and interlocution with the environment, and thereby enables skill and knowledge transfer.

Many cognitive psychologists and educationists presume that the work of a skilled person is to do with problem solving, and therefore the only core skills which matter are the problem solving skills. Skill acquisition here focuses on an explicit rendering of knowledge. It is devoid of any 'reflective practice' which embodies capabilities such as 'seeing as', which is a form of unarticulated perception. Professional activity involves both problem finding (problem creation) and problem solving activities, problem solving cannot be separated from the activity of problem finding [38]. A human centred learning framework enables us to consider issues of skill and competence in a holistic manner, within a broader horizons of the tacit dimension and human competence.

Within the human centred framework, core competences are part and parcel of working life and living environments, the social competence is inseparable form the functional competence, and the objective knowledge is inseparable from the experiential and the personal knowledge. While the objective part of core competences in the scientific, economic, and technological domains may be transferred through formal channels such as text books, journal, and electronic media, the tacit dimension (experiential knowledge and personal knowledge) can only be transferred through the exchange and flow of practitioners and expertise.

1.4 A Human Centred Agenda of Technology Shaping & Social Innovation

In the age of the market and global competitivity, technological innovation has become the prerequisite of any innovation, be that industrial, organisational or bureaucratic innovation. The implications are that the development of social, economic and industrial systems is seen primarily in technological terms. It is as if the natural has become embodied in the artificial. For example, the AI and Information Science researchers talk about human-machine interfacing, virtual reality, natural language processing, electronic networking, multimedia technologies, telecottages and computer supported cooperative working in terms of technology as if the human purpose of technology has only a marginal relevance to working and living. This marginalisation of human purpose in technological research leads to the exclusion of human values, ethical, moral, cultural, aesthetical from the design or the assessment of technological systems. These are the very values which are at the heart of social innovation, a new and imaginative way of tackling a social problem or improving the quality of working and living by making use of technological resources. So long the citizen continues to be defined in economic and technological terms, the mechanistic world view of innovation would continue to prevail. The challenge is how to shape technology which sustains and develop the interrelationships between the individual, community, and society.

1.4.1 The Limits of the Artificial

The limits of the artificial can reasonably be defined in terms of the nature of 'artificial intelligent machine' and its impact on the shaping of the industrial culture. This debate therefore can be viewed within wider horizons: social, economic, cultural and political. Toulmin [42] and Cooley [7] place the debate on the culture of the artificial within the wider debate on the shaping of science and technology in the Western tradition. The shaping of science and technology, they emphasise, is rooted in the basic themes of 'the dream of the exact language', 'one best way' and the 'sameness of science'. Through its 'dream of the exact language', the 'ideal of certainty', and 'rational method', the artificial machine expounds the dream of the 'symbolic man', replacing the 'natural, by the artificial'. Does the charm of the *artificial* lie in its *characteristica universallis* alluding to the supposed liberation of the individual from the realities, complexities and uncertainties of diversity? Does this charm lie in its outlining the contours of 'secular technological culture' transcending the national, cultural, linguistic and religious boundaries? Or is the 'artificial' about the celebration of the dream of the separation of the individual and the community, private and public, reason and the emotion, function and the social, work and living, technology and society? Or is it about redefining and redirecting societal issues and social agenda in terms of the culture of 'sameness' and the science of the 'one best way'?

1.4.2 The Limits of 'Productive Functionality'

'Productive functionality' has been a powerful driving force of industrial and bureaucratic innovations. These notions of innovation arise out the concerns of the governance with the 'productive functionality' which is at the heart of the decision making processes of the industrial cultures. This view of functionality has been shaped by two powerful industrial processes, the mechanisation of industry and the bureaucratisation of organisations, both of which are rooted in the mechanistic world view. The notions of 'productive functionality' and the 'one best way' form the basis of the methodologies of 'exclusion': citizens, communities, and societies which are unable to contribute to industrial productivity are excluded from consultation and participation in decision making processes; science and technology which does not fit into the strait-jacket of the 'one best way' is excluded from bureaucratic recognition. The degree of 'exclusion' is determined by the mechanistic criteria of quantitative measurement such as regularity, precision, speed, efficiency which themselves are the product of mechanistic nature of bureaucratic organisations built around the division of tasks, hierarchical structures and problem solving rules.

The 'productive functionality' has been and remains a deriving force for shaping science and technology, industrial cultures, and organisation structures, as well as an instrument of decision making processes. While this functional world view has led to increasing production and consumption and new possibilities of autonomy, especially in the advanced industrial world, it has also led to an increasing alienation of individuals and communities from the decision making processes of their governance. What are the consequences of this view of innovation? The function of the governance has shifted from broader societal concerns to that of the guardian of industrial production; innovations of science and technology are defined in the language of the machine and measured in terms of marketable commodity; Development is identified in terms of consumption; national wealth is measured in terms of the GNP; international cooperation is described in terms of global competitivity.

Those individuals and communities who are not 'productive' have become mere observers of the technological and bureaucratic innovations. The 'productive functionality' redefines the nature and purpose of work, from 'social utility' to 'economic disutility'. In the realm of the new economics, work is not a part of living but living is part of work, social part of living becomes separated from the 'productive functionality' part. Bureaucratic innovations have become concerned with the management of change and controlling product quality for the benefit of the market rather than creating quality of human services such as health, welfare, education or learning for the benefit peoples. In the name of the 'Quality', industrial Taylorism is being implemented in social domains, a form of 'social Taylorism'. The semi privatisation and marketing of the social and welfare services, including health, education and training in Britain illustrates this trend. The old balance of the social and the economic rooted in the civic state is all but vanishing. Within this model of 'social Taylorism', those in power, authority, and control are all producers, and rest of the society are all customers. The governance no longer aspires to the responsibility of the provision of social services, but seeks market as a mechanism for managing and controlling the 'productive functionality' of these services. Managerial innovation becomes a vehicle for redefining social concerns as problems of production and consumption, and the bureaucrats seek quantitative solutions of qualitative social concerns as if there were no difference between quality of life and the quality of industrial product. In this view of 'productive functionality' human work and social provision are regarded just any part of the industrial production, obeying the rules of production and consumption. What happens when, as we are now witnessing, the level and quality of industrial production cannot be sustained and industrial decline leads to social pessimism? Does this mean that neither human work nor social provision can any longer be sustained even at the present levels? Has not the very existence of the social and cultural systems already become dependent on the sustainability of the industrial production systems? If so what price should we are prepared to pay for the technological and bureaucratic innovations which cannot even support the sustainability of social fabric of industrial societies, let alone contribute purposefully to the needs, aspirations and well being of peoples and societies of developing countries?

Recent technological innovations in the form of artificial intelligence, electronic networking, virtual reality and cyborgs give us a glimpse of the electronic shaping of bureaucratic and managerial innovation. In the name of 'productive efficiency', we may already be witnessing the rise of 'electronic functionality', as the 21st Century tool of governance. In the realm of the innovations of new technology, artificial intelligence recasts human relations from the social to the symbolic; information technology defines social and economic wealth in terms of units of information and thereby categorises societies into information poor and information rich; the cyborgs offer a boundaryless world where individual has no social or cultural roots; communication technologies offer the globe as a market of individual opportunities; virtual reality offers virtual tools for redesigning the human itself with no ethical constraints and no obligations. 'Electronic Fordism' in the form of computer networks, for example electronic mail, is bridging the gap between the technological and management of change innovations. We are in the era of electronic cottages, information transfer, distance learning, remote working, virtual design, remote manufacture, virtual planning and electronic management [23,26, 33].

Although the inspirations of the technological, bureaucratic and managerial innovations may have been economic and social progress, in practice their increasing focus on production and consumption has resulted in the separation of the social from the economic, product from the process, information from knowledge, wisdom from action, and individual from the community. In theory, the electronic revolution provides an efficient vehicle for democratic participation, social and economic cohesion, knowledge and skill transfer, and global harmony. In practice, so long as these innovations are defined, expressed, and evaluated in terms of the 'productive functionality' these would continue to strengthen the rigidity of the bureaucratic and managerial control, leaving very little flexibility and adaptability to cope with the uncertainties and volatilities of the future. The danger is that in the virtual world of illusion (of reality), work and living may no longer be regarded as social, cultural or even economic concepts, they may well be just regarded as electronic concepts, totally explicit, symbolic, certain, quantifiable and measurable. There may no longer be any no room for intuition, creativity, uncertainty, error, initiative. The danger of the mechanistic world view turning into an electronic world view is that neither the governance nor the governed would be left with the capacities and capabilities of dealing with the complex and diverse social, cultural, political and economic issues arising out of the industrial decline and the breaking down of the civic, social and cultural boundaries of industrial societies. The cost of the ideology of 'efficiency' may be very high. It is time to reflect on social and human cost of the ideology of 'productive functionality' which has far too long shaped the technological and bureaucratic innovations, and seek alternative concept of 'social utility' as the guiding principle for social innovations.

1.4.3 Social Innovation: a human centred view

The notion of social innovation from the human centred perspective is concerned with the social and cultural shaping of science and technology for making world a better place for living and working, and innovation is seen in terms of social welfare and economic co-development. This view of social innovation extends the human centred tradition from the anthropocentric production domain to broader societal domains such as social citizenship, sustainable systems, working life and living conditions, human development, health, welfare, education, and learning. The human centred approach sees the citizen, not just as a producer and consumer of products, but also as a social and cultural being, a consumer and producer of knowledge, user and a social assessor of science and technology, and a proactive participant in society at the same time. This focus of social innovation emphasises the enrichment of the interrelationships of individuals to the community by building on fundamental social values of cooperation, collaboration, interdependence and harmony. These values enable the development of socio-economic, educational and welfare infrastructures and processes by building on social and cultural resources. This approach of innovation promotes notions of codevelopment, coexistence and valorization of diversity . From this perspective of social innovation, the concept of human centredness is essentially a developmental and a learning process which seeks social and cultural understanding of working life, technology and living environments [19-23].

Two British social innovations which illustrate the human centred vision of social innovation are the Consumers' Association and Open University. The Consumers' Association grew out of a Labour Party pamphlet, Small Man, Big World' written by Michael Young, during the radical, relentless and optimistic period of 1945-1951. He was concerned that big government, like big business or big union, was a threat to democracy, since democracy could flourish best in small groups built to scale of the individual. The Association's journal, 'Which?" has become a national institution, and the Consumer Association has led to many new acts of Parliament intended to protect consumers. His book, 'The Rise of the Meritocracy' provided an inspiration for the setting up of the Open University, which was to be open to everyone, with or without qualification. This innovation challenged the rise of the meritocratic elite whose main quality was to have, as children, sailed through the examination system [1].

Some of key issues of human centred perspective of social innovations:

- social and cultural shaping of science and technology which is based on the notions of the 'valorization' of diversity and coexistence.
- the idea of social citizenship which regards the citizen not just as a producer and a consumer but also an active participant in decision making, and a cultural shaper and social assessor of science and technology.
- holistic approaches of human centred design of systems within the broader societal contexts of working life and living environments
- the view of education as transmission, exchange and enrichment of cultures rather than as just transfer of technical skill and competence

- multicultural perspectives of cohesion and developments, holistic notions of sustainability and codevelopment

1.5 Learning as Social Innovation: Towards a Human Centred Framework

The discussion on anthropocentric production systems highlights the need for new forms of education and research which support lifelong learning and enhance human skill and competence. The sections on skill and cognition show the limitations of the cognitive science view of skill and the techno-centric view of working life for an understanding of skill. The technical view of competence freezes skill within the present context and expertise. Its transfer in this static form renders learning into a managed form of training. The danger of this narrow view is that competence may be described as skill devoid of uncertainty, and that training may be used as an instrument for eliminating human judgement and intuition. Furthermore, by rendering explicit the 'secrets' of craft, we prepare the basis of a rule-based system. The disadvantage of this view of training is that it separates learning from people's own knowledge, skills and expertise. Consequently, it prevents learners from enjoying the experience and gaining dignity from transmitting their experiences to the future generations [7]. Moreover, the machine-centred view of skill does not allow any questions about the "validity or sanity of a *system*" which destroys initiative and rots brains", and thereby acts as a barrier to any fundamentally new thinking on work and its purpose [37]. The consequences of this narrow view of industrial culture is that it inhibits educational and training innovations which could enable the transfer, exchange and sharing of skill, knowledge, and experiences within and across organisations and social systems.

The human centred perspective, on the other hand, provides a wider view of the industrial culture. This perspective celebrates human creativity, and skill, and facilitates a purposive view of work and living; it regards work and living as complementary and interdependent activities. The worker is not just a producer and a consumer of products but is also a social citizen with interests and concerns for the creation of socially responsive working and living conditions. This view is shared by the alternative, 'Buddhist view of economics' [37] in which humans have a chance to develop their faculties, overcome their ego-centredness by joining with other people in a common risk, and produce goods and services for a becoming existence. This view of economics emphasises the development, liberation, dignity, freedom, and fulfilment of the worker. it does not measure the standard of living by the amount of annual consumption.

From this wider view of human-centredness, the idea of life-long learning requires a change of perspective on work from a purely production and consumption ethos to the ethos of working and living. This requires a change in the notion of learning from the idea of technical competence and skill to the idea of social competence and tacit knowing . However, this developmental focus of learning requires the adoption of a human centred view of working and purposeful living in which work is measured in terms of production and reproduction of resources rather than solely in terms of consumption. Technology, from this human centred perspective, should be designed as a facilitating tool for social innovation and emancipation instead of as an instrument for technical change.

1.5.1 Social innovation of a learning network

The notion of learning as social innovation takes a developmental perspective of working and living with relationship to both the individual and the society. A central challenges for learning as social innovation is to shape education and research cultures which are based on the notion that "education is about transmission, exchange and enrichment of cultures" rather than about the transfer of technical skills alone. To shape learning organisations requires the cultivation of scope and emancipation in the emerging network society. The idea of social innovation builds upon social competences and widens the learning horizon from the idea of acquiring cognitive competences within the narrowness of technological innovation. Social innovation here means organising change rather than just managing change. It is about acquiring social competences for working life and living conditions rather than about acquiring cognitive skills to cope with technology embedded organisational structures. It places emphasis on the processes of change and not just the results of change, and it is about problem finding rather than just problem solving. The Seake Centre's project 'Parosi' [16-18] emphasised the notion of social innovation and evolved an approach for acquiring the necessary competences to deal with the realities of complex socio-cultural and socio-economic domains. The learning environment provided a complex social environment in which participants were able to act as learners, as teachers, as experts and as social mediators at various levels of knowledge exchange. The knowledge and language skills acquired by the team were not just of benefit for the project duration but were also of benefit for future use in other learning and real life practical situations. Emphasis was placed on the knowledge, experiences, intuition, expectations and cultural backgrounds of learners. The project consisted of a human network of adult learners, tutors, education officers from the local education authority, volunteers from the local community as well as student volunteers from both the local universities, voluntary and full time tutors, professionals and community experts, as well as researchers from both the university and continuing education sectors. The project was based in the local community centre and was linked to local schools and further education centres. It involved 38 adult students and about 60 volunteer tutors in the form of a learning network. It was a "learning organisation without walls", and has since been regarded as an important experiment of 'learning as social innovation'. The project subsequently became a basis for the EC - Social Fund pilot project on New Technology, Numeracy and Life Skills for Adults (1983-1985).

Social innovation in the form of "The Futures Circles" illustrates an other perspective of learning through participation which was the central focus of PAROSI project. The Futures Circle are an interesting new design by Leif Dambo in Sweden. Each circle will consist of five to eight people, with a trainer. The group will uses adult education facilities to debate future issues and then to design a project. The idea is that the future is created by you. This is your right - and your duty. If you do not do it, some one will on your behalf. By taking apart in Futures Circles you can actively influence the course of events, and create the future here and now. And creation is always an act based on knowledge. To create the future you need tools: knowledge, experience, insights, methods. The Futures Circles are a forum for sharing different ideas, knowledge, experience - the future is a group product [1].

'PRELUDE' (Programme of REsearch and Liaison between Universities for DEvelopment) is an example of a learning network which extends the learning philosophy of 'PAROSI' from a local level to an international level. PRELUDE [40] is concerned with the transfer of scientific and technological skills and expertise and their appropriation through the auspices of an associated network of individuals. The networks are particularly active in a range of countries in the South and are composed of 'voluntary researchers from different backgrounds, disciplines and horizons'. The network is action oriented and challenges the rationalist view of development. It seeks social structures and functions that operate in harmony over time. Thus "inventiveness and long term efficiency go through pro-active suggestions for alternatives" requiring much individual involvement.

It recognises that a world governed by economic issues, with competition and short term views as the rule, encourages a techno-science where there is global domination of the technological, economic and financial processes. Therefore orientation is required for long term sustainability. However the notion of sustainable development does not signify subjecting humanity to single law: judicial or economic. In relation to diversity of need, action research should seek individual autonomy, and freedom.

The concept of codevelopment changes the meaning of knowledge and skill transfer. "It is expertise and skills which are exchanged, and not established and institutional knowledge or technologies". The network approach enables complex, highly heterogeneous situations to be tackled in a systematic and global fashion... by putting into perspective the different symbolic, economic, educational, ethical, social, political, organisational and ecological components and dimensions. "Far from replacing institutions, associated networks complement them; they give institutions back their capacity to institute, and in so doing displace acquired balances. This is a pathway which promotes new centres of creativity within institutions and thus increases their capacity to innovate" [40].

In order for enterprises to undertake organisational innovation, it is necessary develop learning environments which promote continuous self learning and self development, as well as motivation, team work, autonomy and responsibility. In this scenario of the learning organisation, the focus is on group learning or working situations where people have different interests, needs, aspirations and assumptions. In finding a harmonious balance between individual and group learning, dialogue acts as catalyst of change. Cultural assumptions are part of peoples cultures. They are expressed in the form of relationships. Dialogue helps people to resolve conflicts and work out these relationships. It is not the content of opinions or assumptions which matters but the process of working out relationships. In dialogue we seek coherence and order which is purposeful. We seek coherence through participation, communication, and sharing. Participating in a dialogue means partaking of the whole and taking part in it; not merely the whole group, but the whole. This holistic view of dialogue provides an important conceptual handle for developing learning organisations which involve the sharing and exchange of knowledge and experiences. Docherty [9] gives a management perspective of learning and points out that the nature of the learning organisation is very dependent upon the organisational culture, for example a 'closed administrative culture' gives low priority to personal involvement and self learning. A 'change-oriented culture' promotes personal learning and is characterised by communication and delegation. He comments that the Japanese 'Human Resource Intensive' strategy recruits personnel with high skill levels and invests highly in the individual. Compared to this, the Anglo Saxon countries focus on the 'mobility' strategy which recruits personnel with high skill levels, but relies on the market and the individual to exhibit initiative and flexibility. Docherty compares international strategies for skill development. The Anglo Saxon market led strategy shows once again some limitations for creating organisational cultures which enable participation, dialogue and life long learning. He cites Peddler's observation that "the learning organisation is not an entity but a 'generative theory', mobilising energy to shape shared perception and the will to change, as well as leading to concrete actions". This notion of the learning organisation is an interesting concept for further development.

Human centred concepts such as transcendence, shaping, sustainability, renewal and human purpose extend the dialogical process between the individual and the group at a societal level. This perspective of human centredness thereby provide a wider societal framework for the learning organisation.

1.5.2 An Institute without "Walls": innovation of a human centred systems research model

The idea of setting up an international research institute of human centred systems (IRIHCS), an institute "without walls" grew out of the foundation work of LUCAS PLAN, Greater London Technology Networks (GLEB, London), The ESPRIT 1217 Project, and the work on social innovation and learning of the SEAKE Centre, University of Brighton. The purpose was to create an international network of concerned researchers and practitioners to develop, share and disseminate innovations and practices in human centred education and research. As a first step, an international journal of human centred systems, *AI & Society* was launched in 1987 followed by a new book series in Human Centred Systems in 1989, both published by Springer-Verlag, London. These developments were followed by setting up a European Research Network on Human Centred Systems sponsored by the ERASMUS Programme of the EC (ERASMUS 1990-91).

IRIHCS was set up in 1992 to create an international framework for human centred systems research, and provide a forum for a strategic debate on socially and culturally responsive technology. The Institute's human centred tradition provide an alternative humanistic traditions of science and technology to the 'mechanistic paradigm' through concepts such as diversity, human purpose, participation, equality, social responsibility, ethics, and creativity. The work of the Institute is underpinned by human-centred traditions such as the British tradition of Human-Centred Systems, the German tradition of Social and Cultural Shaping of Work and Technology, the Scandinavian tradition of Democracy, Dialogue and Participation, as well as by the cultural traditions of the East such as diversity, harmony, order, balance, empathy and beauty.

The Institute's influence derives from its individual members, its links with supporting research centres, and associated institutions. The Institute is a human network rather than a physical entity in the traditional sense. Its members are not bound by any constitution. They work together because they share a common belief in enabling people to shape new technology appropriate to their working and living environments. The Institute is coordinated by a Secretariat. The Institute facilitates international collaboration on human centred research. Through its members, it organises international workshops, symposia and conferences. It facilitates the exchange of researchers and students between institutions and across national boundaries. (IRIHCS, SEAKE Centre, University of Brighton).

Current work of the IRIHCS includes the setting up of the European Postgraduate Studies in Human Centred Systems which is built upon the European Research Network in Human Centred Systems. The postgraduate studies aims to develop a design and technology culture which deals with the relationships between technology, social and industrial systems. In Europe, there exists a diversity of industrial and cultural traditions which can be used to elaborate a shared concept of human-centredness. This European programme is coordinated by the SEAKE Centre, and involves 16 European universities of Aalborg, Aarhus, Odense, Roskilde, Lyngby (Denmark), Amsterdam (The Netherlands), Bremen (Germany), Urbino, and Padova(Italy), University College, Dublin (Ireland), Lund (Sweden), Technical University and New University, Lisbon (Portugal), Crete (Greece), and Brighton and Warwick (UK).

The concept of human centredness is undergoing continuous development, based on an ongoing research process which supports the development of a shared meaning of human-centredness. Central to this is an understanding of the cultural dimensions of working life, technology and living environments. The Inter-University network of Human Centred Studies aims at the elaboration of a multi-perspective notion of human centredness taking into consideration the existence and possible contradictions between different rationalities: economic and organisational, individual and social, cultural and technical. The aim is to establish an interdisciplinary European approach to designing socio-technical systems which responds to challenges arising out the growing penetration of information technology in almost all areas of working life and living environments. This development is part of the European research initiatives on social and cultural shaping of technology and social innovation of learning which build upon the foundation work of the LUCAS PLAN and the current work on anthropocentric production systems of the FAST (EC) Programme.

1.6 Conclusions

The Human Centred research promotes humane forms of working life and living conditions, and emphasises holistic forms education and research which cultivate human knowledge and skill. This approach enshrines human purpose, participation and emancipation, and thereby provides a wider societal horizon for shaping learning. To shape learning from a wider societal perspective, however, requires the creation of new alliances between universities, enterprises and communities. Learning from this societal perspective can be seen as a process of social and organisational innovation rather than a practice of 'exclusion' and ''demarcation' of the traditional university education and industrial training. The projects, 'PAROSI' and the PRELUDE exemplify learning as a social innovation process, and share a vision of enterprise innovation with the APS programme. These network models of enterprise and anthropocentric models of production provide a way forward for developing human centred frameworks of learning as social and organisational innovation.

The foundational concept of human centredness is essentially a developmental and learning process. It seeks a social and cultural understanding of working life, technology and living environments From this wider societal perspective, it regards learning essentially as a process of social and cultural innovation.

References

1. Alby, N. (ed.): The Book of Visions: an encyclopaedia of social innovations. Virgin Books, London, 1992
2. Ardigo, A.: Artificial Intelligence: a Contribution to Systems Theories of Sociology. AI & Society. 2.2 (1988)
2. Bannon, L. Robinson, M. and Schmidt, K. (Eds): Proceedings of the second European Conference on Computer Supported Cooperative Working. Amsterdam 1991
3. Belussi, F.: Benetton Italy: Beyond Fordism and Flexible Specialisation. The Evolution of the Network Firm Model. In Computer-aided Manufacturing and Women's Employment (S. Mitter. ed.). Springer-Verlag 1991
4. Brodner, P.: In Search of the Computer-Aided Craftsman. AI & Society. 3.1 (1989).
5. Bruno, S. et al: Modes of Usage and Diffusion of New Technologies and New Knowledge. A Synthesis Report, FAST, European Commission June 1991
6. Charles, T. Charles, R. and Roulstone. A.: Prospects for Anthropocentric Systems: Production Systems in Britain. APS Research Series, Report FOP 252. FAST, European Commission 1991
7. Cooley, M.: Architect or Bee?: the human price of technology. Hogarth Press 1987

8. Cooley, M.: European Competitiveness in the 21st Century. FAST, European Commission June 1989
9. Docherty P.: The Utilization of Information Technology: A management Perspective on a Learning Issues. In Developing People's Ability to Learn (B. Nyhan. ed.). European Interuniversity Press. Brussels 1991
10. Dodgson, M. (ed): Technology Strategy and the Firm. Longman 1989
11. Eichner, V.: Organisations and Concepts in German Industry. APS Research Series. Report FOP 270. FAST, European Commission 1991
12. FAST: Prospects for Anthropocentric Production Systems. APS Research Series. Reports. FOP. FAST, European Commission 1991
13. FAST: Science and technology and the socio-economic cohesion of the European Community. Prospective Dosier 1. FAST, European Commission July 1990
14. FAST: Panel's Consensus Statement. FAST Consensus Conference. Science, Technology and Community Cohesion. Louvain-la-Neuve, European Commission. 2-4 December 1992
15. Fontela, E.: Diversity and Quality in Europe: Cohesion, Diversity and Quality. The Quality. September/December 1991
16. Gill, K.S. (ed.): Artificial Intelligence For Society. John Wiley & Sons. Chichester 1986
17. Gill, K.S.: Artificial intelligence and social action: education and training. In Knowledge, Skill and Artificial Intelligence (B.Goranzon and T. Josefson. eds.). Springer-Verlag 1988
18. Gill, K.S.: Reflections on Participatory Design. AI & Society. 3.4. 1989
19. Gill, K.S.: A Summary of Human Centred Systems Research in Europe. NTT DATA Tokyo, Japan 1990
20. Gill, K.S.: Artificial Intelligence for Social Citizenship: Towards an anthropocentric technology. Journal of Applied Artificial Intelligence. 5.1. Hemisphere 1991
21. Gill, K.S.: Human Centredness: A 21st Century Paradigm for Industrial Cultures. In Human Centred Systems in the Global Economy (Y. Masuda. ed.). Springer-Verlag 1992
22. Gill, K.S.: Socially Sustainable Technology: an agenda for human promotion, in le Nuove tecnologie per lepromozione umana (A. Ardigò. ed.). Angeli. Milano 1993
23. Gill, K.S.: A Human Centred Agenda for Social Innovation. The Social Sciences Workshop. STOA, European Parliament. Strasbourg 19-20 April 1993
24. Gill, K.S.: Summary of Human Centred Systems Research in Europe (Japanese Edition). RISS, NTT DATA, Tokyo (Document 90-04J(0015), pp 1-34 (1993)
25. Gill, S.P.: On Two AI Traditions. AI & Society. 2.4. 1988
26. Haraway, D.: A Manifesto for Cyborgs: Science, Technology, and Socialist Feminism in the 1980s. In Feminism and Postmodernism (L. Nicolson. ed.). Routledge 1990
27. Jones, B: Work and Flexible Automation in Britain. In Work, Employment and Society. 2.4. 1988
28. Mitter, S. (ed): Computer-aided Manufacturing and Women's Employment, Springer-Verlag 1991
29. Negrotti, M. (ed.): Understanding The Artificial. Springer-Verlag. 1990
30. Noble, D.: Cockpit Cognition: Education, the Military, and Cognitive Engineering. AI & Society. 3.4. 1989

31. Nyhan, B. (ed): Developing People's Ability to Learn, European Interuniversity Press, Brussels 1991
32. O'Siochru, S. and Dillon B: Prospects for Anthropocentric Production Systems in Ireland. APS Research Series. Report FOP 258. FAST, European Commission 1991
33. Petrella, R.: Three Anaylses of Globalisation Technology and Economy. FAST - Europrospective II. NAMUR 1991
34. Rasmussen, L.B.: Human Centred Methods of Social and Technical Design. Working Paper. Technical University of Denmark. Lyngby 1993
35. Rosenbrock, H H: Machines with a Purpose, OUP 1991 October, 1991
36. Rosenbrock, H.H.: Technology and its Environment. AI & Society. 7.2. 1993
37. Schumacher, E.F.: Buddhist Economics. In The Best of Resurgence (J. Button, ed.). Green Books. Bedford, Devon 1991
38. Schon, D. A.: The Reflective Practitioner. Basic Books 1983
39. Senker, J.: The Contribution of Tacit Knowledge to Innovation. AI & Society. 7.3. 1993
40. Thill, G.: The Relevance of Associated Networks for/in a Sustainable Information and Communication Society. 2nd EC-Japan Conference on The future of Industry in the Global Context. Essen, Germany March 15-19, 1993
41. Thorpe, J.: Learning, Experiences and Learners. Working Paper. SEAKE Centre University of Brighton 1991
42. Toulmin, S.: The Dream of the exact language. In Dialogue and Technology (B. Goranzon B and M. Florin. eds.). Springer-Verlag 1991
43. Wittrock, B.: Polity, Economy and Knowledge in the Age of Modernity in Europe. AI & Society. 7.2. 1993
44. Winograd, T. and Flores, F.: Understanding Computers and Cognition: A New Foundation for Design. Ablex. New Jersey 1986
45. Wobbe, W.: Anthropocentric Production Systems: a strategic issue for Europe. FOP 245. APS Series. FAST, European Commission 1991

2. An Industrial Perspective of Human Centred Systems

Andrew Ainger

Human Centred Systems Limited, Quantum House, Hemel Hempstead, Hertfordshire, HP2 4SJ

Abstract. The benefits of Human Centred Manufacturing Systems are far reaching. There is a ground swell towards these types of system throughout Europe. However, the design, production and installation of Human Centred Manufacturing Systems has to be tackled in a completely new way if the full benefits are to be realised.

This paper outlines an industrial perspective of human centred systems as applied to a large UK based multi-national organisation. It covers the background on which the human centred systems were based, indicates the principal targets of the system and why the human centred approach was adopted. It also provides a brief outline of human centred systems themselves, indicates some of the principal benefits and describes the main methods by which the human centred systems were developed.

Keywords. Human centred computer integrated manufacture, batch manufacturing, manufacturing cells, cell scheduling

2.1 Industrial Background

A large UK based multi-national organisation was, during the mid 1980s, striving to achieve an improved world-wide competitive position. Initially, The Company was attempting to achieve this by an analysis of its manufacturing organisations throughout Europe. The purpose of the analysis was to identify common strands or problem themes that would apply to the majority of their organisations. This work would enable the development of new and improved manufacturing systems that, once installed, would significantly improve the competitive position of the companies concerned. This research [1] was concluded in 1985.

Major findings indicated that all companies within the group were suffering from:

1. Long lead times
2. Poor due date performance
3. High inventory levels

These results came as no real surprise and four manufacturing organisations were chosen and studied in further detail. The production departments of the selected manufacturing organisations were further analysed and the principal performance measures identified. The performance measures were numerous and varied but common themes emerged. All the organisations studied placed great emphasis on two principal factors and almost none on the third. The two performance measures of significance were:

1. Machine utilisation
2. Product Output Value (POV)

The effects of these two performance measures were quite startling. It was found that the measurement of machine utilisation had the effect of driving batch quantities up. For example, when a customer requested a certain quantity of a product, the production department tended to round that quantity up so that they would be able to supply the next customer ex-stock. Unfortunately, many such products were not requested again and as a result finished goods stocks increased steadily.

Using the Product Output Value (POV) as a performance measure would appear, at first glance, to be logical. Let us assume that a company has a turnover of £50m ECUs per year. From this figure it can be deduced that the output per month has to be around £4m ECUs. As a result, the production department strove to achieve the £4m ECUs per month figure regardless of the consequences. Striving for monitored perfection led to the process of 'cherry picking'. If towards the end of the month production output was down, the production department would select and manufacture a high-value future order, to boost the month's POV. Thus the effect of having Product Output Value as a performance measure in the product department led to the factory changing due dates without reference to the customer requirements and to products being delivered early and late, but rarely on time.

The measure of customer delivery performance was never or very rarely used. Eventually, it was seen that the production department's performance measures of machine utilisation and product output value militated against using customer delivery performance as a performance measure.

During the extensive investigations of the European operations mentioned earlier, a market trend was identified (Figure 2.1). In general it was found that the product quantities of a particular order were reducing, whilst the product varieties requested were increasing. In many organisations where this trend was identified, it was found that managerial and supervisory staff tended to look backwards in time and try to obtain economies of scale, as there had been in the past. These attempts always led to failure. The market had changed and there were no longer any substantial benefits to be obtained from economies of scale. What should have been sought were economies of scope (variety). Systems and procedures should have been devised and implemented that enabled the companies concerned to obtain new forms of benefit; benefits that had hitherto been thought impossible; benefits from virtually one-of-a-kind production.

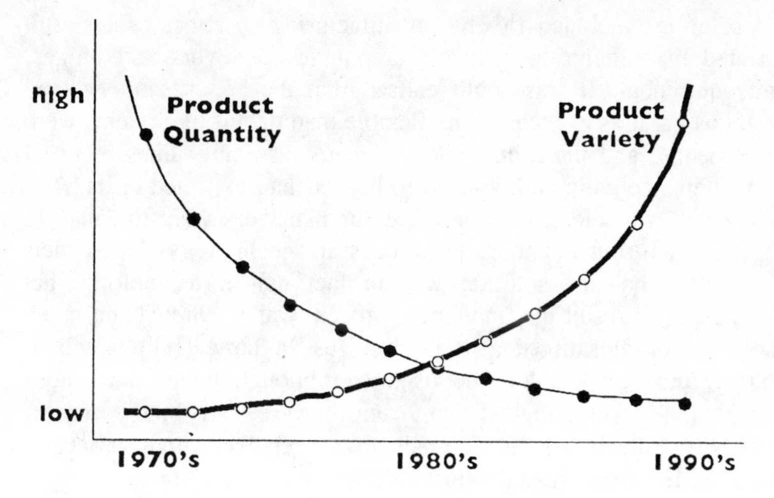

Fig. 2.1. Market trend

In a survey (Figure 2.2 [2]) it was deduced that the semi or unskilled workforce would be reduced from 41% in 1980 to just 10% in the year 2000. In the same period, it is estimated that the technical and engineering staff would be increased from 6% to 40%. This trend indicated that the workforce of the future would be far more technically oriented than the workforce of today. Consequently, the company concerned ploughed much effort and resource into technology.

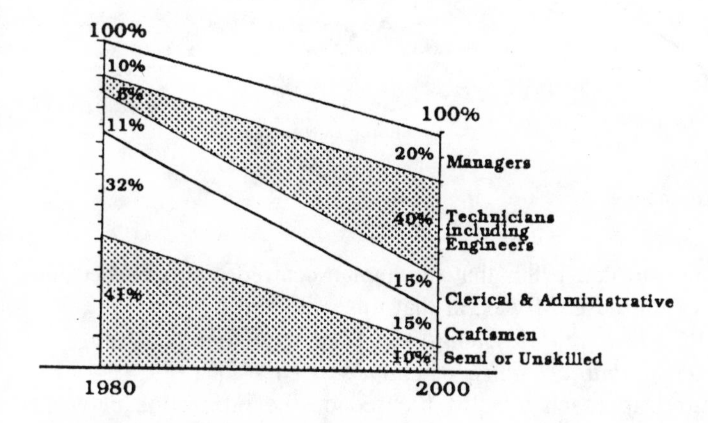

Fig. 2.2. Current trends in skill levels

It was realised that, to get a company from Point A to Point B (Figure 2.3), there has to be both organisational and technological change. During the early to mid-1980s many millions of ECUs were spent on so called 'technical solutions'.

These technical solutions included flexible manufacturing systems, robots, full computer integrated manufacturing systems, automatic conveyors and bigger, faster plant and equipment. It was soon realised that the benefits of such an approach were not as great as expected. The flexible manufacturing systems were not as flexible as people and the robots and automated assembly lines required high levels of maintenance which all equated to higher than expected costs.

During the late 1980s a selected group of senior managers went to Japan to study Japanese manufacturing methods, techniques and technology. Upon their return it was deemed that the solution was in fact not in technology, but organisational issues. As a result the 'modern approach' was attempted and much effort was placed on organisational aspects, i.e. Just-In-Time (JIT), Kanban, Group Technology, etc. Once again the benefits, although better than those obtained through the 'technological approach', were, in many cases, disappointing. This was attributed, in the main, to the relatively high variety of products produced in European manufacturing organisations (Figure 1).

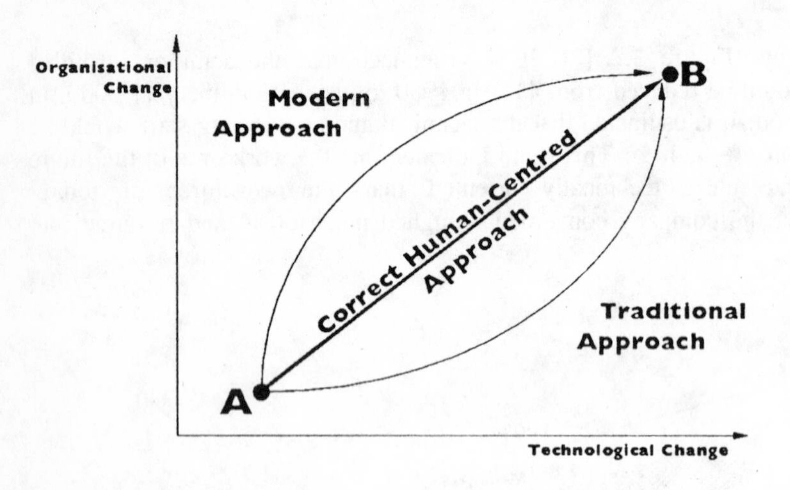

Fig. 2.3. Approaches to change

It was during the mid to late 1980s that the human centred approach became better known. Human Centred CIM was, at that time, defined as:

a new approach to CIM where the system is designed around human beings and integrates their capabilities, skills, inventiveness etc. [3]

Here the human centred approach to CIM focused on the interaction between technical issues, organisational issues and the most important asset any company possesses, its people, (Figure 2.4).

It was realised that computers were good at:

1. storing and processing information
2. performing routine and repetitive tasks
3. consistency

4. being constantly vigilant
5. multi-variable monitoring, etc.

whilst people, humans are good at:

1. working as a team
2. fast, adaptive decision making
3. dealing with unforeseen events
4. handling complex quality criteria
5. changing tasks rapidly
6. using attributes such as perception and intuition and suggesting design improvements.

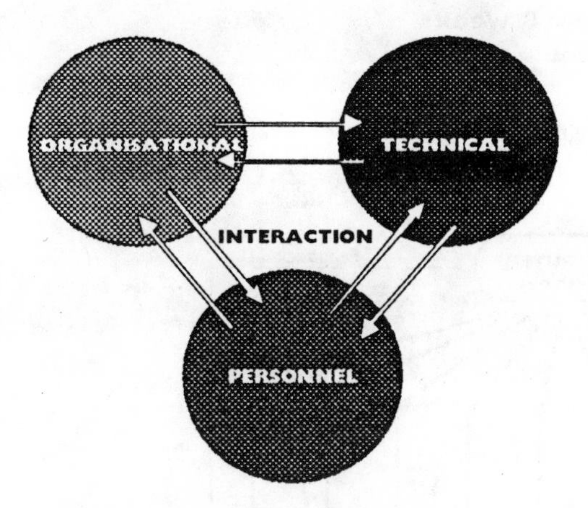

Fig. 2.4. Human approach to CIM

2.2 The Project Focus

With this background of high variety, low volume batch manufacture, etc., it was realised that a focus had to be adopted if progress was to be made. In this case, the focus was on a human centred approach to production planning. This, it was hoped would result in improved due date performance, reduced delivery times and also, simultaneously, improved customer satisfaction.

It was realised that focusing on the speeding up of a particular machine or process would not have the required effect (Figure 2.5), i.e. a massive 50% reduction in machining time would only improve door-to-door time by about 1%. What was needed was a renewed emphasis on production planning which combined organisational aspects, backed up with the appropriate technology. It was therefore decided to move away from the traditional systems centred factory (Figure 2.6) where the computer system tries to dictate and orchestrate what each individual machine does, when it does it, and how it does it and move to a cell-based approach (Figure 2.7).

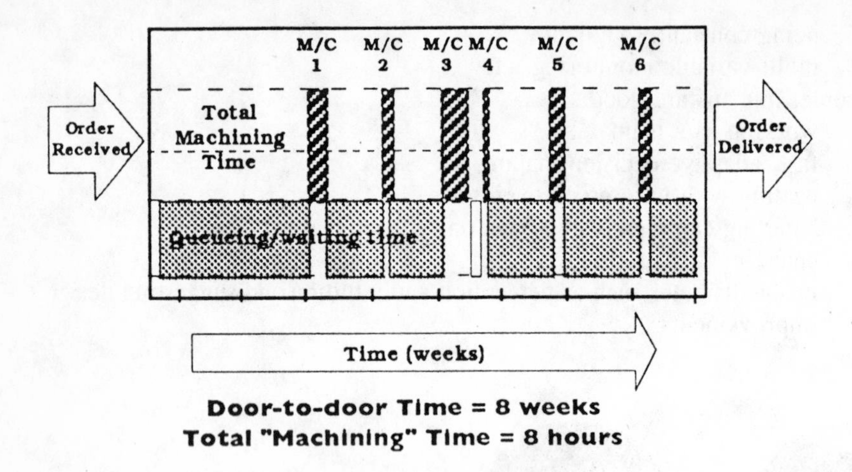

Fig. 2.5. Typical job profile in a European factory

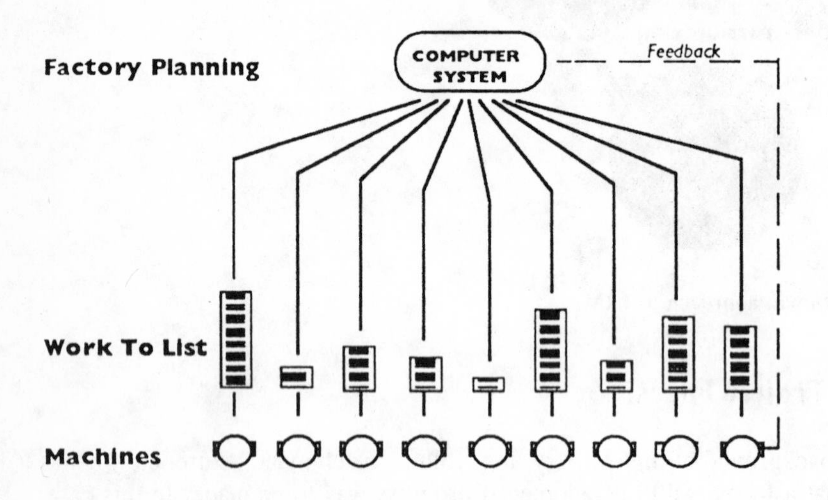

Fig. 2.6. Traditional Systems-centred factory

In the traditional system centred factory, the feedback path, although there in theory, was very rarely used in practice. The management hierarchy tended to hinder effective feedback of information. What was important to a machine operator was less important to his supervisor and had an even lower priority as far as his manager was concerned, etc. By the time the corrected information reached the computer system operators who had to update the computer system, the information was either out of date at best, or more often the case, never reached the Systems Department in the first place.

In the cell-based approach (Figure 2.7) a simplified factory planning system was provided, which down-loaded order lists to manufacturing cells. The cell

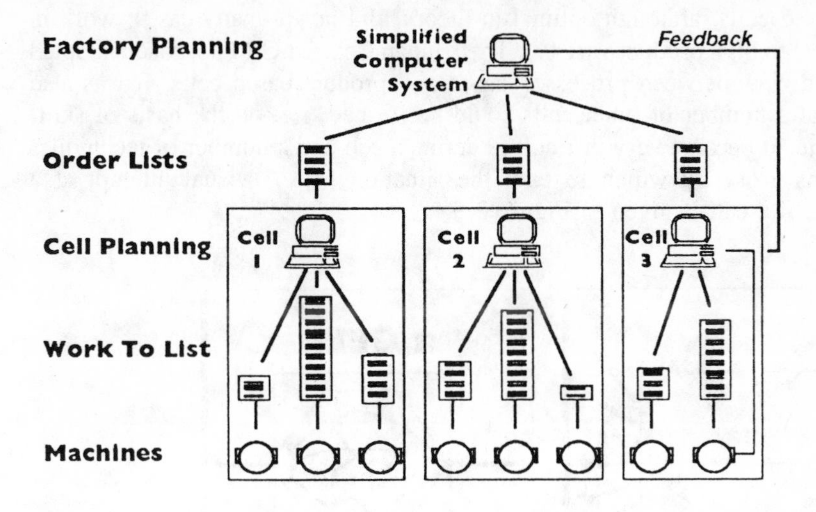

Fig. 2.7. Modern cell-based factory

leaders, line managers, etc., were then able to down-load to the machines within the cells work lists. In this case, the feedback mechanism worked extremely effectively. The cell managers only down-loaded jobs to machines that they knew, from their local knowledge, were capable of running them. Similarly, the cell managers only accepted order lists from the factory planner that they knew from personal knowledge the cell could manufacture. In this way, fast and efficient feedback was provided at all levels in the manufacturing organisation.

The way the factory was divided into cells then became critical. In the past (the MRPI days?) the departments/workshops tended to be process based (Figure 2.8).

When the first drive to cell-based manufacture emerged, there was a great

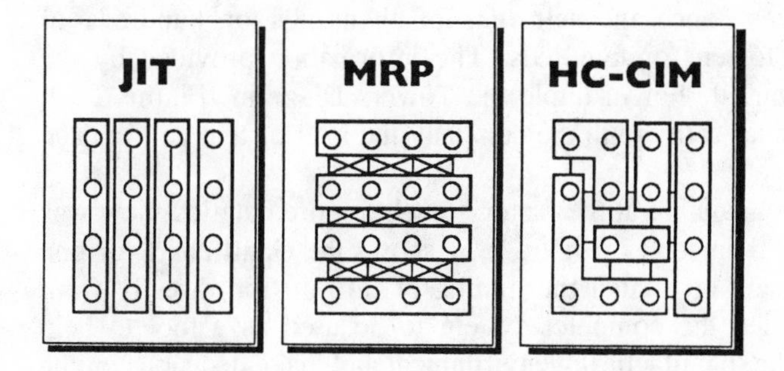

Fig. 2.8. Diagrammatic representation of JIT, MRP & HC-CIM

tendency to move towards product-based cells and the adoption of Just-In-Time (JIT) principles. It was not realised that slavish adoption of the JIT approach and product based cells, although optimal in theory, did not in many cases, work in practice (due to high product variety). The Human Centred CIM approach adopted a pragmatic view between processed based and product based cells. It was also realised that a number of other cells could be formed, i.e. on the basis of skill, material, etc. It became very difficult to define a cell and a number of techniques and systems arose by which to ease the situation [4]. A visual attempt at a 'definition' of a cell is given in Figure 2.9.

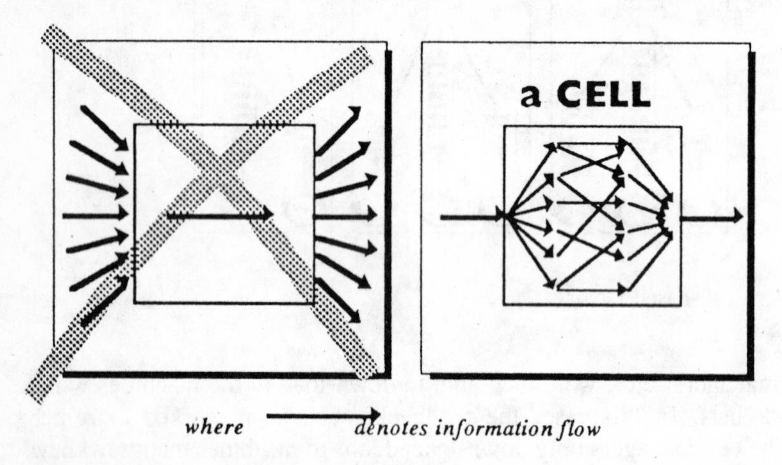

Fig. 2.9. A visual 'definition' of a cell

2.3 The Solution

The implementation of what is thought to be the world's first human centred system was installed on the south coast of England in September 1989. The company produced a variety (47,000) of electrical connectors for the electronics industry. The batch sizes, once in their tens of thousands or hundreds of thousands, had reduced to tens or hundreds. The information provided by the systems was wide and varied. For example the Towers Diagram (Figure 2.10) indicates for each individual cell within the company the load of that cell in each time period.
Whilst this overview was available at the factory level, a more detailed view was available within the cells themselves. Figure 2.11 shows the Gantt chart for one particular cell. Mechanisms facilitated the mining of information directly from these screens. This enabled the computer system to be used as a tool to help people both learn about the manufacturing environment and make decisions on the information provided.

A typical systems architecture is given in Figure 2.12. The PC-based system can be installed and implemented in modules, one cell at a time as and when required.

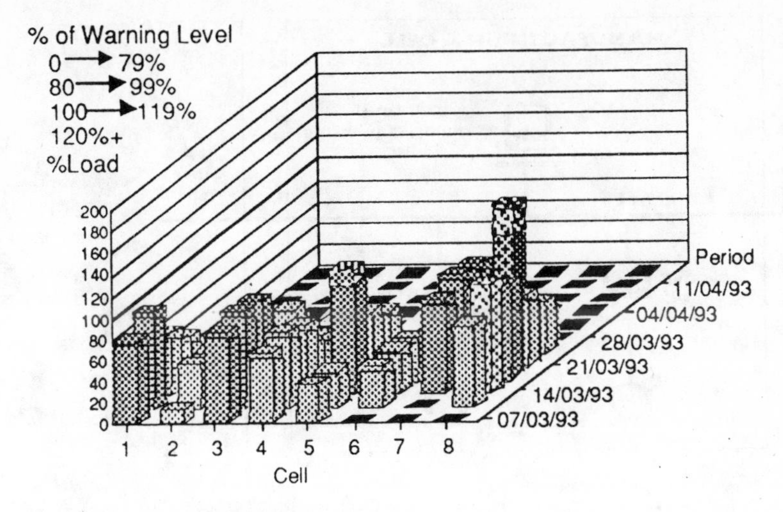

Fig. 2.10. Factory loading

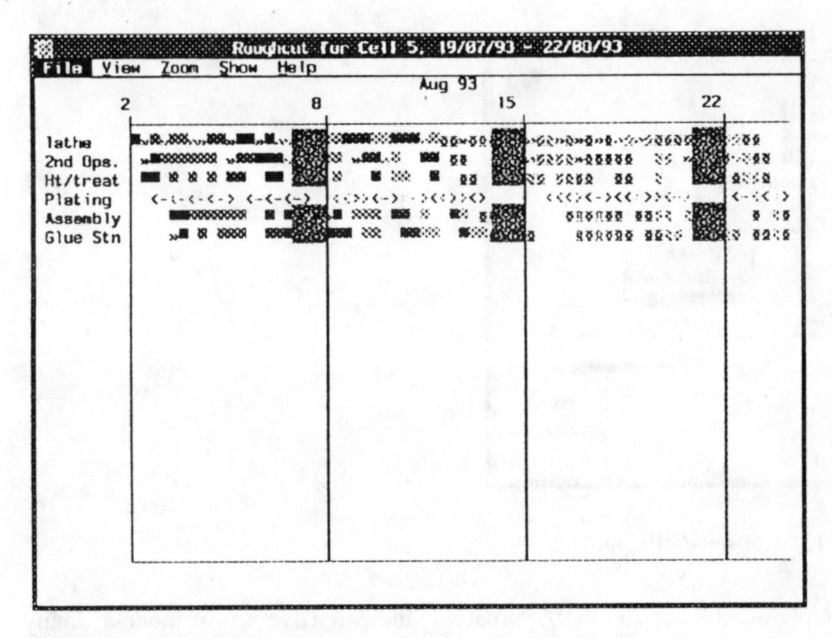

Fig. 2.11. Gantt chart for a cell

The method by which this human centred system was developed and introduced followed the Helical Project Life Cycle [5]. It is firmly believed that the Helical Project Life Cycle procedure greatly facilitated and eased both systems development and implementation, resulting in the significant benefits [6].

The Helical Product Life Cycle enables many of the problems associated with the traditional waterfall approach (Figure 2.13) to be overcome.

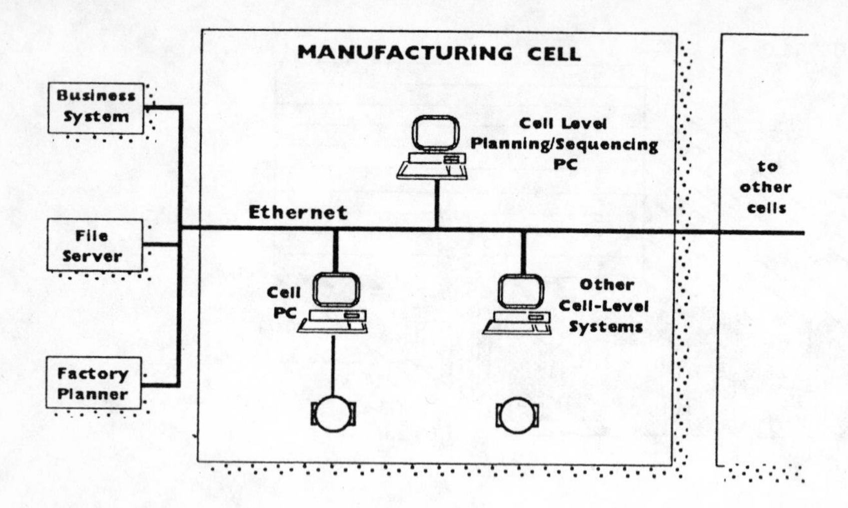

Fig. 2.12. Typical systems architecture

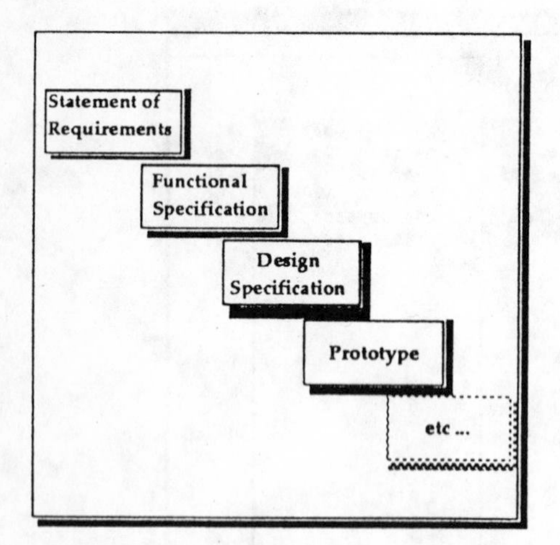

Figure 2.13. The waterfall approach

The principle behind the Helical Approach is the extensive use of models. Many models/mock-ups of the system are made. The models have physical, psychological, diagrammatic and verbal attributes. The benefits of such an approach are significant and it was the Helical Approach that was instrumental in enabling the first human centred system to be designed, built and installed.

2.4 Benefits and Conclusions

The benefits of installing the human centred system into the company concerned were high. 50% improvement in throughput can be seen in Figure 2.14. Figure 2.15 details the 75% reduction in overtime. The 100% delivery performance for a typical manufacturing cell with the Human Centred Computer Integrated Manufacturing (HC-CIM) approach is given in Figure 2.16. The benefits have been so good that the Human Centred Computer Integrated Manufacturing System has now been commercialised. Its commercial name is ACiT (Appropriate Computer integrated Technology) and is available throughout the UK various other companies via Distributors [7].

In conclusion, the benefits of implementing human centred systems have been significant. They have not been limited to financial benefits, but also extend into the organisation as a whole. The people using the systems appear to be more motivated and have more control and say over their local environment than before. They also have, at their figure tips, far more information (as opposed to data) by which decisions can be taken that benefit not only the cell concerned, but also have a significant impact on the company at large. It is this increased transparency, the provision of information and the use of appropriate human centred computer systems (ACiT) that has enabled the company to earn through learning and to succeed.

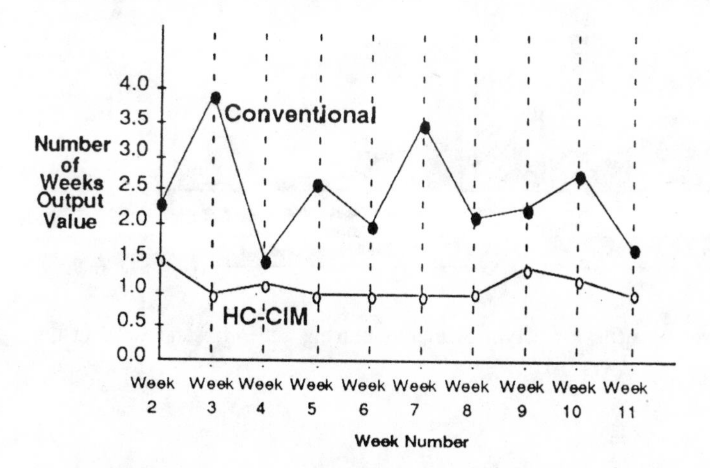

Fig. 2.14. Improvement in throughput achieved by the use of HC-CIM scheduling by a reduction in work in progress, expressed in weeks of sales (at standard cost)

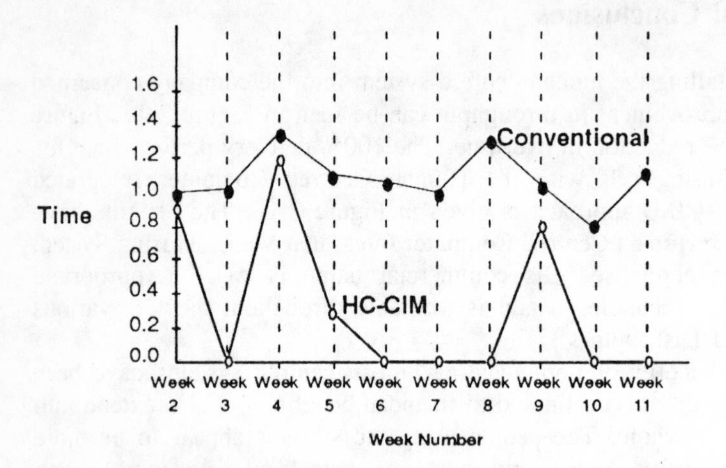

Fig. 2.15. Comparison of excess hours required by a typical manufacturing cell with and without the benefits of HC-CIM

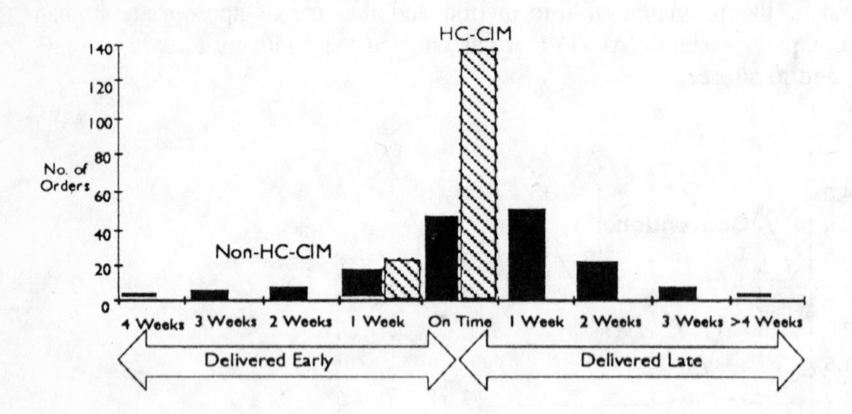

Fig. 2.16. Order delivery profile for a typical manufacturing cell with and without the benefit of HC-CIM

References

1. Ainger A, 1988 Human Centred CIM Systems, Technology in Action, BICC, UK.
2. Hancke T, 1990 Training Needs of Small to Medium Size Enterprises Implementation and Operating Human-Centred Manufacturing Systems, Delta 7064, Imperial College, London, UK.
3. Cooley M, 1986 Human Centred CIM Systems E/P 1199, ESPRIT Conference, Brussels, Belgium.
4. Maher R, 1993, Manufacturing Cell Formation System, 2nd Year Project Report, Brunel University, UK.

5. Ainger A, April 1991, Manufacturing - A Practical Human-Centred Perspective, Engineering Management Journal, IEE, London, UK.
6. Hamlin M, April 1989 Human Centred CIM, The Professional Engineer, UK.
7. ACiT 1993, Available from Human Centred Systems Limited, Hemel Hempstead, Herts, HP2 4SJ, UK.

3. A Business Strategy Perspective in HCS

Nigel Slack

Warwick Business School, University of Warwick, Coventry CV4 7AL, UK

Abstract. Although the performance of the manufacturing function, and therefore implicitly its constituent manufacturing systems, is central to company competitiveness, system designers are sometimes reluctant to evaluate the effectiveness of their designs at the level of the firm. Yet without a clear and unambiguous link between the way in which a company competes and the performance of its manufacturing system, the manufacturing function will never achieve its potential to enhance competitiveness. To make this link, system designers must first place the performance of their systems in terms of the generic manufacturing system performance dimensions - quality, speed, dependability, flexibility and cost. Second they must judge the relative importance of these dimensions against their importance to customers. Third, they must judge their system's performance against that of their competitors. Finally an Importance - Performance matrix is illustrated which can be used to prioritise the development needs of manufacturing systems

Keywords. Manufacturing Strategy, Competitiveness, Performance Objectives

3.1 Introduction

Manufacturing systems, however configured, form part of the greater manufacturing function, which in most companies represents the bulk of its assets and the majority of its people. Yet it is misleading to think of manufacturing as mere 'bulk'. It is the operation's anatomy, its bones, sinew and muscles. Hence its importance, and implicitly the importance of its manufacturing systems. A healthy manufacturing function gives the company the strength to withstand competitive attack, the endurance to maintain a steady improvement in competitive performance, and perhaps most important, the operational suppleness which can respond to increasingly volatile markets. Yet there seems a reluctance amongst some manufacturing system designers to acknowledge the importance of their efforts at this level - the level of the firm, and its competitive position. Their focus is either at the level of the single 'micro system', or at the societal level.

The contention of this paper is that the main contribution of manufacturing systems should be judged at the level of the individual company's competitive position. After all, their influence can handicap a business' performance no matter how sharp is its strategic sense. Many companies know the frustration of their best laid strategic ambitions rendered impotent by manufacturing system's inability to translate them into effective action. Strategy only means anything when it can be translated into operational action. It remains an abstract set of aspirations if it is devised in an operational vacuum.

Competitive strategy cannot hope to be successful in the long term unless it expects the manufacturing system's role in creating a strategic advantage to be both pivotal and direct. This means more than simply acknowledging the limitations of the system, though it will have limitations. It means that it must recognise the sheer competitive power which an effective manufacturing system can give the whole organisation. (Skinner 1973).

3.2 Competitiveness Through a Manufacturing System Advantage

The question therefore is, "what should a company be expecting of its manufacturing system?" In all too many companies manufacturing systems are little more than an irritant, a drag on the company's competitive effort. Many a manufacturing manager's time is spent fire fighting. Rarely if ever do manufacturing system designers contribute directly to strategic decision making, except to act as a constraint. Often the manufacturing system is the reason why the company can't do what it really wants to do. Contrast this with the role which manufacturing system designers perhaps should play. Here the competitive success of the whole company is a direct consequence of its manufacturing function having a superior performance to any competitors. Its products have a specification closer to the customer's needs than those made by any competitor, they are made and reach the customer 'error free', they are delivered in a lead-time faster than any competitor can match, and they always arrive at the time they are promised. Furthermore the manufacturing function has the confidence to change its stance, to adapt as the competitive environment itself changes (Slack 1991).

The gap between these two very different pictures of the manufacturing system's role is defined by their achievements relative to two sets of people - customers and competitors. Both of these groups should be central to manufacturing systems designer's thinking.

3.3 Customers are the Arbiters of what is Important

Constructing a set of aims and objectives for manufacturing is a matter of translating the needs (and potential needs) of customers into terms which are meaningful to it. It involves, for example, deciding whether price is more important to customers than lead-time, or product range or delivery dependability, or anything else. And if price is a more important factor, by how much? And which is the second most important factor? Further, do different products or product groups compete in broadly the same way, or are there significant differences in the relative importance of their needs? In other words how do customers value the things which manufacturing can contribute to the operation's performance? A common response to this idea is to claim that all aspects of performance are important to customers. And so they might be, but not equally important. Some must have a greater significance to customers than others.

A particularly useful way of doing this is to distinguish between "Order Winning" and "Qualifying" objectives (Hill 1993).

Order Winning Objectives are those which directly and significantly contribute to winning business. They are regarded by customers as the key factors of competitiveness, the ones which are the most influential in their decision of how much business to give to the company. Raising performance in order winning objective will either result in more business or improve the chances of gaining more business.

Qualifying Objectives may not be the major competitive determinants of success, but are important in another way. They are those aspects of competitiveness where the operation's performance has to be above a particular level even to be considered by the customer. Below the critical level of performance the company probably won't even enter the frame. Above the 'qualifying' level, it will be considered, but mainly in terms of its performance in the order winning factors. Any further improvement in qualifying factors above the qualifying level is unlikely to gain much competitive benefit.

It is customers then who totally define what manufacturing should consider important. Their needs should be manufacturing's priorities, their concerns should be manufacturing's concerns. Yet customers concerns are rarely static. They change with customers' own competitive priorities, and they respond to activity from competitors. What was regarded as acceptable performance before can be rendered inadequate by a competitor raising their own, and possibly the whole industry's standards.

3.4 Competitors' Performance Defines your Performance

If the first part of manufacturing's contribution to competitiveness is understanding customer needs and shaping its values and interests accordingly, the second part is to reach levels of performance which make it pre-eminent in the eyes of its customers. Yet although it is the customer who is to be impressed by the operation's achievements, it is not against the customer standards on which performance should be judged - it is against competitors. All improvement in performance is, at least potentially, worthwhile, but that marginal step which takes a company beyond the performance level of its competitors is by far the most valuable. The most significant boost to competitiveness will come when the performance of order winning factors is raised above those of competitors. Conversely any reduction in the relative performance of qualifying factors will be particularly serious if it drops below the industry's 'qualifying' level of performance. It becomes, in effect, an 'order losing' factor.

It may never be easy to assess competitors' performance with absolute accuracy, but most operations seem to spend a totally inadequate amount of time and effort tracking it. Knowing how your rivals are performing has obvious advantages in terms of anticipating their competitive position and in being able to learn from their successes and failures. But the longer term and ultimately greater benefit is in the way constant comparison with competitors establishes the idea of competitiveness itself within the operation.

3.5 The Manufacturing Advantage Means 'Making Things Better'

Both customers and competitors are central to a competitive manufacturing operation because they define its aims succinctly - to satisfy one and be better than the other. A successful manufacturing operation relies on bringing a strong sense of both customers and competitors right on to the shop floor. Customers to act as a constant reminder to the operation of what aspects of competitiveness are important to it. Competitors provide the measure against which its own performance should be judged. But more than this, by bringing a customer derived measure of importance together with a competitor derived measure of performance, priorities for improving the operation can be formulated. Remember that the aim is to develop a manufacturing system which can give the company an overwhelming advantage in its market place. A manufacturing based advantage is one which relies on the manufacturing function to provide the main ammunition in the competitive battle. In fact all the fundamental aspects of competitiveness are clearly within the mandate of the manufacturing function. It has direct influence over such aspects of competitive performance as producing error free products, getting goods to the customer quickly, invariably keeping delivery promises, being able to introduce innovative new products on a timely basis, providing a range of products wide enough to satisfy customer requirements, being able to change volumes or delivery dates to customer demands. And, always important, it determines the company's ability to offer products at a price which either undercuts the competition or gives a high margin, or both. In effect manufacturing is the custodian of competitiveness for the whole organisation.

3.6 Manufacturing System Strategic Performance Objectives

At its most basic, the role of the effective manufacturing system is to 'make things better' than competitors. This can be broken down into a number of discrete objectives.

It means *making things right* - not making mistakes, making products which actually are as they are supposed to be, products which are error free and always up to their design specification. Whichever way it is put, by doing this the manufacturing system gives a *Quality Advantage* to the company.

It means *making things fast* - achieving an elapsed time between starting the manufacturing process and the product reaching the customers which is short than competitors. In doing this the manufacturing system gives a *Speed Advantage* to the company.

It means *making things on time* - keeping the actual or implied delivery promise. This implies being able to estimate delivery dates accurately (or alternatively accept the customers required delivery date) clearly communicate this to the customer, and then deliver on time. In doing this the manufacturing system gives the company a *Dependability Advantage*.

It means *changing what is made* - being able to vary and adapt the operation, either because the needs of customers alter, or because of changes in the production process, or perhaps because of changes in the supply of resources. It means being able to change far enough, and being able to change fast enough. In doing this the manufacturing system gives the company a *Flexibility Advantage*.

Finally it means *making things cheap* - making products at a cost lower than competitors can manage. In the long term the only way to achieve this is by obtaining resources cheaper and/or converting them more efficiently than competitors. In doing this manufacturing gives a *Cost Advantage* to the company.

These then are the manufacturing system's five generic *performance objectives*, they are the basic building blocks of competitiveness. Any manufacturing system designer should be able to rank the relative importance of its performance objectives and judge its achievements in terms of each of them. In other words, an effective methodology of prioritizing the system's performance objectives is necessary. One such relies on the twin strategic influences of customer requirements and competitor performance to develop priorities for the system designer to address (Slack 1991).

3.7 The Importance — Performance Matrix

In effect, customers and competitors define the relative importance and the relative performance of each characteristic of a manufacturing system. Both these dimensions can be (arbitrarily) quantified on some kind of scale. The following are suggested and have been empirically tests (Slack 1993).

3.7.1 A Nine Point Importance Scale

For the products manufactured on this system, does each performance objective...
Order Winning Objectives

1. Provide a crucial advantage with customers — it is the main thrust of competitiveness.
2. Provide an important advantage with most customers — it is always considered.
3. Provide a useful advantage with most customers — it is usually considered.

Qualifying objectives

4. Need to be at least up to good industry standard.
5. Need to be around the median industry standard.
6. Need to be within close range of the rest of the industry.

Less Important Objectives

7. Not usually come into customer's consideration, but could become more important in the future.
8. Very rarely come into customer's considerations.
9. Never come into consideration by customers or is every likely to do so.

3.7.2 A Nine Point Performance Scale

In this market sector, or for this product group, is the achieved performance of the manufacturing system in each of the performance objectives ...

1. Consistently considerably better than our nearest competitor.
2. Consistently clearly better than our nearest competitor.
3. Consistently marginally better than our nearest competitor.
4. Often marginally better than most competitors.
5. About the same as most competitors.
6. Often within striking distance of the main competitors.
7. Usually marginally worse than main competitors.
8. Usually worse than most competitors.
9. Consistently worse than most competitors.

Figure 1 illustrates how these two scales can be used to derive priorities for manufacturing system development. A number of the manufacturing system characteristics have been scored as to their importance against customer needs and their performance against competitor performance. Those which fall in the bottom right corner of the matrix are clearly in need of urgent attention. They are the dimensions of performance which customers value but where current performance lags competitor performance. They should therefore be given first priority in terms of systems improvement. These dimensions of performance which fall below the "lower bound of acceptability" line, but are not in the first priority area, are accorded second priority of improvement. The lower bound of acceptability is an arbitrary line which will differ depending on a company's competitive position, but is often as shown in Figure 1. Above this line performance is generally appropriate. However should any attributes of performance fall in the top left corner of the matrix they should be examined to ensure that excess design capability has not been expended on achieving them. These dimensions of performance are those where actual performance seems to exceed customer requirements.

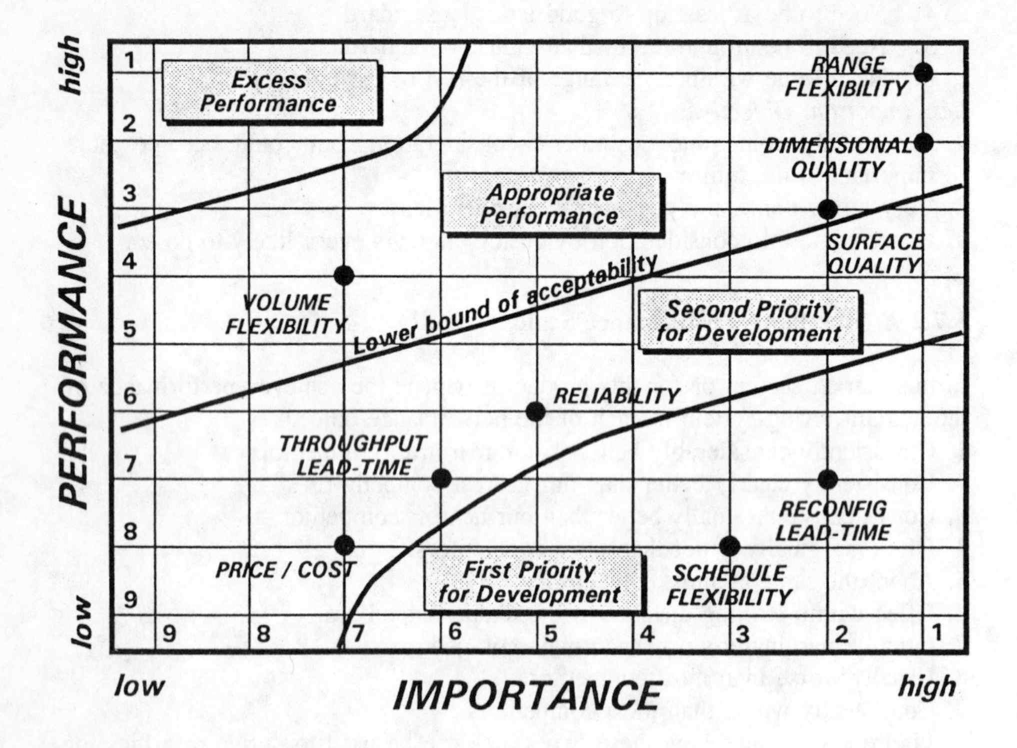

Fig 3.1. Example of the Importance-Performance Matrix used to Prioritise a System's Performance Characteristics

References

Hill, T "Manufacturing Strategy". Second Edition, Wiley, 1993

Skinner, W "Manufacturing in the corporate strategy", Wiley, 1978.

Hayes, R H & Wheelwright, S C "Restoring our competitive edge", Wiley 1984.

Slack, N "The Manufacturing Advantage", Mercury Business Book, 1991.

Slack, N "Using the Importance - Performance Matrix to judge internal priorities" Proceedings of the 8th OMA Conference, Warwick, 1993.

4. Prospects for Anthropocentric Production Systems in Europe

Werner Wobbe

Commission of the European Communities[1], DG XII MONITOR-FAST-Programme, B - 1049 Brussels

Abstract. New socioeconomic parameters have emerged in the last decade, changing the framework for industrial production. In particular, markets for customised quality products have increased, demanding flexible manufacturing patterns instead of those for mass production. A new paradigm for manufacturing has developed which puts organisation and human competence in the forefront and which requires adapted technologies. Anthropocentric Production Systems (APS) are fulfilling these requirements.

The present contribution explains what is meant by APS. It explores factors fostering and hindering its implementation in Europe and examines the role of public authorities and the C.E.C. as well as in the European member states. Finally it reasons about action necessary to further the adoption of Anthropocentric Production Systems in the European Community.

Keywords. Anthropocentric Production Systems, Research and Development Policy, Organisations Research, Manufacturing, Industrial Culture, European Community, European Forum

4.1 Introduction

A paradigm shift in the use of technology and labour and its organisation has emerged recently, placing emphasis on organisational factors to raise productivity rather than on technology. Until the 1970s, manufacturing concepts for Europe had been derived mainly from the precepts founded on mass production in its American context. These concepts still influence the thinking and beliefs of industrial managers. They will be detrimental to the process of adaptation of industry in Europe, a sector of the economy which is composed mainly of small and medium enterprises.

---

1 The opinions expressed are those of the author alone; under no circumstances should they be taken as an authoritative statement of the views of the Commission.

Over the last decade, a market shift towards customised quality products has occurred at the expense of standardised mass products. Industries based on mass products and open to price competition have lost out to the Far East and might in future also face competition from Eastern Europe.

The increase in product variants and quality features, smaller batch sizes and the decrease of product life cycle length and the reduction of repeat orders have had dramatic consequences for management and organisation in the manufacturing industries. In the 1980s, it became evident that the demand for flexibility could not be met by new technologies on their own. The challenge for management exists in finding the right combination of skilled personnel, flexible organisation and technologies adapted to these prerequisites. This combination is called *'Anthropocentric Production Systems'* (APS) and underlies a new manufacturing paradigm contrary to the traditional one based on a high division of labour and the step by step automation of the production process.

APS has been proved to be economically very successful in industrial sectors affected by steadily changing demands, volatile markets and the need for high adaptability to customer requirements, more so than 'lean production'. Lean production principles are focused on the needs of the automotive industry, where they are applied to modernising the large scale methods of production. APS can be taken as a European approach, suited best to the diversified small and medium sized firms in industries such as machine tool production, engineering, wood work, textiles etc, predominant in Europe.

4.2 A Brief History of the Paradigm Shift in Manufacturing

4.2.1 Developments of the 1970s and 1980s

The expanding markets and the global competition typical of this century have led to enforced division of labour and to Taylorist and Fordist principles of work organisation. Achieving maximum scale of production via specialisation and automation were the guiding concepts for managers. Increased labour specialisation and automation have been complementary processes.

When, in the 1970s and 1980s, fragmentation of markets and product complexity grew and the lack of production flexibility became a threat, computer aided technologies seemed to offer a solution to cope with this challenge in manufacturing. Therefore, in these two decades, the technological imperative, the technocentric manufacturing paradigm, became dominant in managers' minds and thus resulted in public support for technological R&D. At the end of the 1980s, however, the first critical conclusions were drawn by researchers observing the diffusion pattern of the computer aided technologies, giving the following results:

- industrial robots, the symbol of industrial automation, have progressed far below expectation in industrial development [2],
- FMS (Flexible Manufacturing Systems) hardly ever become economic if applied together with Tayloristic forms of work organisation [4],

- 30 % of CAD Systems have been abandoned immediately after implementation[1],
- MRP-Systems (Material Resource Planning and Control Systems for the shopfloor) are claimed to have caused misinvestments to the tune of 100 mio. DM in Germany,
- assembly automation in the European automobile industry has been abandoned and in certain instances, installations have been dismantled[2],
- information technology in manufacturing has been applied very differently depending on social constellations [1],
- in the Danish context, the paradox of a combination of increasing technology application and diminishing productivity has been observed [2].

We can therefore state that, from the late 1980s, the manufacturing paradigm inspired by information technology and aiming at the 'peopleless automated factory' has been questioned quite fundamentally.

At the same time, recognition of the complex interplay between man, technology and organisation and its management has come to be understood as a system. As a transitional phase, measures fostering the acceptance of new technologies and training to adapt people's competence, but leaving the old fashioned Tayloristic concepts of manufacturing organisation intact, have been of crucial interest.

Now, in the early 1990s, influenced by the studies at the Massachusetts Institute of Technology (MIT) of 'lean production'[10] and the EC on 'Anthropocentric Production Systems' (APS) [7, 9], it has become clear that the manufacturing organisation, the use of skilled and competent labour and a proper management of this system is at the core of the solution of the problems witnessed before. Therefore, the manufacturing paradigm is in the course of shifting from a 'technocentric' focus to an 'anthropocentric and collaborative' focus.

4.2.2 The Background to the Paradigm Shift

As already mentioned, the attempts at 'understanding' manufacturing either through the spectacles of automation technology only or from the restricted viewpoint of the users of mathematical wisdom and information technology alone are, evidently equally inadequate.

These 'biased views' of manufacturing stem from academic groups and also from military based research and manufacturing funding in the United States. For European manufacturing, it is relevant to understand that product markets are

---

1 According to an ILO Survey of 1989.

2 FIAT has abandoned an automatic assembly line while VW kept its own but has not gone further with its famous automation showpiece of Halle 54 and announced, instead, the development of group work. A big automobile manufacturer paid 9 mill. DM to an equipment producer to 'de-automate' a welding line.

being transformed. This market shift is the economic background for the success or failure of both old and new manufacturing concepts.

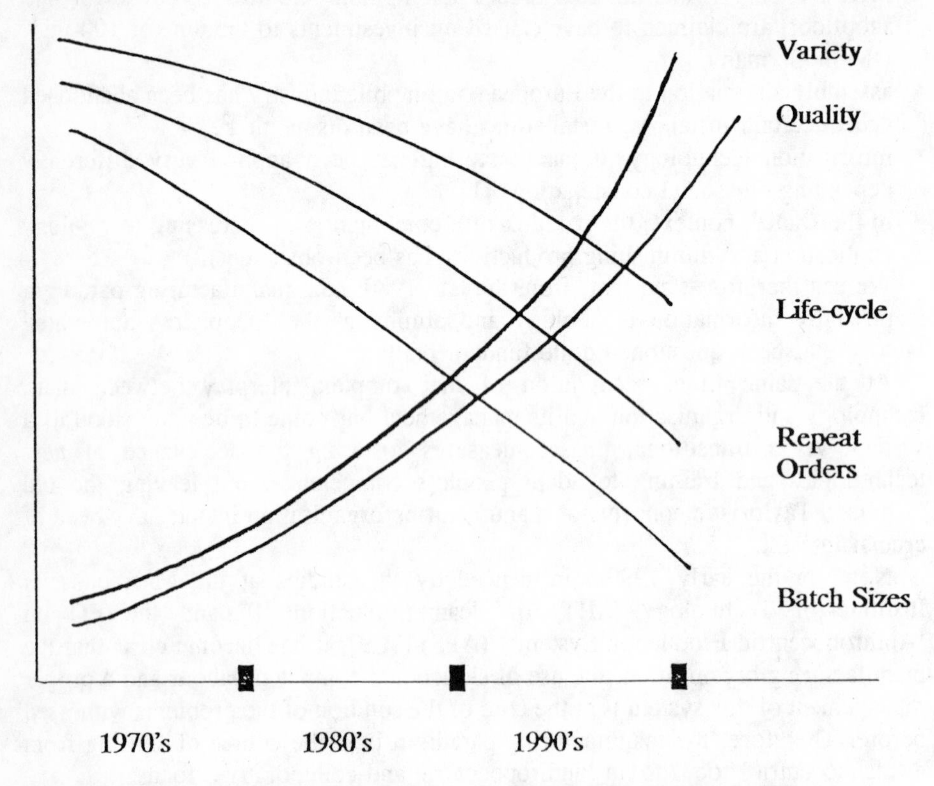

Fig. 4.1. Market trends in a few decades. Source: FAST (W.W.), P. Kidd

As Western societies have become more affluent, so have the market demands for customised products become more sophisticated. New quality features have come into play — not only those of functionality and reliability but also those of additional features and designs. While the cheap and price sensitive products are more and more frequently produced in low wage countries, the markets for customised quality products are expanding in Europe. This increase of the customised quality economy has dramatic consequences for manufacturing.

The example of a big British producer of electromechanical equipment is typical of this development. The company had to restructure its operations completely to respond to the changes and to cope with their effects.
All efforts of this corporation to reduce the number of variants had been unsuccessful. On the contrary, the number of product variants was steadily being increased, coupled to a parallel demand for quality upgrading. Concurrently, the life cycle of products decreased and with it the size and incidence of repeat orders. Also, batch sizes were reduced dramatically due to the decision of customers to minimize stocks and to ask for delivery of the right lot sizes when

LEVEL	TECHNOLOGY
WORKPLACE	* shopfloor programming systems for machine tools and robots * decision support systems * analogue user support mechanism to control the manufacturing process * symbolic representations of complete pictures for information, processing and decisions * skill supporting and learning techniques
GROUP	* scheduling and planning systems for group work * computer aided cooperative work techniques for information, planning and decisions
INTERDEPART-MENTAL	* IT systems to facilitate interactions and dialogue between office and shopfloor * transportable analogue design sketch pads
FACTORY	* information systems to support network organizational structures
GENERAL	* adaptable and natural language human/computer interfaces * highly transparent support systems for collective and individual decision making * new vision and symbolic representation systems

Fig. 4.2. APS Technology. Source: FAST (W. W.)

needed. In other manufacturing industries too, and even in chemicals production, this trend can observed. These contradictory trends in manufacturing — resulting in a dilemma in the philosophy of price competition — can only be brought to a new balance with a different way of manufacturing.

4.2.3 The New Paradigm for Management, Labour and Organisation: APS

As already mentioned, anthropocentric production systems have been developed to cope with the 'customised quality' economy. APS require:

- comprehensive use of human abilities and performance,
- permanent learning of the work force and corporate structures which facilitate such behaviour,
- decentralized production units,
- reduction in the division of labour,
- collaborative forms of organisation,

- adapted technologies.

The last point in particular means that technology development has to start from the organisational and human requirements to perform production and not from the technological possibilities available. Therefore, these new systems also need new technology and new technological research. What we mean with this is indicated in Fig. 4.2 'APS Technology'.

4.3 Industrial Cultures and the New Concepts

4.3.1 Collaborative Structures are Essential

The traditional manufacturing paradigm has worked well with a hierarchic form of organisation, high division of labour and clear task description. The new manufacturing organisation needs overall collaboration to adapt steadily to new requirements and changes to the product(s). Collaboration is demanded at different levels and in varying situations using a number of means:

- team work at all levels of production,
- blue/white collar communication,
- interdepartmental cooperation,
- collaborative industrial relations,
- cooperation in the supply chain.

These requirements touch attitudes, values, behaviour, social distinction, power and influence in corporations. They are at the core of a given industrial culture — meaning how people and organisations deal with each other and their work. They relate directly to the management of a firm.

The awareness of this fundamental and essential concept of the significance of industrial cultures has developed only over the last few years [8]. Differences in the industrial cultures of Japan, Europe and the US can be detected easily but even in Europe, industrial cultures and social constellations are very different from country to country.

In a basic sketch of the structure of an enterprise, we can distinguish by functional analysis managers, white collar staff, consisting of technicians and engineers, supervisors and clerical staff, commercial and administrative employees. The blue collar workers, often represented at the bottom of the pyramid, if at all, are carrying out production work, maintenance and tool making.

As shown in Figs 4.3, 4.4 & 4.5, illustrating national differences in organisational configurations in France, Germany and the United Kingdom, there are substantially different ratios for the composition of white/blue collar staffing in these countries [6]. While France contains in manufacturing firms on average 41.6% white collar employees and 58.4% blue collar workers, Germany is quite significantly different. It has a white/blue collar ratio of 28.2% to 71.8% while Britain is closer to France with 37% to 63%. Germany thus scores top in allowing work to be executed at the lowest possible competence level, a phenomenon which might be explained by its strong tradition of skilled workers.

The collaborative structures and the distinction between departments and functional areas are also considerably different between the countries. Because of the trade union structure based on professions, the distinction in Britain between technical staff and supervisory staff is strong as is that between production and maintenance workers. The situation is again different in Germany where this distinction is blurred because of the industrial trade union organisation as well as the acceptance and the esteem in which practical and productive work are held in German society.

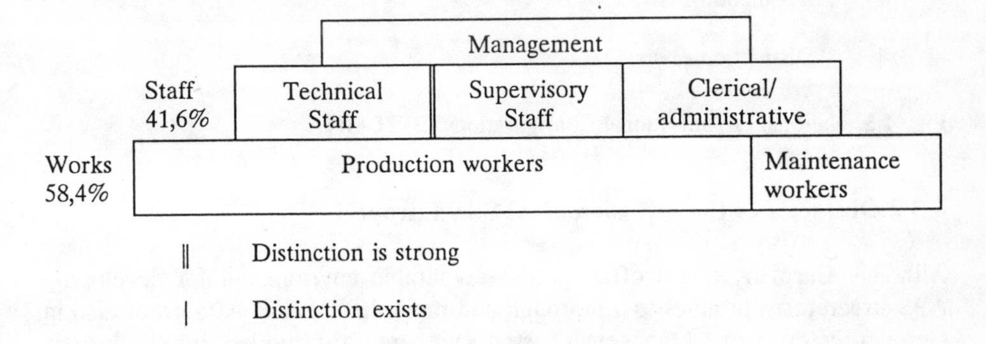

Fig. 4.3. National Organisational Configurations: FRANCE

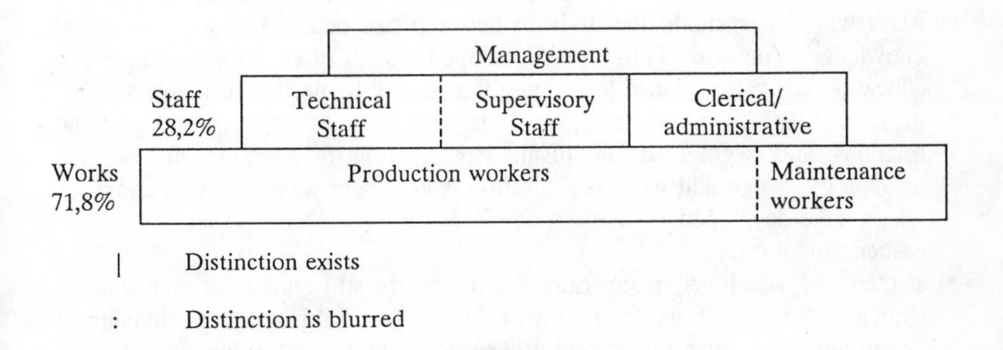

Fig. 4.4 National Organisational Configurations: GERMANY

In conclusion, the cultural context in German industry might be best suited for the application of new collaborative production concepts and it might also explain its industrial strength in certain industrial sectors such as machine tools, automobiles and electromechanical engineering.

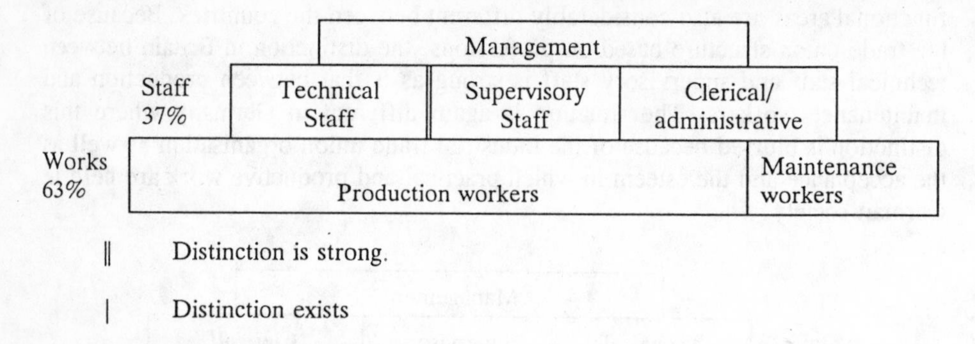

Fig. 4.5. National Organisational Configurations: BRITAIN

4.3.2 Obstacles to the diffusion of APS in Europe

Although Germany might offer quite a favourable environment for developing APS structures, obstacles to a thorough and rapid diffusion of APS occur also in German enterprises. Management strategies are still guided by Tayloristic principles and technocentric application of engineering expertise.

All over Europe, the following observations apply, according to M. Lehner [7], regarding mismatches and obstacles to the introduction of APS:

- qualitative and quantitative deficiencies in some national systems of education and training. These result in shortages of skilled labour as well as narrow skill bases which perpetuate the division between practical skills and theoretical knowledge. Countries with a well developed system of vocational and general education are better placed to provide the new skills needed in industry,
- in several EC member states, there is a climate of 'low trust' industrial relations and segmented unionism. Participation in decision making for technology design and work organisation is generally weak, even in countries which have developed co-determination,
- at the enterprise level, many European firms are still guided by management strategies for new technology which rely upon de-skilling, a high division of labour and short term investment criteria founded on cost reduction,
- public support for R&D has been concentrated on technical development work at the relative expense of social and organisational research and the diffusion of technology innovations for manufacturing,
- technology design of hardware and software is largely 'top down', with a lack of attention to issues such as user interaction, operator control and ability to comprehend the whole production process.

4.4 Europe's Role in Advanced Manufacturing

In general, industry has to solve manufacturing problems by itself. This is to be said in the light of 'socio-cultural' aspects of manufacturing and the spirit of subsidiarity in a double sense: The state should not touch the industrial firm's autonomy and the EC should not hurt the autonomy of the national patterns of industrial relations.

Nevertheless, large differences between member states with regard to the national philosophies of production should be made known to society in order to maintain the EC states' competitiveness at a decent international level. This would mean that the EC has a role to play in communication, knowledge transfer and stimulation and not so much in direct intervention.

In Industry, many enterprises must analyse their position and have to realise the need for:

- better incorporation of users' ideas into system design,
- more effective inclusion of organisational changes and human factors in the strategic plan of the organisation,
- a permanent skills audit of the workforce and systematic development of education and training opportunities,
- reorganisation towards teamwork and reduced division of labour.

Since industry, formed mostly of small to medium sized enterprises, lacks cohesion and a sense of strong common direction, public authorities can play an essential role in two domains:

- fostering a rapid implementation of APS. The public sector needs to take steps to reduce socio-cultural obstacles to APS and to strengthen infrastructures, mainly at the training and educational level,
- expanding the present research and technological development approach of the Community to include a new R&D initiative on the 'organisational dimension of manufacturing'.

This need has been recognised by the CEC and has led to a number of research initiatives. According to the FAST study on anthropocentric production systems [9] action is necessary in the following areas:

- raising awareness about new manufacturing concepts,
- education, training and curriculum reforms at universities,
- research in manufacturing organisations on adapted technologies,
- knowledge transfer aimed at less industrialised member countries,
- stimulation of collaborative cultures,
- fostering rapid diffusion of APS practices by demonstration projects.

4.5 Final Remarks

These recommendations would enrich the EC's new industrial policy to strengthen the industrial base not only in terms of its 'hard' infrastructure but also of its 'soft systems side' which is the industrial culture. Synergy effects between countries and the transfer of knowledge from advanced industries, firms and regions would be beneficial in order to guarantee cohesion in the Community.

In conclusion, these actions are not for centralised state-guided action but a concerted action by those directly involved. This means that it is time for a European Forum on Advanced Manufacturing. The purpose of the Forum should be to raise awareness of actors in business, unions, policy making and the scientific world in order to support rapid implementation of Anthropocentric Production Systems.

References

1. Campbell, A., Sorge, A., Warner, M. : Microelectronic Product Applications in Great Britain and West-Germany, Avebury Grower Aldershot 1989.
2. Deiß, M., Döhl, V., Sauer, D. : Technikherstellung und Technikanwendung im Werkzeugmaschinenbau, Campus Verlag Frankfurt 1990.
3. Gjerding, A.N., Johnson, B., Kallhange, L., Lundvoll, B.A., Madsen, P.T. : Den Forsvundene Productiviteit, Charlottenlund 1990.
4. Haywood, B., Bessant, J.: Organisation and Integration of Production Systems in : Warner, M.,Wobbe, W., Brödner, P.: New Technology and Manufacturing Management, Wiley Chichester, 1990, P. 75. ff.
5. Hirsch-Kreinsen, H., Schultz-Wild, R., Köhler, C., von Behr, M.: Einstig in die rechnerintegrierte Produktion, Campus Verlag Frankfurt 1990.
6. Lane, C. : Management and Labour in Europe, Gower Aldershot 1990.
7. Lehner, F.: Anthropocentric Production Systems: The European Response to Advanced Manufacturing and Globalisation, Synthesis Report, C.E.C. FAST, Brussels 1991.
8. Rauner, F., Ruth, K. : The Prospects of Anthropocentric Production Systems - A World Comparison of Production Models, FOP 249, C.E.C. FAST, Brussels 1991.
9. Wobbe, W. : What are Anthropocentric Production Systems? Why are They a Strategic Issue for Europe?, Brussels, Luxembourg 1991.
10. Womack, J.P., Jones, D., Roos, D. : The Machine that Changed the World, Rawson Macmillan New York, 1990.

5. Getting the Human to the Centre of the System

Janet Rachel

CRICT, Brunel University, Uxbridge UB8 3PH, UK

Abstract. This chapter is written with the aim of demonstrating one way in which Human Centred Systems Design might be understood and thereby realised (that is, put into practice). It takes an Ethnographic[1] look at Systems Design, and draws out the kinds of lessons that might be learned from this perspective in the context of asking how Human Centred Systems might be designed.

Keywords. Ethnography, System Design, User, Technical, Social, Human, Design Methodology

5.1 Introduction

Ethnography is a research method which draws on the history and tradition of Anthropology. Literally, the word *ethnography* can be taken to be the writing (graphing) of the local community (ethno). In practice, of course, there is more to it than that. In order to help me decide what kinds of things to write about whilst studying my particular community (a Systems Design Team in a recently privatised Water Company — henceforth The Customer Project at Freshwater) I adopted the explicit tactic of thinking of myself as if an 'anthropologist visiting a distant and strange tribe'. The 'making strange' of something familiar is a tactic which might be thought of as a kind of lever with which I (the ethnographer) attempted to 'hold open' a view of action which, because it has become so familiar, is usually obscured. This is similar to the move made in Ethnomethodological Studies [2] and developed particularly in Social Studies of Science [4, 5, 6, 7, 8]. It was the explicit intention of the research[2] to try to find 'different' ways of understanding what goes on in Information Systems Design

---

[1] See Cooper, Hine, Low and Woolgar (1994) for a more detailed exposition of ethnographic approaches to technological domains [1].

[2] The research reported here was supported by SERC grant no. GR/H23917: Human Factors in Information Systems Development.

with the hope that this would shed fresh light on the problem of *improving* that process. In the case of The Customer Project at Freshwater, this meant getting the User's voice into the design process. For the purposes of this chapter then, I have interpreted the problem as one of moving the Human (or the Social) into the technical design process.

5.2 Defining the Problem

The first step to take in asking the question 'how to get the human to the centre of the system' is to notice that 'humans' in some form are already there. Of course, we might joke that System Designers are not really 'human', that they are in fact 'techies', and that therefore, the problem of getting the human in still remains. But this should at least alert us to a problem already implicit in our formulation of the question. We are already implying that there are different ways of being human, and the 'techie' formulation is not the kind of human we necessarily want to have in such a central role in the design process.

This makes the ethnographic approach a particularly useful and relevant one for the problem. We have already begun to stake out the ground in the form most accessible to a sociological enquiry. That is, we have identified that there are different modes of 'being human', and that some of these are more desirable if you want to make Human Centred Systems. A socio-logically informed enquiry can draw on a history and tradition of trying to understand how humans go about being humans in different ways and with different things (and here, the thing might be described specifically as computerised technology). The rest of this paper will present my attempt to describe system design as a social process, and illustrate the kinds of issues that arise from this view which have relevance for the question of this book: making Human Centred Design a realistic possibility.

5.3 Freshwater's attempt to get the 'human' into the system

Freshwater was pleased to claim The Customer Project as a major venture which successfully incorporated the User into the design process. In other words, the management at Freshwater also saw the value of opening up the technical design process to a wider group of people: specifically other organisational members, who were often referred to as Users. This management objective was expressed to me in several ways during the course of my ethnographic study[3]. Amongst the senior members of the Project Team (which included a number of senior

[3] I spent 15 months with the Customer Project, 13 of those months were spent working in the office for four days a week, every week. The fifth day (usually Wednesday) I returned to Brunel University to debrief, and to teach Software Engineering to final year Computer Science undergraduates, and Masters Students.

Consultants from a large and well known consulting partnership, which I shall refer to here as DC) there was an explicit belief that the project was achieving this revolutionary organisational form. For example, towards the end of my ethnographic period with Freshwater, I found myself being told a story. I was told it twice within two weeks, and each time I was told it by a senior manager at the end of a management meeting which had been explicitly addressing the Quality of the Customer Project's work. The first time I heard it, it was at the end of a senior management meeting of the Management System Division, and it was the Quality Manager who told it to me; the second time I heard it from a Senior Partner of DC after a Quality Audit meeting of the Customer Project. The story went like this, you've probably heard it yourself:

> "Systems design *used* to be done by a bunch of techies, deep deep deep within the depths of some head office building somewhere. Here they would build their system, test it, test it, test it until they were sure it would work. And then they would throw it over this great high wall, out into the organisation, and hope that the User would catch it."

The story was told with a great flourish of the arm to symbolise the toss of a machine over a high, impenetrable wall, out into the organisation. This helped to form the image of techies protected from the 'real world', safe in their hidden environment, absolved of all further responsibility for the working of their machine. Implicit in the story is the message that the Users, if they catch this 'gift', or more likely, scrape it up slightly damaged from the floor, have a great deal of difficulty making the thing work. Many reasons can be imagined for the failure of the machine from the structure of the story. For a start, the machine has been thrown, and probably dropped. But more important than that, the solid brick wall that keeps the users and designers separate ensures that the user has no idea how to use the machine, and the designer has no idea what it might be used for. In this formulation of design, and in this formulation of the story, we can hardly be surprised that computer systems don't work properly. The solution implicit in this story is: dismantle the wall between Users and Designers.

Given this interpretation of the story, we can see that the Customer Project had acted logically by removing the bricks and mortar between Users and Designers to achieve an integrated design team. It had brought a Team together to work in one room. They were all also networked together electronically through the office computer system provided for their use. There was (apparently) no visible sign to suggest that the Customer Project was operating under the bad old system of separation which was so evidently present in the story.

However. By the time I heard this story, I had been working with the Customer Project as part of the 'Team' for over a year. I had formed a different opinion to the Senior Managers on the state of project integration, and I was beginning to see how the 'brick wall' was manifesting itself in the social practices of the office.

I was invited to address a meeting of Middle Managers in the Management System Division to speak about the kinds of things my study had revealed. Part of the process of my ethnographic study involved me in a continual dialogue with

Freshwater, as I constantly fed back my perspective to the Team in the process of my involvement in the everyday work of the office. By the time I was invited to 'deliver my findings' to the management team, I had already become aware of the difficulty of being heard. To make my findings digestible, therefore, I had to persuade the managers that one of their explicit beliefs about the project organisation was not in fact a useful one. To make my findings of interest to Freshwater, I had to re-articulate the project organisation as a *problem not yet solved*. I decided to make use of the story they had recently told me in order to do this. I chose to retell the 'brick wall' story in the light of my experience with the Project. I told it like this:

> "System Design is done by a bunch of Techies. Deep deep deep within the depths of a head office building somewhere. Here they build their system. Test it, test it, test it until they are sure it will work. And a few weeks before the great toss they send out the Change Management Guys to *describe* to the Users how to catch!"

The response from the meeting was enough to convince me that, although formally the middle managers were as happy to tell the original story as the senior managers, they also recognised that there was still a barrier that kept the technical work separated and protected behind a wall as impenetrable as any bricks and mortar might be.

Now, all (!) that was left for me to do was to point out how the 'wall' was operating in different material form. And it is here that the 'ethnographic eye' was able to demonstrate its usefulness. However, the process of revealing the boundary at work in the everyday life of the Customer Project exposed a different problem. The ethnographic approach might be thought of as *too* useful. It revealed the boundary in dozens of different practices; there were almost too many instances of it to be of any use to Management[4]. My problem, as researcher, then, was to find examples which struck me as instances which would be most productive to deconstruction if the ultimate aim was to get the User's voice into the technical design process.

The process which I will now describe to you comes from my field note books, and is chosen to demonstrate the boundary at work. It shows how the work of the Systems Team and Change Management were linked together in a relationship which can be seen to be governed by each team's relationship with the Project Methodology. (The Consulting Company had installed a sophisticated set of procedures, manuals, computerised documentation, time recording sheets and algorithms for budgeting, to manage the process of design and development. and this is known as the *Project Methodology*). The example dwells on the work practices that reproduced the old 'brick wall' boundary, and shows the results of this boundary as it got written into the system design process. The story draws our focus down to specific instances which might be addressed by management if they really do wish to place the 'human' at the centre of the design process.

---

[4] The Project Report details many more of these, please see Hall, Low and Woolgar, 1992 [3].

5.4 Background: Organisation of the Customer Project

When I first joined Freshwater to begin my ethnographic study, the Customer Project comprised approximately 25 people. It is not possible to be specific about the numbers, as they were in constant flux throughout the project. Consultants and contractors were continually being brought in and laid off; new employees were being taken on, old ones moving on to new jobs. But to give you an idea, there was a Project Manager, and reporting to him were the Head of Systems Development, and the Head of Change Management. The *Change Management Team* consisted of six people who were all Freshwater employees. They had each worked at Freshwater for a number of years and had gained experience in a number of different areas across the range of functions in the business as a whole. They had each been seconded onto the project for differing times, their full time jobs being 'held' for them to return to, once their work on the project was complete. The Change Management Team sat at two blocks of desks in one corner of the office, four of them facing each other (a block of four desks pushed together), the other two sitting just behind them, facing two members of the Systems Team (another four desks pushed together in the same way).

The *Systems Team* is less straightforward to describe. There were four team members who were Freshwater Employees who had worked on other projects before joining the Customer Project. There were another five who had been recruited straight onto the Project from outside the company (either from University, or from other organisations). Three of them were independent contractors, bought in via different agencies. And then there were several members of DC. The only person (apart from myself) who didn't neatly fit into one or other of these teams was the User Representative. Stella was also a long term employee of Freshwater, but she didn't position herself in the Change Management Team. However, she wasn't really a member of the Systems Team either, even though she often sat at a desk that was usually thought of as a Systems Desk.

Apart from the difference in employment patterns between the two teams, there was also a difference in terms of movement. In general, you could typify the Change Management Team as the ones who kept the same desks the office, but moved about the company a great deal (driving to Water Treatment sites, or visiting Sewage Treatment works across the country). The Systems Team hardly ever left the office to travel around the company, but were often moving desks within the office as they reorganised themselves in accordance with the different phases of design layed out in the work Methodology.

There was also a difference between the teams in the way they used the computerised equipment in the office. Although the system was organised to make it possible for all project members to access all files held on the Local Area Network (LAN) (except those that were specifically kept secret), the Change Management Team treated documents on the machine's memory as the property of the writer, rather than the team. They tended to get a copy printed out if they wanted to read someone else's document. The systems team, however, were regularly accessing documents written by others and held on the LAN. The systems team were also adept at using the network facility to send brief messages to their colleagues which would appear with a beep on the bottom line of their screen.

This sketch of the office is meant to begin to alert you to some of the differences which were operating within the same four walls which housed just 25 people. A small team by some standards, and a small room. Yet separate (and separating) patterns were being quietly woven into the fabric of the office life, and many of these were recreating the distinction between technical and organisation that we saw in the Brick Wall story. The final one I shall mention before going on relates to the time sheets. The project management system (the Methodology) required each team member to complete a 'Turnaround' document at the end of the week to help management figure out how the team was progressing, and to help them budget for staffing levels and time requirements. All members of the office (Change Management, System Team, and User Rep) were required to fill these out, but there was an interesting difference in the ways this was done between the teams. The Change Management documents were a constant problem for the management of the team. It was difficult to categorise their work, and (therefore) it was difficult to allocate realistic times spent on each category of work. The detailed manuals and spiral bound booklets that came along with the Project Methodology had already shaped the categorising of work for the system team. Members of the consulting company also continued to play a part in inventing categories for the system team, but the Methodology did not mention the work of Change Management. There was no 'pre-mapping' of any kind to help the Change Management Team define their work in ways which would easily fit into the budgeting model on the machine. The work of defining what they were going to do, and when, and by whom, was down to them to do at the same time as doing the work to be done. This was the first real sign I picked up of the role of the project Methodology in the rest of the office work. Mostly, the Methodology and the time sheets were treated as a low-key, mundane, regular, boring event; they were just taken for granted. The Methodology was apparently a passive part of the working day. However, once I started looking more closely at it, I realised that this passivity was achieving a great deal of invisible work. In other words, although the managers stated that the project was to be done within the overall framework of bringing technical issues into contact with organisational ones, the project Methodology did not agree. And, as we shall see (and unfortunately, for the management of Freshwater), it was the Methodology which was to have the last word on the way things got done in the office.

5.5 Designing and Developing the After Hours System

When I first joined the Customer Project, it was six weeks before the 'go live' date of the first release of the Customer Information System. The systems team were very busy doing system testing, checking for minute errors in the miles of programming code, slogging their way through endless scenarios which they felt might reveal different mistakes they might have made. They were therefore spending much of their time sitting at their machines, in a dialogue with the system, as it were. The Change Management team, on the other hand were busy in dialogue with various parts of the Company. They were out on the road, delivering training sessions to the people out in Water Distribution Depots, or visiting the site of the new Customer Centre which was being fitted out for its future 'high tech' use as a kind of communications centre. The Customer Centre was a brand new thing for Freshwater. Up until now, customers had been able to telephone directly to their local water works or sewage site, and address their queries to the local employees. The Customer Project was changing all that. In an ambitious centralising move, it was changing the company's relationship with its customers by establishing what it called a 'one stop shop'. A central unit (the Customer Centre) was to be established, which would receive all customer calls, deal with 80% of them, and distribute the remaining 20% to the local responsible site. This meant the Change Management Team were responsible for equipping a building with telecommunication lines for phones, faxes, and computer networks capable of linking all parts of the business, to realise the new centralising strategy. A manager had been seconded to run the new centre, and he (together with Stella) was busy recruiting staff (mainly from outside Freshwater) to answer the phones and operate the new computer system (ie record the query on the data base, and if necessary send a message to another part of the business, asking for work to be done). Stella was also involved with some of the Consultants and Change Management Team in designing (and later delivering) a six week training programme which would equip the new recruits with all the skills they would require for carrying out the new job.

As you might imagine, the Change Management Team (six people) had their work cut out. They were tremendously busy, and travelling large distances between sites to spread the news of the impending system. Meanwhile, across the other side of the office (maybe five strides away) a small team in the systems team was being formed. This team was called the *After Hours Team*. They were being brought together to begin the process of designing Release 2 of the Customer Information System. While their colleagues in the system team continued with system testing of Release 1, they began the process of User Requirements for Release 2.

They were following the process laid down by the Methodology. User Requirements was the first phase of system design, and it had already been allocated a segment of time in which to accomplish this work, and a number of people to do it. The planning and budgeting machinery, ie the Project Methodology, had already decided who was to carry out this work, and how long it would take them. The people who were to do this work came exclusively from the Systems Team. I noticed this at the time, and mentioned it to the Change Management Team. It was rather like trying to talk to someone as they shot past you on a high speed train.

"Eh? What? They're doing what in the systems team? Starting Release 2? You think we should be involved in that? Well, sorry, got to dash, I've got to get to Bushywood by 2pm, maybe we could talk about it later?"

As I walked back across the office, I could feel the tension lessen, the concerns of the Change Management Team slipped off me as I walked back into the After Hours Team discussion. Although we were all quite close (physically) to each other and visible across the office, there was an almost complete separation of concern. The System Team were not really aware of what was going on in the Change Management Team, and the Change Management Team were not really aware of what was going on in the Systems Team.

The After Hours Team took their lead from the Methodology, the time and resource plan that had been worked out by one of the consultants, and began the process of design. So, in December, without general announcement or office-wide awareness, one of the systems team went out to visit various parts of the business where he interviewed a number of key managers about the current practice of organising work (the night time and weekend work rosters) outside normal working hours. On his return, he and his colleagues in the systems team used his interview material to devise 'data flow diagrams', and to work out 'entities' and 'data elements'. Quiet discussions were held with the DataBase Manager (Roy) and the Technical Architect (Cecil) at casual moments during the normal working day.

I was explicitly trying to join in with this process, but even so I found it difficult to know when discussions were happening that concerned this work, it was done so 'invisibly', and so 'nonchalantly'. I was constantly reminding the After Hours team that I wanted to be part of this process. Asking if I could join in on interviews, and especially to join the discussions between the database manager and the technical architect. I wanted to do this to find out why this work was thought specifically 'technical', and thus delegated to the systems team. I wanted to know whether there was something peculiar to this work which explained why the Change Management Team were thought to be irrelevant to this part of the process. As far as I could see, this part of the process was not obviously 'technical'. William had gone to visit managers about the company, and talked to them about the work practices of their staffs. William was a new recruit to Freshwater, so much (practically all) of what he was being told was new to him. It seemed to me that Change Management already had much of the knowledge that William was seeking in his interviews. His discussions with Roy or Cecil however, began to reveal the source of a difference. William was trying to reinterpret his interview material to fit a two dimensional scheme which could 'fit in' with the existing scheme that had been planned into the structure of Release 1. The complexity of the different Rosters which were at work in Freshwater were being straightened out in order to fit the existing system design. In practice, however, it was not within the scope of William's power to 'straighten out' the complicated Roster practice as it operated in the company. So, instead, the *scheme* of it that he was writing got straightened out. What this meant was that the process of drawing data flow diagrams and defining data entities is a process which defines the responsibility of the System Team in the ensuing organisational change. In effect, the scope of the computerised system was being dramatically scaled down in these small conversations in the office. Although everyone else in the Customer Project continued to speak about the grand change that they would be able to achieve in the business with this new computerised system and the new Customer Centre, the computerised bit of the system was itself looking less and less ambitious, quite ordinary, in fact.

But the Project Methodology continued to insist that this work be done, and done then in that time frame. So, a prototype was put together, a presentation was delivered to a few carefully selected managers. Commitments were made. Documents were written. Future budgets were drawn up. Future Staffing levels were agreed. And then, *then*, Change Management were brought in. They began their own process of interviews and designs. By this time, the System Team were already firmly established along the path laid out in the pre-structured Methodology. They were beginning 'technical design' as Change Management were beginning to get a feel for the size of the problem. In the process of all the discussions between the systems analyst, the data base manager, and the technical architect, much of the complexity of the various Rosters had had to be dropped; it was not possible to computerise very much of this process. So, when Change Management picked up the challenge, they found themselves in a difficult position. Management commitments had already been established, a date had been fixed for the 'go live', and a scenario of what 'The Customer Project' could achieve had been sewn in the thoughts of a number of significant organisational actors. The Change Management Team found themselves in the unenviable position of figuring out all the things that must be done (how many vodaphones must be bought, how the radio system must be changed, what kind of training should be delivered, who to, how many new staff might have to be recruited, what procedures would have to be written, what forms would have to be invented, what job changes should be instituted, what office space was available for this new operation ...) to allow the computerised system to slide gracefully into operation on go-live day, dignity and integrity intact!

What is particularly interesting here is that it was the explicit intention of the project management to bring a Change Management Team into the process of systems design to capitalise on organisational knowledge during the process of design. Even though this was an intention up front, the Project was unable to realise it because the Work Methodology in use did not allow for the possibility in its time plan, nor did it encourage the possibility in the structure of budgeting. Perhaps even more relevant is to notice that bringing this knowledge into the process of the design (by drawing attention to it at the time) was also not enough to affect a change. So, there was intention, and there was knowledge, but practice continued to move in a different direction.

This draws attention to a number of different questions. First, there were only certain specific opportunities in which to make a significant difference to the management of the project. It was not enough to raise these issues in casual moments of the normal working day (which I did, constantly), but in order to have a clear *effect*, I had to wait until invited to address the middle management meeting at the end of my period of study. Second, and directly related, it was my role as 'outsider' that gave weight to my words. I was not saying anything revolutionary, I was merely giving voice to a set of questions which regular members of the team might also have spoken, but their words, like mine during the study, had fallen on deaf ears. The third point I wish to make here is that the desired change was in accordance with the stated aims of the management of the project. Given the strength of intention to develop this information system by incorporating organisational members into the process (which I take to be a similar motive for making a Human Centred System), and the difficulty of achieving that in practice, we must ask: "what is at stake in so doing? what else is going on?"

To restate the position. Several members of the project were saying the same thing as I was saying, and we had been saying it for quite some time, but with no effect. This is more remarkable when we remember that it was a specific objective of the management to do what we were suggesting. There appears, then, to be something else going on which was more important, at least to some members of the Project, than turning the Project into a User Centred one.

I chose to focus attention onto the Project Methodology because it was performing a vital function in the relationship between the Consultants and Freshwater. It seemed to be occupying a crucial role which brought together the senior managers from Freshwater and from DC in a particular relationship. This relationship was often very tense during the course of the project, and the Project Methodology was called upon at these times to account for the progress of the project towards its goals in terms of time, money and performance. Control over the figures and what they stood for, was therefore a crucial issue. The consultants were constantly in a better position to interpret the figures produced from the methodology, as they knew (or claimed to know) the algorithms which produced the figures. That this was a particularly contentious and painful relationship might be explained by referring to its use as a tool for deciding how many consultants should be recruited onto the project, how long they should spend on the work, and therefore, how much money Freshwater should pay to DC.

During the course of my study, the operation of the methodology and the turnaround documents was only ever successfully accomplished if done with the help of a consultant. I got the impression that if the consultants hadn't been there, the methodology would have fallen into disuse and time plans and budgeting would have been done in a very different manner. It is not too difficult to imagine a project team which would have been able to reorganise itself and redistribute work to take better advantage of the experience and skills of the people at its disposal. This suggests that the methodology was doing much more work than I have even yet revealed. Much seems to depend on the control of the methodology, and so, to suggest changes to its operation seems to imply significant changes in many different relationships. So, although it had been my intention to target the most productive point for deconstruction, it might have been *too* important to deconstruct.

However, work in the Customer Project after I left did change to take more account of the similarities between the work of the Change Management and Systems Teams. People who started out in the systems team were now doing work marked Change Management, and more users were being incorporated into the systems team. However, the methodology continued to be used as the significant guide to working patterns, and so the systems team continued in its privileged position, even though it was now openly acknowledged that much of the work labelled 'technical' was understood to be organisational in its most political and potent form.

5.6 Conclusions

This chapter began by asking 'how to get the human to the centre of the system?' It realised that humans of some kind were already at the centre of the system, so then turned to ask what is it about the 'techie' that is not desirable to have at the centre and what is it about the User, or other Organisational member that is desirable at the centre of the system?

This question was being asked against the organisational backdrop of the Customer Project at Freshwater. The Customer Project was explicitly put together with the intention of overcoming the usual technical/organisational divide. It was a team which included organisational experience and technical competence in the form of two teams (Change Management and Systems Design) and User Representatives. However, the ethnographic study I carried out revealed that the divide was still very much in operation. I then described how I set about persuading the organisation that they still had a problem, and they needed to address it. I went on to describe one way in which the boundary was working, and I chose the example of the After Hours Team. This example enabled me to draw attention to the Project Methodology. It was here that the boundary seemed to be most powerfully recreated. If the Customer Project was different to the scenario painted in the first Brick Wall story, it might be that the 'techies' protection has been increased! Not only are they protected behind the Methodology, but they also have the Change Management team wrapped around them, acting as a kind of 'buffer' or 'sponge'. Change Management seemed to be absorbing much of the 'shock', or the 'flack', that the project was invoking in the organisation.

Finally, I questioned what was at stake in removing the 'brick wall', which was thought in this case to be the Project Methodology. I pointed out that the Methodology was performing a number of other functions which had hitherto not been noticed. Amongst these functions was the crucial mediating role between the Consulting company and the Freshwater Management. Control over the Methodology seemed to be maintaining the Consultants in a particular bargaining position vis a vis their client.

The upshot of this analysis is to bring into view what is often overlooked (perhaps the term 'organisational politics' might be invoked here). Tensions between different groups of people were put into the foreground of the analysis and situate it in a vital role in the production of a new information system. In doing this, I hope that I made it clear that it is impossible to eradicate this dimension (the 'political dimension') from the organisation of work, let alone the design of information systems. However, it must be addressed if anything at all is to be done about changing the pattern of technological design and development.

References

1. Cooper, G, C Hine, J Low, S Woolgar (1994): "Ethnography and Human Computer Interaction", The Social and Interactional Dimensions of Human-Computer Interfaces, Cambridge University Press.
2. Garfinkel, H (1967) Studies in Ethnomethodology, New Jersey: Prentice Hall.
3. Hall, P, J Low, and S Woolgar (1992) "Human Factors in Information System Design: A project report", CRICT Discussion Paper series, No 31
4. Knorr-Cetina, K (1981) The Manufacture of Knowledge: An essay on the constructivist and contextual nature of science. Oxford: Pergammon
5. Latour, B and S Woolgar (1979, 1986) Laboratory Life: The construction of scientific facts, New Jersey: Princeton
6. Low, J and S Woolgar (1993), Managing the Social-Technical Divide: Some aspects of the discursive structure of information systems development. in Quintas, P (ed) (1994) Social Dimensions of Systems Engineering: People, Processes, Policies, and Software Development. Ellis Horwood.
7. Lynch, M (1985), Art and Artifact in Laboratory Science: a study of shop work and shop talk in a research laboratory London: Routledge and Kegan Paul.
8. Traweek, S (1988) Beamtimes and Lifetimes: the world of high energy physicists. Harvard University Press.

6. Human-Centred Computer Integration in Manufacturing

Felix Schmid[1], Simone Creux[2] and Angela Martin[3]

[1] Dept. of Manufacturing and Engineering Systems, Brunel University, Uxbridge UB8 3PH, UK
[2] Abteilung für Betriebs und Produktionswissenschaften Eidgenössische Technische Hochschule, Zürich, Switzerland
[3] Dept. of Mechanical, Manufacturing and Software Engineering Napier University, Edinburgh, Scotland

Abstract. The move towards computer integration of manufacturing operations is only one of many changes which have affected the production of artefacts since the early times of human evolution. However, its impact is viewed as much more significant than even the industrial revolution. The authors of the present paper attempt to place Computer Integrated Manufacturing in this wider context and put forward a case for a particular approach to creating a form of advanced manufacturing environment, the BESTMAN methodology.

Keywords. Manufacturing, Industrial Production, Human Factors, HCCIM, Work, Change, Transformation, Strategy, Industrial Revolution.

6.1 Introduction

'Productivity and the Future of Work', a symposium on the changing face of industry, provided a panoramic view of all the issues, both well known and emerging, which affected people's relationship with their work in the mid-1980s [Munich, 14-16 October 1986]. Poignantly, the participants in the symposium addressed the questions of whether there was and whether there should be a future for human work. The starting point for this discussion was the original 'job of work' carried out by an individual in a fixed time frame and following more or less detailed instructions according to the worker's abilities and qualifications. At the time, in 1986, it appeared that both in manufacturing and service industries, most of these 'simple' jobs would disappear, people being replaced by advanced technology solutions which would offer better all round performance.

Much of what the contributors predicted has happened: computers and computer controlled machines and systems have replaced people in many roles at most levels of a wide range of organisations. However, only a proportion of the jobs have simply disappeared, many have been changed to adapt to the new environment. This process has resulted in the development of the theory and practice of Human Centred Computer Integration starting in the early 1980s. Depending on the sector of human activity concerned, approaches have ranged from ergonomics to complete socio-technical systems solutions, some of which are very significant. The following discussion will be confined to the problems arising in manufacturing industry. However, most approaches can be transferred to other areas of human activity.

6.2 Industrial Revolution and the Use of Computers

6.2.1 Background

The changes brought about by the emergence of powerful computer technologies are often compared to the changes which resulted from the industrial revolution: many authors have described this transition from craft work to factory production, the change from individual skill to the division of labour with its emphasis on dexterity and speed rather than an awareness of the process as a whole. The transformation meant that, instead of small quantities of expensive goods, industry could supply standard products of repeatable quality, with vastly improved productivity. While these changes led to entirely different working conditions in the production of artefacts, the creation of markets for mass produced goods also meant that industry had to recruit workers from backgrounds which previously had had no involvement with manufacturing. This development was very welcome in a period where:

> "The continual rise in the population made it indeed impossible to provide work for everyone in the English village. Agriculture had absorbed all the hands it required. Great national industries, like cloth, were migrating back out of the country districts to which they had moved in the later Middle Ages..." [P.486, Trevelyan 1942].

However, at the same time, a great many craft based businesses such as hand loom weavers, disappeared, with their skilled workers ending up in abject poverty. But:

> "An important group had even accepted, indeed welcomed, industry, science and progress (though not capitalism). These were the 'artisans' or 'mechanics', the men of skill, expertise, independence and education, who saw no great distinction between themselves and those of similar social standing who chose to become entrepreneurs..." [P.90, Hobsbawm 1968].

Although this group of 'engineers' was not very large, it created its own myths, including that of the superiority of machines over people. Very often the men became successful businessmen (gender specific labels intended) in their own right.

In general, however, the situation in the cities was barely better than that in the countryside. Between 1800 and 1840, entrepreneurs had to employ workers on subsistence wages because much of the value added was not reinvested in the system by their backers. The new markets were only being established and workers were not yet perceived as potential customers. Naturally, people changed a great deal as a result of all the pressures and experiences, as observed by Robert Owen:

> "The general diffusion of manufactures throughout a country generates a new character in its inhabitants; ... it will produce the most lamentable and permanent evils ... The manufacturing system has already so far extended its influence over the British Empire as to effect an essential change in the general character of the mass of the people." [Owen 1815]

Not only Owen but also a number of other 'modern' industrialists, such as Titus Salt in Bradford, developed models of industrial communities which showed the way towards creating a better environment for workers.

> "Some time in the 1840s all this began to change, and to change rapidly,... the readiness to accept legal supervision of working conditions - as by the admirable Factory Inspectors - increased. ... British industrialists now felt rich and confident enough to be able to afford such changes." [PP.123-4, Hobsbawm 1968]

For a while Britain had become, to use a cliche, the 'workshop of the world'. New hierarchies and new opportunities for training, education and personal development for the masses emerged. Working hours became regulated and salaries rose to levels where most people could live without constant fear of the future — apart from the Great Depression of the 1930s.

6.2.2 Recent Developments in Industrial Production

The industrial society whose social patterns persisted in Europe until the mid 1980s, the type of society to which many 'threshold countries' aspire, thus existed only since the late 19th century. Major cracks in the system appeared around the time of the first oil crisis of 1973/74. However, the seeds for a new revolution had already been sown during World War II: the new levels of mass production necessary for the war machine led to the development of mechanically programmable machine tools followed by the advent of numerically controlled machines (invented at the MIT in 1947) and then the computer controlled systems of the late 1970s and early 1980s. Productivity and quality of output could grow at rates not even imagined before and thus provided the foundation on which 'mega-corporations' could be built with scant regard to overhead costs.

By the mid 1980s though the process of industrial concentration and the move to ever larger and more complex manufacturing facilities had ceased as low cost producers emerged in the 'third world'. Changing markets threatened industrial stability and with it the social fabric. The European industry had to change. Often this process was and is compared to the industrial revolution of the 19th century. However, there are some key differences:

- the capabilities of modern technology are far more advanced, by orders of magnitude, than those which replaced craft based industries
- first world markets are no longer expanding in quantitative terms but purely qualitatively, with increased product diversity in some sectors and very much reduced variety in others

- the emerging new markets are often poor, volatile and very price-sensitive
- improved communications and better transport links have rendered competition worldwide and therefore unpredictable
- productivity in most sectors of the economy has risen dramatically and the productive capacity far outstrips demand
- the needs of a large population can often be satisfied by a proportionally very small workforce
- the cost to acquire and maintain advanced technology is very high

People displaced by technological or economic developments in one industry can no longer expect to be re-employed quickly elsewhere. The skill levels required to operate and manage the new technologies in their pure forms are very different from those available amongst existing workforces. Computer Integration is only one of the many applications of advanced technologies to manufacturing. It has received more attention than many others though, not just because of the fascination with its 'pseudo-intelligent behaviour', but because of its scope for displacing human workers at all levels of an organisation, rather than simply replacing manual workers. It is also believed to have further long term implications which cannot yet be predicted.

6.3 Computer Integrated Manufacturing

6.3.1 Setting the Scene

Computer Integrated Manufacturing (CIM) has been described as:

> 'the uninterrupted flow of electronic information throughout an enterprise' [OU CIM video, ca. 1985].

In this relatively early quotation, CIM is viewed not so much as the creation of a synergy between the traditional strengths of manufacturing organisations and the data and information handling capabilities of computers but rather as an add-on to businesses' existing structures.

Whilst it was expected that computers would one day have a major impact on manufacturing as a whole, until the early 1980s most organisations became more and more vertically and horizontally structured to cope with the complex manufacturing environments of the time. Attempts were made to tailor computer systems to these situations, rather than simplifying the organisations to ease the introduction of computer oriented approaches. The move from 'computers in manufacturing' to CIM progressed in stages:

After early experimental work, from the mid 1960s onwards, computers played an increasingly important role in manufacturing industry, although, in a first phase (1960 to around 1970), only in such areas as payroll management, bill of materials production and mathematical modelling. Such activities were ideally suited to mainframe computers operating in 'batch' mode with very significant support from data processing departments. In fact, this amounted to the invention of the concept of 'islands of automation' which brought significant improvements in the areas where the systems were installed but which had little or no impact on the manufacturing organisation as a whole. Dan Elder of Honeywell, quoted by Wedeking [1991], states:

> "... we were able to learn from other companies' experiences and avoid many of the pitfalls associated with 'islands of automation' ... Our charter is to develop an integrated environment that will help us fully implement a concurrent engineering or team approach to product development. We want to reduce our development cycle from an average of two to three years to a year and a half or less. At the same time we want to ensure that we are achieving the highest possible product quality and delivering cost-effective systems to our customers."

As the capabilities of computer systems were enhanced, the scope of their use could be extended, for example, to include drafting and design and machine tool control. Soon the performance of computer systems in one functional area of a plant could be improved by using data from another system directly rather than through the intermediary of paper based systems or people: the myth of the dichotomy between 'reliable computers' and 'unreliable people' was born. Any information which could be transferred by a keyboard stroke or, better still, automatically was perceived to be 'good information' whereas any process involving people was expected to lead to 'corrupted data'. Since people's attention span will always be limited, it is inevitable that they make mistakes, sooner or later. The relatively basic computers of the period though were well suited to simple tasks such as the forwarding of information. In this second phase (from about 1975 to 1985) of the computerisation of manufacturing, the emphasis was clearly on communication between subsystems.

During the third phase (starting around 1985) of the computer integration of manufacturing, most of the efforts were concentrated on using computers as automatic decision and control devices for whole manufacturing plants or particular subsystems. Computers, on the one hand, were seen to be objective and accurate, 'able to take impartial decisions'. People, on the other hand, be they managers or shop floor staff, were viewed as 'subjective and easily influenced'. Because manufacturing operations require a constant stream of decisions, most of which are time-critical since they concern the loading of manufacturing equipment, computers were adopted as the ideal tools. Very quickly though it became apparent that the amount of data required and the need for absolute accuracy during initial acquisition of data made the move to 'intelligent' computer systems excessively expensive.

The complexity of early integrated factory management systems was such that their performance could be assessed only once completed products started to emerge from the process. Systems operation was non-intuitive and could only be described in mathematical terms. Any interference with the automatic operation of the system, made necessary, for example, by a customer's change of plans or equipment problems, could trigger major disruption and an overall failure to achieve scheduled deliveries.

6.3.2 Computing Euphoria

At the same time (around 1985), however, microprocessor based systems started to emerge, offering automation possibilities beyond engineers' and managers' wildest dreams. High speed data networks became available, together with the necessary central information storage devices. The concept of the 'lightless factory', often described as a Japanese invention, was the result of these technological advances, a concept promising high productivity, flexibility, top quality and very low labour costs, due to the almost automated design of products and the development of the corresponding automatically controlled means of production, the automatic handling of goods at all stages of manufacture and the reduction in labour costs to almost zero.

This scenario did not materialise, however, since it became apparent very soon that the investments required to achieve such performances were beyond the resources of even the biggest and most powerful manufacturing organisations. A prominent victim was General Motors of the USA, where the company management spent a sum, equivalent to the price of acquiring one of its Japanese competitors, on developing a fully automated car factory, an enterprise resulting in a failure which brought the company close to collapse.

What went wrong? Some critics maintain to this day that the systems used were simply not powerful enough, that software and hardware were still flawed. As technological optimists they are convinced that better systems will fulfil the early promises. Technological pessimists though argue that any system whose complexity exceeds a level at which it could still be operated by a human being will ultimately be doomed to failure. Both groups tend to overlook one of the factors which was mentioned in section 2.1: productivity of the industrial workforce had risen to such an extent in the 1960s and 1970s that direct labour costs no longer represented a major factor in product costs. Its complete removal could therefore not be achieved in a cost-effective manner. The relatively indiscriminate use of computer based system was aimed at displacing the 'lower' levels of industrial workforces but, at the same time, created many new support and management functions elsewhere in the companies. Rather than being able to establish a lightless factory run by a few experts from home, industrialists were faced with top-heavy organisations with high wage bills and under-qualified machine minders and cleaners on the shop floor.

6.3.3 Finding an Alternative

While it would be facile to take sides with one or other of the groups mentioned, we would run the risk of denying manufacturing the use of powerful tools which can enhance its effectiveness and thus profitability. The data and information handling capability of computer systems must be used if manufacturing is to continue to provide a contribution to Gross National Product (GNP) and to offer challenging and reasonably paid work to a proportion of a country's population.

It is thus necessary to develop a new paradigm for the computer integration of manufacturing, a paradigm based on people and computers as partners.

It is to be expected, unfortunately, that such an approach will only be applicable to some areas of manufacturing, particularly to 'leading edge' production, where competition is not purely on cost but includes factors such as timeliness. While it would be theoretically interesting to eliminate competitive pressures by means of trade barriers, McKinsey & Co [1993] state in a recent study that global competition is essential if productivity, measured as value added per hour worked, is to increase and thus create conditions ensuring company survival. It must, alas, be accepted that this free international trade will militate against human oriented work designs as long as there are no internationally binding agreements or consumer pressures which guarantee comparable levels of industrial employees' welfare in all markets. Such a levelling of the 'competitive playing field', although desirable from the human work angle, will also result in a levelling of living standards between newly industrialised and developed nations. There is, clearly, a built-in conflict between different goals.

6.4 Human Centred Computer Integrated Manufacturing (HCCIM)

6.4.1 The Meaning of Human-Centredness

The concept of 'Human-Centredness' and the ideas that underlie the approaches were first developed and formulated by Howard Rosenbrock in the early 1980s [Rosenbrock, 1983]. The phrase 'human centred' is often replaced by the term 'anthropocentric'. The concept of human centred design goes along with and includes many principles well known in the field of 'human work design': personality promotion, skill-based manufacturing and complementary design of man-machine systems [Schmid, Hancke & Wu, 1993].

In general, a human-centred technology is one which extends human skill and its application to real life situations. The technology itself must be designed so as to optimise the synergy between human skill and computer power. The work within the factory must be organised such that in all areas people are able to apply a substantial range of their skills rather than just a small 'useful' part thereof. Individual skill and competence should be increased through a balanced combination of learning by doing and formal training and education.

In a human-centred system, traditional design and manufacturing skills are used to their fullest extent. The range of activities for which each operator is responsible is maximised, to include, for example, production work as well as quality and planning related duties. As a result, each person will develop a general knowledge of the whole production process, and must be given the freedom and opportunity to comment on any aspect of it. Cherns [1975] developed ten principles of socio-technical design, some of which are at the heart of HC systems:

- compatibility: the way in which a job or system is designed should be compatible with the objectives of the design, for example a system requiring participation for its operation must be designed in a participative manner
- minimal critical specification: the specification of a job or system should identify and specify no more than is absolutely essential
- information flow: information for action should be directed first to those whose task it is to act
- power and authority: those who need resources to carry out their responsibilities should have the power and authority to command those resources

The concept of human-centred manufacturing relies on skill enhancement rather than skill replacement. There are many ways of increasing human-centred working within as well as outside manufacturing industry through the application of computers. True interactive computer-based systems are needed and are being developed for a variety of human work situations, in areas such as banking and air-traffic control perhaps even more so than in manufacture. The reason for such an optimistic generalisation is that the use of the computer has forced people to think deeply, perhaps for the first time, about the fundamentals of processes, both qualitatively and quantitatively. This need for reflection on the key issues is not limited to management. In manufacturing, the integration of computers involves everyone engaged in the production process.

Computer systems, if they are to be subservient to human beings must be designed in a human centred way, Rosenbrock [1983]. Such design efforts must not be limited, as a matter of course, to interface improvements such as the use of mice, windows and graphics. The efforts must be aimed at sharing meaningful tasks between person and machine, for example, allowing human operators to decide on the rate of injection of plastic into the mould, based on their experience and, used as backup, a number of proven time profiles stored in the computer. Since the technology is new, there is a chance for cross-disciplinary teams to work together not only in establishing the new technology but also in getting this technology accepted by the users. Thus, radical changes in working procedures, large process innovations and skills properly managed give opportunities for new, more satisfying and thus human-centred ways of working.

The development of human-centred computer based tools provides people with assistance in the management of complex situations. The combination of human skills, such as fast and adaptive decision making, with computer capabilities, such as quick storing, processing and retrieval of information, offers a good approach to dealing with highly dynamic problems. The computer based tools either simply provide information to the user in a structured form or they help by offering options for approaching the solution of problems. Thus they can be viewed as elements of a decision support system. Algorithms for decision making can either exist in the system or can be added by users as and when required. It is important that the user can check the method of operation of the algorithm at any moment. In some instances, it may be necessary to limit the level of the information provided by the computer systems so as to leave sufficient scope for the work of the human.

Various projects have been set up to design alternative methods of implementing technology in the form of "flexible manufacturing systems in which the operator is not subservient to the machine". The European Community project on 'Human Centred CIM Systems', described by Hamlin [1989], was one of the key projects concerned with Human Centredness. The objective of the project was to produce human-centred CIM components, in which human skill and its application are optimised, in harmony with leading-edge computerised manufacturing technology.

6.4.2 Company Transformation

To remain competitive in world markets, manufacturing enterprises must take full advantage of the potential for increases in productivity, better quality and greater flexibility provided by more responsive organisational structures, better utilisation of human skills and experience and the power of modern computer-aided technologies. To achieve these goals, a skilled, cooperative and motivated workforce is required. Traditional management hierarchies and forms of control must be modernised. More participation by employees is needed at all levels, in planning, designing and implementing new technologies and systems. Technical systems must be designed not just to meet economic and technical goals, but also to satisfy organisational and human requirements.

Experience suggests that manufacturing systems do not operate effectively and do not yield expected benefits unless attention is also paid to the organisation and people issues during design and implementation. There is now an increased recognition that organisation and people issues are important, but most companies adopt a fairly narrow approach as to how these issues should be addressed. Management attempts to find ways of overcoming the resistance to change and the reluctance of people to accept new technology but fails to provide an entirely new environment and philosophy. Lang [1990] discusses this reluctance of companies to move from interfacing to integration because it requires more change than quick and easy projects.

Some companies have started to change the way they use technology and have begun to consider organisation and people issues in some depth. The changes needed are at times quite simple but must be structured well. Organisation and people issues should be considered at all stages, from business strategy right through to manufacturing systems design and implementation. Instead of looking for the technological fix, companies need a broader and more balanced approach that addresses manufacturing organisation, people and technological systems. It is necessary to overcome the belief that technology provides the answers to all problems. Managers must develop a new and broader vision of the 'Factory of the Future'.

The change process from an existing mix of organisational methods and technical tools needs to be planned in a way which is appropriate to humans. Most people are disinclined to handle rapidly varying rates of change with high peaks. Company transformations should therefore follow an approach as shown in Fig. 6.1, graph 2. The diagram illustrates the need for a balanced process of organisational and technological transformation where humans are able to adapt to a changing work environment. The third axis of the main graph would show the rate of change in training and attitude required of the humans involved in the process.

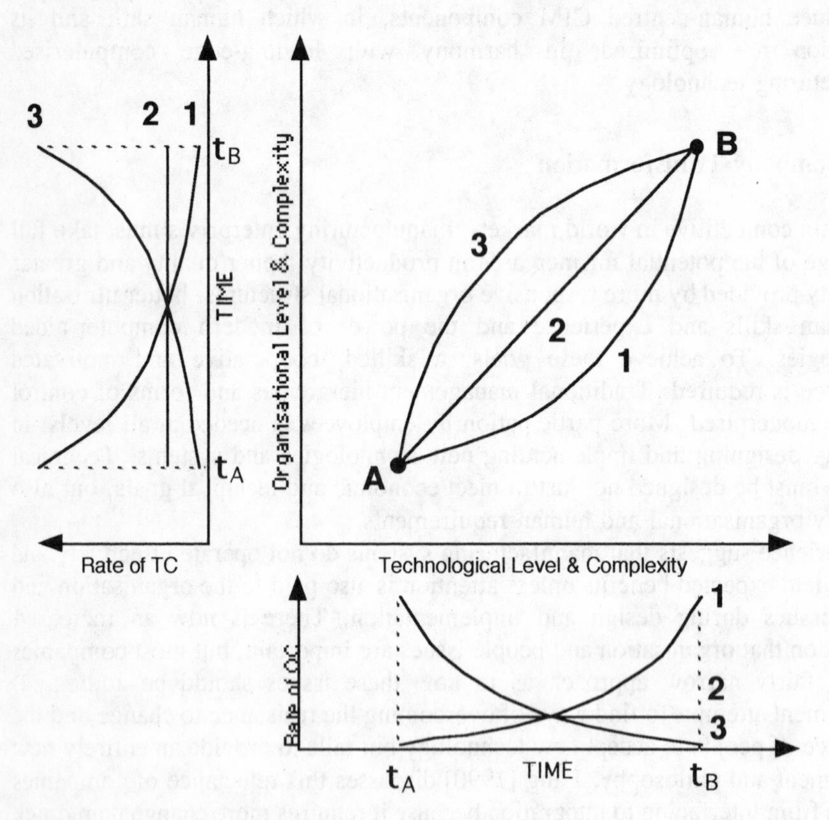

Fig. 6.1. Human centred change process

A new vision is provided by the idea of using organisation, people and technology to develop a manufacturing strategy that will enable companies to respond to the dynamic markets of the 1990s.

The requirements for flexibility, adaptability, improved responsiveness, as well as the need to motivate people and to make use of their skills, judgement and experience, create an impact on organisations, work practices and technology. These facets of an enterprise must be developed in a way that will allow highly trained people, at all levels of the company, to adapt their work strategies to the variety of situations which they will have to face. There is a need, therefore, to set up a new organisational model based on:

- flat organisational hierarchies
- cell-based factories
- decentralisation of decision making and control
- increased competence and authority for shop floor staff
- multi-skilled employees
- team working
- skill supporting technologies
- continuing improvement involving all employees.

Typical benefits of a balanced manufacturing strategy based on people, organisation and technology can include: shorter throughput times, reduced inventory, improved product quality, more economic operating conditions, and improved responsiveness. Other advantages are simplified material flows, easier production planning and control and improved job satisfaction which can lead to more highly motivated people.

These ideas are the basis of the MOPS initiative for the improvement of manufacturing companies in the United Kingdom.

6.5 MOPS Programme: The Enterprise Initiative

The DTI's Manufacturing Organisation, People and Systems (MOPS) programme was launched in April 1991. MOPS helps industry (particularly small and medium-sized companies) to manage change within their manufacturing environment. It does this by supporting collaborative industrial research and development projects that involve organisational and people issues.

The programme focuses on the research and development of strategic issues, support tools and methods and software packages. These will help industry to improve manufacturing system design practices, introduce new organisational and management structures and develop better and more effective technical systems, taking full account of the people issues.

The MOPS programme supports six subsidiary projects in the area of management improvement, one of which, BESTMAN or BEST practice cellular MANufacture, is described here.

The concept of BESTMAN revolves around the proposition that any company can move from its present level of organisational competence to a position of excellence in terms of people, organisation and technology (POT). It particularly addresses the transformation of companies using the principles of cellular manufacturing, since the resulting 'federal' structure assists the process of distributing authority, responsibility and power in a motivating manner.

6.5.1 The Generic Model

A six level model was created as a result of Human Centred Systems' (HCS, a UK based consultancy and research organisation) research experience with a number of organisations, accumulated during the feasibility study phase. The purpose was to create a tool with which a company could identify its own current position and also understand the measures necessary to move forward towards BESTMAN. The philosophy behind the Generic Model can be likened to the organisational application of Maslov's theories on individuals' needs and motivation. As in the case of Maslov's models, organisations, just like people, must be moved through the levels, not leap from bottom to top. As BESTMAN encourages focus on the people within an organisation, the Generic Model can become a wide-ranging tool for positioning the organisation and then motivating and developing the moves up the steps to BESTMAN.

"Bestman" - Best of Best

Empowerment Level

Pro-active Level

Directive Level

Re-active Level

Survival Level

Fig. 6.2. BESTMAN Generic Model [HCS Ltd., 1993]

To implement best practice cellular manufacturing, redesign work must encompass the refashioning of the enterprise as a whole. Figure 2 shows the Generic Model illustrating the stages of development through which an organisation has to move. Positioning a company is the first step, followed by an individually tailored plan to move through the levels. Some typical characteristics of companies found at each level are listed below.

6.5.2 Company Classification

1. *Survival level*
   late deliveries, poor quality, long cycle times
   poor customer/supplier relationships
   poor teamwork, ownership and initiative
   unclear strategy and focus

2. *Re-active level*
   responding to priorities — customer, products, etc.
   islands of conflicting groups or departments
   isolated, conflicting systems and processes
   several diverse strategies

3. *Directive level*
   a strategy is determined
   priorities and goals are established
   communications are promoted
   conflicts are brought out into the open
   'Hit Squads' are created

4. *Pro-active level*
   squads become teams
   people continue to set goals and seek approval for initiative
   integration becomes the norm
   customer and supplier focus is paramount
   knowing your customer becomes a culture

5. *Empowerment*
   shortened chains of command
   greater trust and responsibility
   elimination of non-value added activities
   secure, proud culture

6. *Best of the best*
   continuous improvement in all areas (organisation, people and technology including product)

While MOPS is a programme with a wide overall remit, the focus of BESTMAN is the transformation of complex organisations into effective businesses with a strong slant towards cellular manufacture, matrix management and therefore methods of operation suited to human skills and aspirations.

6.5.3 Example: Before and After BESTMAN

In this example the authors describe the structure of a typical company and one of its business processes (order management cycle). They then present the changes introduced by implementing BESTMAN. The organigram and the process are shown before and after BESTMAN and typical characteristics are outlined.

Research allied to the BESTMAN project on the technology front has helped to identify tools that will assist in this process. These include system tools which enable the users to construct easily and quickly a virtual and transparent 'mathematical' matrix model of their factories, hence deriving a first rough cut version of the factory's cell structure.

Whilst the above can be algorithm and CAD based, other tools are oriented more towards providing qualitative advice. For example, companies at the Survival or

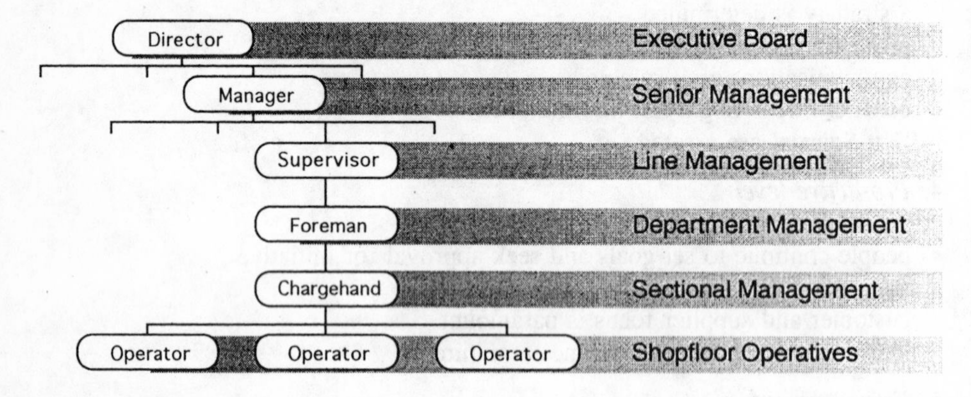

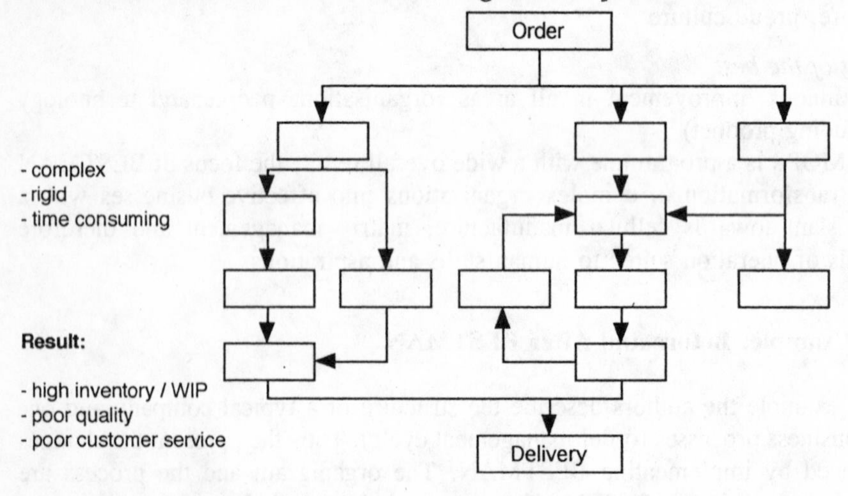

Fig. 6.3 BEFORE: A Traditional Company

Reactive Levels need a lot of help in setting up basic systems, procedures and disciplines before process simplification and cell formation. Substantial advice and

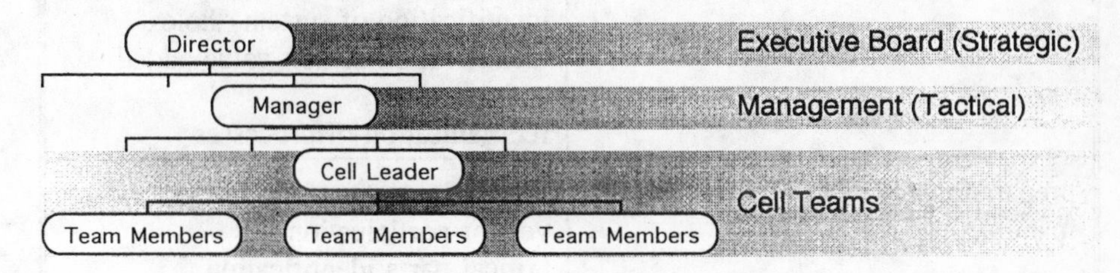

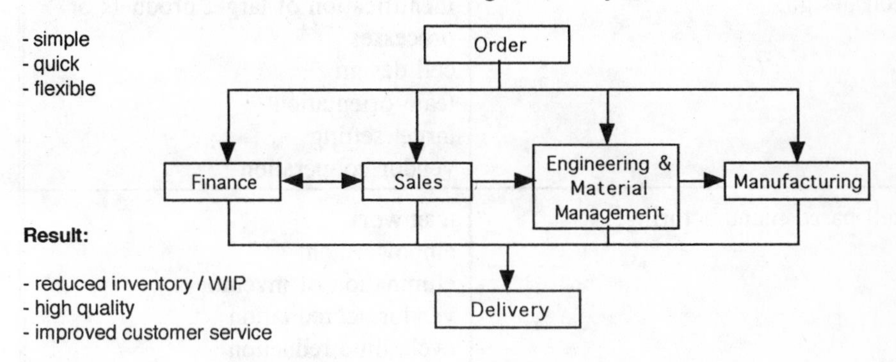

Fig. 6.4. AFTER: A BESTMAN Company

education must be given to lay a foundation. Many internal tasks have to be carried out and, therefore, coordination and project management is critical.

As organisations move up the steps of the Generic Model, the specific nature of the services changes. Advice on Kanban, vendor accreditation and relationships, integration and teamwork become more relevant.

The closer a company comes to the empowerment level, the more the emphasis of the change programme will be on team workshops and continuous improvement. Many factors will be taken into consideration. A sample of these factors is listed below:

basic procedures and systems:	organisation of data validation of data organisation of the business flow process identification of system "holes" identification of non value-added activities reorganisation of processes
preparation for cell based manufacturing:	production rationalisation vendor participation critical parts identification inventory reorganisation team identification
cell design:	identification of target products or processes cell design team orientation target setting vendor cooperation
cell-based manufacturing:	teamwork empowerment elimination of inventory vendor accreditation cycle-time reduction continuous improvement

In each of these areas there are included activities ranging from advice and guidance, education, training, hands-on management through to support activities in a continuous process.

6.6 Conclusion

The appropriate starting point for the development of a human-centred system is the consideration of strategy. Two strategic components must be considered here:

(1) the corporate strategy and, associated with this, how computers can help realise business objectives

(2) the method and priorities adopted by the organisation in the development of its computer systems

As British Standard BS6719 states, users are often disappointed in the system as delivered and one reason given for this is inaccurate specification of users' requirements. It is perhaps unkind to imply that this is all the user's fault, as it is often the case that the people for whom the system is intended are left out at critical stages of the development process and, even when they are asked to participate by the computer professionals, they are often not adequately briefed or guided when stating their requirements. It is essential that both these points are addressed in order to improve the situation. This would involve not just a new methodology, but a change in attitude by all concerned.

It would appear that object-oriented design and analysis offer the best approach to the development of systems of this kind, since both modularity and re-usability are conducive to more careful software design. Object-oriented design in combination with techniques such as Joint Application Design (JAD) and Participant Design (PD) should result in rigorous and well structured approaches which effectively cater for the needs of all the people involved — system developers, users and other stakeholders.

Although a number of methodologies exist and others are being developed to reflect new approaches to systems development, evidence seems to suggest that no single methodology can guarantee successful systems development on its own. As a general rule, it can be stated that usable methodologies must be flexible and adaptable to almost any given situation. It may be better to have a set of guiding principles which reflect the key issues and allow system developers to use these as tools in a manner which is appropriate to a particular organisation rather than prescribing an all purpose methodology.

A tool which has recently received much attention is multi-media technology. It is felt that this could contribute to more user-friendly computer systems and be helpful for information presentation in the systems development process itself. Its particular strength lies in the capability to display information in a manner which can be adapted to both the subject covered and the recipient of the information. In many cases, it is possible to provide, at extra cost, the same information in several forms.

An exercise in systems design, Case Based Reasoning Process Planning, carried out as part of the NATO ASI 'People and Computers', illustrated that multi-disciplinary teams have much to offer in terms of eliminating guesswork and utilising the expertise of each member at an early stage in the process. In fact, it is feasible to see overlaps in knowledge although the same ideas may be given different labels by each sub-group, depending on their 'home' discipline. However, one important consideration here is group size: complex design tasks are best tackled by small teams of well-briefed individuals whose expertise has been closely matched to the problem and each other.

Perhaps, the development of methodologies and techniques is only part of a larger consideration: the question of tangible returns must be resolved if industry is to continue to put effort into supporting the design of human-centred systems. Developers, users and, perhaps more importantly, stakeholders must be able to ascertain clear benefits. The criteria for determining benefit is usually based on financial and functional issues and may not include consideration of what is best for the people involved. The passage of time and the study of the philosophical issues surrounding human work, 'tools' and automation may point the way to optimum integration of people and computers. Maybe one day tasks involving the co-operation of people and computers will again be viewed as 'jobs of work' rather than complex social and psychological problems.

References

ANON., 1987. Proceedings of the International Symposium 'Productivity and the Future of Work', Munich, October 1986, Published by RKW, 1987.

Cherns, A., 1975. 'The Quality of Working Life, Vol.1, Problems, Prospects and the State of the Art', New York, 1975.

Hamlin, M., 1989. 'Human-Centred CIM Systems', ESPRIT Project 1217 (1199) Deliverable 27: Final Report, BICC Technologies, Hemel Hempstead, 1989.

Hobsbawm, E.J., 1968. 'Industry and Empire', London, 1968. Volume 3 of the Pelican History of Britain, Penguin, 1975.

Lang, R.G. 1990. 'The Path of Least Resistance and the Path of Highest Return in the Pursuit of a Computer Integrated Enterprise', Proceedings of Rensselaer's Second International Conference, Rensselaer Polytechnic Institute, Troy, New York, IEEE Computer Society Press, Los Alamitos, California, 1990.

McKinsey Global Institute, 1993. 'A Comparative Study of Industrial Productivity in Six Key Nations', McKinsey & Co, New York, 1993.

OU CIM Video, Open University, ca 1985. Teaching video introducing the IBM Warwick demonstration CIM facility

Owen, R., 1815. 'Observations on the Effect of the Manufacturing System', 1815, quoted from Hobsbawm.

Rosenbrock, H.H., 1983. 'Flexible Manufacturing Systems in which the Operator is not Subservient to the Machine', Research Project Mimeo, UMIST, Manchester, 1983.

Rosenbrock, H.H., 1990. 'Machines with a Purpose', Oxford, 1990.

Schmid F., T. Hancke and B. Wu, 1993. 'The Human-Centred Approach to the Implementation of Computer Integrated Systems', in 'Control and Dynamic Systems, Vol. 61; Computer Aided Manufacturing: Computer Integrated Manufacturing (CAM/CIM)', Academic Press, San Diego, 1993.

Trevelyan, G.M., 1942. 'English Social History', London, 1942. Pelican edition 1979.

Wedeking,E.L. 1992. 'Maximising your Return on Investment by Integrating Mechanical and Electronic Design Automation', Proceedings of the Third International Conference on Computer Integrated Manufacturing, Rensselaer Polytechnic Institute, Troy, New York, IEEE Computer Society Press, Los Alamitos, California, 1992.

7. The Impact of Information Technology and the Informating Capacity of the Organization on the Enterprise's Performance

Kate Laskowitz

Organizational Leadership and Supervision, Purdue University, West Lafayette, IN 47907 -1420, USA

Abstract. This proposal provides a framework to assess the relationship between a firm's output and collaborative decision-making structures, technology, and the informating capacity of labour at the firm level. The model suggests the level of 'informating' can be characterized as the relationship between labour's training, the level of information technology available and the kind of decision-making structures in the organization. The informating capacity of the organization can be understood by one or more of the following three *a priori* hypotheses: informating impacts directly on labour's input; impacts by its effects on technology efficiency; and its corresponding effects on economies of scale of the enterprise, all which have been proven to have a measurable and positive effect on the firm's performance. To assess this relationship, a simulated production system is suggested as a way to evaluate the weights of the variables used to define:

- labour education (training)
- decision-making structure
- technology.

It is hypothesized that collaborative decision-making variables will show a significant and positive impact on the output of a production system.

Keywords. Collaborative decision-making structures, Technology choices, productivity, performance, team-based decision-making

7.1 Introduction

We are currently at the crossroads of technological choices and organizational imperatives. We can continue to develop information technology which increases organizational efficacy but if there is not a corresponding development in the human resource areas and changes in the organizational decision-making structures, the benefits of technological innovation will fall short of the potential that has been created. Often, enterprises are confused by the availability of new technology and emerging approaches to decision-making restructuring on one hand, and the dilemma of whether or not to invest in these innovations. And rightly so. While engineers and social scientists alike have observed the boom in the capacity of manufacturing due to technological innovations, the gains in productivity have been disappointingly and unpredictably slow.

Management and Business schools have attempted to solve this enigma by approaches such as Total Quality Management (TQM) and Lean Production methods. TQM is touted, not only as a refinement of quality circle techniques but as a new paradigm, much as lean production was thought of just three years ago (Womack, et.al, 1990). The MIT study reported, in *The Machine that Changed the World*, that lean production, as a new paradigm, has already outpaced Taylorism and Fordist production methods (Womack, et.al., 1990).

TQM and lean production only bring us a little closer to solving the dilemma. If mass production is based on interchangeable elements (including labour), assigning workers to tasks with few requirements in discretionary decision-making, then lean production and TQM require employees to be trained in collaboration and team decision-making. Whether encased in TQM terminology or lean production, engineers are consigned to enlist workers' intellects, rather than just replace the industrial work environment with robots (Schefler, 1989) or hire more managers to control the production process. But neither TQM nor lean production are based on the integration of the current level of information technology, the needed changing structures of decision-making, and the needed increases in the capacity of organizational learning. And this is their failure. A better way to approach the dilemma might be to understand our historical roots of paradigmatic changes of production due to other technological innovation.

Some have suggested that the introduction of information technology can be compared to the past innovation and introduction of electricity to the production process, which shifted the industrial paradigm (David, P.A., 1990). The claim made is that today, as then, we suffer from a 'diffusion lag' due to a lack of corresponding organizational adaptation as well as a lack of measurement techniques, which can be used to quantify the new structural changes and their effects on productivity (David, P.A., 1990). The lag, then, can be attributed to the lack of understanding of how, and which organizational variables enhance the 'informating capacity' [increasing the intellective, discretionary level skills according to Zuboff, (1988)] of the work organization. In other words, we need to determine which decision-making structures enhance information technology, using productivity and other performance measures of the firm as an objective standard. Concomitantly, once the variations in decision-making structures are understood along with the variations of information technology, one needs to develop a methodology and technique to measure the impact of these variables on the firm's performance. So firstly, we need to address the forms and structures of the organization which put unnecessary drag on the organization's efficiency. Secondly, we need to understand how these variables can be enhanced or changed by assessing their impact on the relationship to the firm's performance.

Intrinsically the level of informating can occur and be measured by the relationship among labour's training, the level of information technology available, and the kind of decision-making structures in the organization. Based on previous research, this paper provides a rationale and method to assess the relationship among collaborative decision-making structures, technology, and labour's training and their effects on output at the firm level. It is hypothesized that informating will show a significant and positive impact on certain performance measures of the enterprise. Additionally the new models will provide a useful predictor for planning the need and utilization of new decision-making structures and information technology in enterprises. A longer-term objective, beyond the proposed research, will be to investigate the new model in an international comparative framework.

7.1.1 Informating and Productivity

Information technology offers managers a choice or a 'moment' (Barley, 1986) to introduce organizational changes in the decision-making structures which empower employees. New methods in manufacturing, in arenas where there is increased uncertainty and velocity of change in the market, have resulted in needed changes in decision-making structures. Whereas automation required capital improvement, there generally followed a 'shock' response to either reskill or deskill labour to control the automation process. Zuboff (1988) differentiates the process of informating from automation in the new work environment. Informating is a logical extension of automation. Zuboff (1990) suggests that a higher order is now not only possible, but necessary. Informating necessitates all employees to think strategically (Zuboff, 1990). Informating, according to Zuboff, *"cannot be exploited without the further development of human skills in ways of thinking that are conceptual, inferential, procedural, and systematic"* (Zuboff, 1988, p. 172).

The distinction Zuboff makes becomes more insightful when understanding the productivity paradox. The paradox refers to the increasing capacity of the organization, due to the increasing innovation and introduction of information technology, yet at the same time productivity gains are stagnant. Denison (1985) identified the factors responsible for the productivity decline in the US since 1973. A partial explanation is found in the declining potential of the traditional inputs, capital and labour (Denison, 1985). Secondly, Denison observed that the bigger share of the measurable productivity decline can be attributed to the managerial and 'organization' forms and structures (Denison 1985, p.40). To further investigate this issue, a summary of productivity analysis and organizational variables will be surveyed.

7.2 Related Research and Methodology

7.2.1 Discourse on Productivity

It has been noted that previous studies measuring the impact of technology and structure on productivity have made some serious flaws in their assumptions (Landau, 1991). Any analysis which continues to promote the impact of technology as having only a direct impact on output, is outmoded. One such mistaken assumption is that the relations between technology and structure are orderly and that the pattern of the relationship holds for all cases (Barley, 1986). The role of technology is now understood as having a multiplier effec,t found in the embodied and reinforcing form within each of the basic factors of production (Landau, 1991). Some of the most important advances in productivity analysis can be found in assessing both the interactive or intermediate effects of certain factors and determining the multiplicative and additive nature of the factors (Barua and Kriebel, et.al, 1991). In assessing the impact of information technology on the overall performance of the firm at the enterprise level, one thesis states that:

> *"impacts or contributions (to performance) of information technologies (if any) occur at lower operational levels ... or near the site where the technology is implemented"* (Barua and Kriebel, 1991, p. 5).

Shop floor economic analysis is rather new. Although micro-economics is based on the firm level, the primary focus of micro- productivity models is on the technical factors of production with assumptions of labour homogeneity and 'marginal utility' used to describe capital's and labour's contributions. As a result, neo-classical economists conclude that labour's productivity, equivalent to the price of labour or wages, is determined by market forces. Harvey Liebenstein takes issue with this when he argues, "the theory as currently constructed cannot handle differential motivation," upon which is what Liebenstein's X-efficiency theory is based (Liebenstein, 1981, p.100).

> *"Our theory argues that in order to understand productivity changes we have to understand how the economic environment operates as an incentive towards more or less effective effort levels...and how the environment influences incentive structures. Mainline theory does not really study such questions because it does not address itself to the non-market production activities within the firm..."* (Liebenstein, 1981, p.105).

Liebenstein's theory and critique of mainstream economics is insightful. But Liebenstein assumes that X-efficiency theory will lead to maximization of effort via changes instituted at the top of the hierarchy, due to their increasing knowledge of market conditions. While the aspects of organizational efficiency, differential motivation, and effort (derived from Liebenstein's notion of effort-entropy) are necessary ingredients to understand what contributes to changes in productivity, to formulate a theory with the assumption of centralized decision-making is a deficiency of the theory.

Taking it one step further, to include an analysis of decentralized, organizational variables, recent studies have begun to measure and link organizational designs and decision-making structures to a firm's performance. Some studies show a significant and positive relationship between certain organizational variables and the firm's performance (Shibata, Tse, et.al., 1991; Cooke, 1989). Those industries which are characterized by rapid technological change and market uncertainty, show a strong relationship between decentralized organizational norms of decision-making and performance, although it is concluded that the specific pattern of the relationship is not easily identifiable (Shibata, Tse, et.al., 1991).

In another study, using managerial perceptions, the data indicate that certain organizational variables, including payment schemes and participation programmes, had different levels of success; gain-sharing, profit-sharing and participation programs made significant contributions to improved plant performance (Voos, 1989.) The measurements for the organizational norms were taken from survey data without any direct measurements.

The weakness of these studies and others is in the methods used to quantify the structures of decision-making. They were derived from manager's perceptions. The proposed model uses direct measurements of the inputs and output to determine the impact relationships. In addition, the proposed model emphasizes the inter-relationship of decision-making structures, labour's training, and information technology in the organization. This was not done by the previous studies.

7.2.2 International Comparisons

International comparisons of different industrial relations and organizational structures have also demonstrated some interesting links between different organizational variables and the firm's performance. In one study, it was concluded that the Japanese informal (not legally binding) Joint Consultation Committees (JCCs) show positive associations between information sharing and firm profitability (Morishima, 1991). The Cressey and DiMartino (1991) study also was based on a comparative framework evaluating European participation paradigms including joint decision-making, negotiations, consultation and information sharing.

Based on the British experience with different participation programs, in a recent study, Jones and Pliskin (1989) conclude that decision-making structures need to be assessed by multi-variable structures to pick up the dynamic influences. Measuring one variable alone would not suffice to identify the structural equation for a decision-making variable.

7.2.3 Decision-Making Structures, Information and Productivity

The IDE study's findings suggest that:

"...The degree to which employees have an opportunity to participate in decision making can be seen as an aspect of how the administrative

structure of an organization is arranged...The way in which, and the extent to which, employees are mobilized in some kind of system that will represent their interests will probably affect both their degree of actual participation and their attitudes towards the system" (IDE, 1981, p. 115-116).

Employee team-based or collaborative decision-making structures have been identified for their synergistic value as well as for their reduction of employee resistance (Cherrington, D.J., 1991; Cooke, W.N., 1989; Katz, H.C. et.al., 1983;). Collaborative decision-making has also been shown, under certain conditions, to benefit the output of the system; links are made between the intensity of the collaborative process and performance improvements (Cooke, 1989).

It was found that technology innovators are more likely to have introduced organizational change. In a survey analysis, 71% of those organizations which introduced some form of technological innovation (CAD, CAM, robots) also had innovations in organizational changes (Newton, 1989). These changes were found in the areas of wage systems; work organization; and joint decision-making structures (Newton, 1989). When introducing technology, often reorganization of the production process comes with the potential for the blurring of line managerial decision-making and employee (team-based) decision-making.

A National Academy of Science (NAS) study evaluated 16 plants in the process of managing innovation through technology introduction. A major issue identified for successful management of the technology was the structures which empowered employees by granting greater amounts of discretionary decision-making. This concurs with Zuboff's notion that two conditions are critical to provide for increases in the informating capacity; an organizational strategy that is built on learning and a leadership vision which engenders redistribution of authority and high levels of employee participation (Zuboff, 1990).

In the past, under Taylorist modes of production, the hierarchical boundaries "...tend to maintain the more intellectually substantive tasks within management ranks" (Zuboff, 1988, p. 207). What is entailed in creating the conditions for such deep rooted authoritarian structures, according to Zuboff, is the hierarchical relations (Zuboff, 1988, p. 217). It is contended here that different forms of decision-making, heirarchical forms of decision-making, are needed. Some studies attempt to describe the different participatory format and suggest a new paradigm is emerging (Cressey and DiMartino, 1991). In Cressey and Di Martinio's study (1991), they assess the different forms of participation and characterize levels of decision-making accordingly: no involvement, information only, consultation, negotiation, joint decision-making. Through case-study analysis these systems were evaluated to more thoroughly understand the country-specific nuances of organizational adaptation.

In the US, employee participation schemes have evolved in many areas, some increasing collaborative decision-making, others exploring rewards tied to performance. Let's start from the premise of a multi-divisional firm and its corresponding need for a high degree of decentralization and independence, with regards to operational decisions. In this case, the perspective of analysis is from the shop floor decision-making structures. Analysis begins with three styles of decision-making: rights of information, consultation, or co-determination (IDE, 1981). A managerial structure takes shape as these styles of decisions are juxtaposed with three levels in the hierarchy of management: shop-floor level, management level, and top management/board-room level. The grid depicted in Figure 1 corresponds to the IDE study's findings (IDE, 1981,p.50).

Figure 1: Styles and Level of Decision Making*

Time Perspective	Operational	Personnel	Economic	Level of Decision-making
Short Term	Task assignment (c) Personal Equip (c,cd) Working Conditions (cd) Working Hrs (c,cd)	 Training (c) Transfers (cd) Holidays (cd)		ii ii iii ii/iii iii ii/iii iii
Medium Term	Programming (I,c) Maintenance (I,c) Trouble-shooting (I,c)	Dismissals (c,cd) Hiring proced (I,c) New Dept head (I) Appoint. Superv (I)	Wages(cd) Reorganiz(I)	iii i i/ii ii ii
Long	Technology Investment (n) New Product (n)	 Diversification (n) Structural Decision-Making (n)	Investment term Capitalize (n)	i i i i

* Adapted from the IDE study
Types of Decision-making styles:(I=information; c=consultation; cd=co-determination/negotiation, n=no obligations; i=centralized; ii=decentralized;iii=democratic)

The IDE study characterizes the three levels of decision making accordingly:

i centralized *de jure* decision making: top management, the highest hierarchical level, holds either a veto-power or can make the decisions in their own right.

ii decentralized *de jure* decision-making: supervisors and middle management control decisions.

iii democratic *de jure* decision-making: all decisions with at least prior consultation with representative bodies; sometimes representative bodies have veto-power (IDE, 1981,p.141).

From the grid, it is apparent that medium and long term decisions are areas where workers have the least influence and participation. The levels and types of shop-floor participation are variegated, with the greatest inequality found in long term decisions and the least inequality in short term decisions (IDE, 1981).

Moving from short-term to long-term decisions, there is an increasing tendency of management's obligations to go from joint decision-making or co-determination towards unilateral decisions, only providing information and consultation with employees or their representatives.

7.2.4 Information Sharing and Productivity

With regards to information sharing, although there are no conclusions about the overall impact of information sharing, it has been concluded that the levels of information sharing do have a perceived significant impact on decision-making (Morishima 1990; Ogden 1992). While there are no conclusions, there is tension among the different managerial hierarchies and tensions between line employees and management at the point of production, as more information is accessible and allows for autonomous decision-making structures. Consequently, upper layers of corporate management are both pulling back and extending their once unilateral decision-making authority (Colling and Ferner, 1992).

Yet some argue that disclosure of information is perceived as counterproductive to the organizational goals (Ogden, 1992). The major contention is that employers will only be willing to share information and certain decision-making areas when and only when employees give unequivocal commitment to management's decisions (Ogden, 1992).

This possibly helps explain why employees are generally excluded from most of the medium and long-term decisions, with access to information only. Yet, the new operating environment appears to be imposing very strong decentralized, more autonomous, dynamic, and flexible managerial decision-making structures upon the corporation (Colling and Ferner, 1992) and consequently upon employees at the point-of-production. In the US, firms have been experimenting with different forms of employee involvement. These employee participation schemes have evolved in many areas, some increasing collaborative decision-making, others exploring rewards tied to performance. Gain-sharing and profit-sharing plans tie workers' wages to profits, while ESOP has the potential to involve employees in more in-depth decision-making. They have knowledge and information about the operations of the corporation and have a well-defined community of interest (Poole and Jenkins, 1991). In effect, they provide a check and balance of managerial expertise to the shareholders. In one study it was found that employees favoured employee ownership for the following reasons (in preferential order): financial gain; entrepreneurship; greater influence and participation in decision-making; a direct benefit from one's own efforts; and cooperative relationship between management and employees (Poole and Jenkins, 1991.) But there is some controversy as to whether ESOP or gain-sharing plans impact positively on productivity. Voos concludes that ESOPs might not play such a positive role in today's economy (Voos, 1987.) The data, based on managers' perceptions, indicate that gain-sharing, profit-sharing and participation programs made significantly greater contribution to improved plant performance than ESOPs (Voos, 1989). While perceptions are important, no study has included an empirical model to measure and control for both ESOP and employee participation programs. One part of this paper examines the role of collaborative decision-making structures, ESOP and their corresponding impacts on productivity. Some studies point to micro-level analysis at the firm level to assess the relationship of information sharing, decision-making structures and productivity (Ogden, 1992; Morshima, 1990). Where specifically does shared decision-making have positive impacts on the firm's performance?

In order to explore the relationship between decision-making structures and their impact on the firm's productivity, structural and empirical models are developed (See Appendix A and B). To test the hypothesis, the following case-study was made.

7.3 A Case-Study of Kaiser Aluminum

In 1975-76, the aluminum industry faced economic turmoil. During the 1970s and starting with the nationalization of the Oil cartels, there was a marked increase in nationalization of bauxite mines. This resulted in a lack of control of raw materials in what had been a ready supply of alumina at a relatively fixed cost. This caused production constraints on Kaiser and the Aluminum industry as a whole. These trends persisted throughout the late seventies and well into the beginning of the eighties. With high energy costs accruing in the production of aluminum ingots, the company invested heavily in numerical data control systems, linked to the electrolytic process. Employees were retrained to manage the new technology. Meanwhile, demand for aluminum continued to decline, due to increases of aluminum substitutions and over-supply, causing the price of aluminum to drop to very low levels. There was little economic incentive for the aluminum corporations to continue producing under the same arrangements with its suppliers and employees. In an attempt to overcome this situation, Kaiser Aluminum and Chemical Corporation initiated major changes in its operation ranging from down-sizing and decentralization of decision-making to changes in basic decision-making structures.

The first stages of this restructuring effort for efficient production (and to ward off takeover bids) involved a transformation of the collective bargaining pattern to implement what is today known as an Employee Involvement program (EI). The company decided to alter its operational and financial decision-making by developing collaborative decision-making structures and mechanisms. This allowed employees and their representatives major inroads into business planning meetings and up-dated financial information on a regular basis. Both corporate level officers and national officers of the Union, along with elected leadership from the Local USWA affiliates of Kaiser met every six months to participate in business and financial planning meetings. A decentralized plan included collaborative operational decision-making structures as well. Employee involvement in decision-making was to reach down to the shop-floor level, through a team-based structure labelled as Employee Involvement (EI). Wage concessions were given in exchange for an ESOP program and more involvement in long-term decision-making. These programs were put into effect during the years 1986 to 1987.

To measure the impact of these programs, a case study was conducted at Kaiser's largest primary aluminum facility, the Mead plant in Spokane, Washington. Its capacity is approximately two-hundred thousand metric tons per year. It employs from 800 to 1,000 production workers and approximately 150 salaried employees. The Union, the United Steelworkers of America, (USWA) has represented the Kaiser-Mead production and maintenance employees since the World War II years when Kaiser Aluminum got its start in aluminum as part of an anti-trust settlement against Aluminum Company of America (ALCOA). Union and Management have a reputation for always being able to settle their grievances and contract disputes without any long term work stoppages. Currently there are three managerial groups: operations production management, employee involvement management, and industrial relations management. Operations management includes the supervisors, engineers, and top managerial decision-makers at the Kaiser-Mead location. The EI management team includes a small group of managerial personnel giving direction to the company's EI program; it also includes supervisory personnel. The Industrial Relations team is involved with day-to-day personnel policies and the collective bargaining process. It represents the company in the grievance process and provides leadership to the decision-making involving the collective bargaining contract.

7.3.1 Discussion

A two stage regression method was used to carry out the fit of the structural equation (1) and (2) (see Table 1). Both estimation equations have approximately the same coefficient of determination. With only the nominal financial collaborative decision-making variable included (E), the model, equation (1), is able to predict 97 percent of the variation of output (see Table 2). The variables, ESOP and Labour, have positive and significant effects on output. Equation (2) also predicts 97 percent of the variation of output. But by adding the other collaborative decision-making variables, labour hours' impact on output is increased. According to the results, the variable which is statistically significant and positive is collaboration at the national level (strategic level). These results concur with Jones and Plaskin (1989) in their conclusions that any effects of financial shared, decision-making may depend quite significantly on the institutional setting and specifically, on employee participation in decision-making.

Labour hours account for close to 49 percent of all explained variation in one unit of output. The labour hours coefficient is highly significant and positive. Top-level collaborative decision-making structures, proxied by the ESOP variable, is only significant when no other decision-making structures are included in the analysis. In equation (1), ESOP explains 14 percent of the variation of output. The collaborative team-based decision-making at the shop-floor according to this analysis, is not statistically significant and seemingly has a negative impact on output. At best, this might be a short-term phenomena. One interpretation of this is that it is in the process of change and certain current pathways of authority are impeded due to the changes being instituted.

7.3.2 Summary of Kaiser Case-Study

This study was intended to demonstrate that collaborative decision-making structures have measurable impact on output. While any conclusions drawn from this case study are tentative, it does begin to suggest that ESOP along with collaborative strategic decision-making and operational decision-making enhances labour's contribution to productivity. This becomes important in determining what types of decision-making structures and information sharing are necessary to increase labour's contribution to the organization. There is a need for further research in the area of multiple programs which are designed to enhance labour's contribution to the firm.

In comparing the impact of ESOP and team-based shop-floor decision-making, this study suggests that decentralized team-based decision-making might initially impede and frustrate current pathways of authority and bureaucracy. And that in the short-run, information sharing and team decision-making structures might not have overnight results. Improving the capacity of capital and labour through collaborative strategic decision-making structures has the potential to impact positively on output. Yet this study only addresses one part of the equation.

A limitation of this study can be found in the lack of analysis and measurement of how information technology effects structural changes in decision-making and how it directly affects output. The following study proposes to evaluate the impact of the informating capacity of the organization on a firm's performance when controlling for decision-making structures, levels of technology and the labour's training.

7.4 The Model of Informating

The model developed in this research explicitly defines the relationship among the informating variables—collaborative decision-making structures, levels of information technology and levels of training and education of employees. In addition, the model is designed to measure the impact of the informating capacity of the organization on a firm's performance and in so doing, explore the additive and multiplicative relationship among the informating variables.

The model uses three (3) variables to measure the elements of the informating capacity of the organization. These three variables are employees' education and experience, collaborative decision-making structures within an enterprise, and information technology (E,D,T). These three variables will be inserted into a Cobb Douglas Productivity function as independent variables. The dependency and weighting system are determined initially by Ordinary Least Squares (OLS) and Two Stage Least Squares (2SLS) analysis. (See Appendix C, D and E for the notation, and methodology). The explicit relationship of the factors of informating and their impact on output will be explored in the mathematical modelling section of this paper.

7.5 The Components of Informating

The education (E), represents the level of education, training and experience of the team members. This is determined by the following components:
Education and Training of Labour
e_1 = training (job specific)
e_2 = education (college, vocational, etc)
e_3 = experience (length of service on tasks)

The decision-making structures represent the level and type of control or unilateral discretion and autonomy the team members have. It is based on levels of information-sharing and the number of organizational layers or hierarchy. The type of decision involves the nature of the decision as to its relevant time frame — short-term to long-term. The style of decision includes such components as amounts of collaboration determined by different degrees, such as consultation with other groups, and negotiations.

7.5.1 Decision-Making Structure

d_1 = level of decision-authority
d_2 = types of decision (short-term, med-term, long-term)
d_3 = style of decision (information only; consultation; negotiation)

The level of technology needs to consider the complexity of the accessibility and sophistication of data and information. To control for these variables, three basic levels of informating technologies will be assessed. These are:

(1) traditional MIS (Management Information Systems), in which information is available, but not easy to access by non-MIS personnel
(2) Networked MIS, where communication networks provide wider and random access to the information
(3) CTCT (Coordination Theory and Collaboration Technology), alternatively termed CSCW (computer-supported collaborative work) which allows workers to cooperate as team-members.

Each level of the three provides better access to information sharing, but requires larger technology investments and more sophisticated training of the users. These three alternative levels will be simulated in our labs, as well as studied in the industry case-study. (The specific relationship among the Informating variables will be explored in the mathematical modelling section of this proposal.)

7.5.2 Information Technology

t_1 = speed of technology (time to access correct information)
t_2 = sophistication (limits or constraints of information)
t_3 = accuracy (output - errors)

The specific measurement of the elements of each of these levels will include the number of data bases one could access, along with the distribution and interfacing that would need to be taken into consideration. The speed to access the information will be a proxy for these elements. Also, another element is the limits or constraints of the hardware and software provided. Constraints and limits are also found in the interfacing components within the system. These components will be evaluated and will be represented in the sophistication level of the information technology. The degree of accuracy will also be considered. In order to assess the differences, three basic levels of informating technologies will be introduced into the model.

Taken together, these variables defining the informating capacity, represent the quality and type of decisions made at the point closes to the point of production. This is a discretized, continuous variable and represents a hierarchical cumulative process. The range of the discrete variable is between 1-O, with 0 representing an immeasurable or insignificant amount of informating capacity to 1 which represents a high level of informating capacity.

7.5.3 The First Hypothesis — Limiting Factors

It is assumed that labour's experience, the accuracy of the information technology, and the style of decision-making are limiting factors. It is also assumed in this model that these limiting factors are dependent on the scale of the enterprise, therefore, the limiting factor is scaled exponentially. This suggests that as the size of the operation increases, so too will the magnitude of certain of the informating components increase, in comparison to the other components. The concepts of scale and limiting factors are adopted in the following informating model:

$$I = e_3^{\,i}(e_1 + e_2) + t_3^{\,i}(t_1 + t_2) + d_3^{\,i}(d_1 + d_2) \qquad (1)$$

7.5.4 The Second Hypothesis — Scale of the Enterprise

The second hypothesis introduces the training and information technology speed as limiting factors. In addition, the training and technology speed is shown to have dependence on the scale of the operation. This model adopts another change as well. It suggests that the type of decision qualifies output in a reciprocal manner within the production function. The second hypothesis is modeled accordingly:

$$I = e_3^{\,i}(e_1 + e_2) + t_2^{\,i}(1/t_1 + t_2) + 1/d_2^{\,i}(d_1 + d_3) \qquad (2)$$

7.5.5 The Third Hypothesis — Reciprocal Relationship

Another model is arranged which eliminates the exponents, establishing that scale does not impact on informating. This model reflects the factor of speed of information technology in a reciprocal relationship to the firm's performance.

$$I = e_1(e_2 + e_3) + 1/t_1(t_2 + t_3) + d_2(d_1 + d_3) \quad (3)$$

7.6 Conclusion

Often, enterprises are confused by the availability of new technology and emerging approaches to decision-making restructuring on one hand, and the dilemma of whether or not to invest in these innovations. Based on previous research, this paper provides a method to model and assess the relationship among collaborative decision-making structures, technology, and the informating capacity of the organization and their effects on output at the firm level. The structural models presented in this proposal suggest that the level of 'informating' can be measured by the relationship among labour's training, the level of information technology available and the kind of decision-making structures in the organization. The methodology used to understand this relationship between the informating capacity and the firm's performance is a production function that includes both additive and multiplicative relationships. Three *a priori* hypotheses about the production model will be explained. The paper presents a previous study used to set up the *a priori* hypothesis and then proposes how these hypotheses can be assessed.

It is hypothesized that informating and decision-making structure variables will show a significant and positive impact on certain performance measures of the enterprise. Additionally the new models will provide a useful predictor for planning the need and utilization of new decision-making structures and information technology in enterprises. A longer-term objective beyond the proposed research will be to investigate the new model in an international comparative framework.

Appendix A

Notation of variables in Production Function

In developing a model which explicitly describes the impact of collaborative decision-making structures on output, the following notation is used in addition to that previously described. Let:

L = the number of labour hours during the observation period

A_0 = intercept — often considered the technical efficiency variable

b_s = regression coefficients for the independent variables,

LagQ = Output in the previous period (t-1),

Q = output of aluminum, measured in metric tons during the observed time period,

The Collaborative Decision-making Variables

The Participation variable (P_s), represents collaborative decision-making on the operational level. It represents the type and level of decisions made at shop floor. This is a discretized, continuous variable and represents a hierarchical cumulative process. The range of the discrete variable is between 1-5, with 1 representing a low amount of worker involvement in decision-making and 5 representing a high involvement.

The participation variable (P_n), represents collaborative decision-making at the national or strategic level. It is a discretized, continuous variable and represents a hierarchical cumulative process. The range of the discrete variable is between 6-10.

Employee Stock Ownership Program (E), represents the number of stock owned by employees and also represents at least nominal collaborative decision-making in investment decision. This is a discrete variable.

Appendix B

Two Production Functions

The data will be used to estimate the following equations:

$$LnQ = lnA_0 + \alpha lnL + ß lnE + u \qquad (4)$$

Where: $\alpha + ß = 1$

$$LnQ = lnA_0 + \alpha ln\ L + ß ln\ E + \sigma lnP + \pi lnP + u \qquad (5)$$

Where: $\alpha + ß + \sigma + \pi = 1$

Equation (4) only includes the ESOP variable, while equation (5) has both ESOP and the participation variables. A two-stage least squares regression analysis will be used to determine the weights of the variables L,E, P_s, and P_n. (See Table 1 and 2 for results.)

Appendix C

Informating Capacity Notation and Hypothesis on Structural Equation of Informating

In developing a model which explicitly describes the impact of the informating capacity of collaborative decision-making structures on output, the following notation is used:

L = the number of labour hours during the observation period,

K = the amount of capital needed for the system during the observed period

A_0 = intercept — often considered the technical efficiency variable,

Q= output during the observed time period,

LagQ = output in t-1 period

I = information capacity (derived from measurement of the amounts of education, information technology, and collaborative decision-making structures — See below).
Lag I = information capacity in t-1 period
(The lag variables will be used to assess the problem of autocorrelation in the production function.)

$$\ln Q = A_0\ \pi \ln I\ \alpha \ln K\ \beta \ln L \qquad (6)$$

Q=Output; K=Capital intensity; L=Labour, I=Informating capacity and:

$$I = f(E,D,T) \qquad (7)$$

Where: E=Education, D=Decision-making structure, AND T=level of technology

Appendix D

Hypotheses

It is hypothesized, *a priori*, that Q (output) is dependent on I (informating) in one of three ways; as a parameter (or contribution) to the labour variable or to the technical efficiency factor; or that I is a parameter to both labour and the technical efficiency factor. To test for the fit of I and its effect on Q, first the function is transformed to a log-linear relationship:

$$\ln Q = f(A_0\ \sigma \ln K\ \beta \ln L) \quad \text{where: } L = g(G_0,e,t,d) \qquad (8)$$

The first hypothesis (8) argues that the informating level measured by (e,t,d) contributes to the labour variable in the productivity function. This suggests that labour hours are qualified (either increased or decreased) according to the level of informating.

The second *a priori* hypothesis (9) is that informating is a parameter to the technological efficiency factor.

$$\ln Q = f[g(A_0, \pi \ln I)\ \sigma \ln K\ \beta \ln L] \quad \text{where } I = f(P_0,e,t,d) \qquad (9)$$

The third *a priori* hypothesis (10) shows that the informating variables, e,t,d are parameters to both labour and the technical efficiency factor.

$$\ln Q = f(A_0,\ \pi \ln I\ \alpha \ln K\ \beta \ln L) \quad \text{where } I = f(P_0,e,t,d) \text{ and } L = g(\beta_0,e,t,d) \qquad (10)$$

The theoretical model will be empirically tested first in a simulated production system.

Appendix E

The Methodology of Determining the Informating Capacity

The model adopted for this study uses a weighting system which is based on the dependent nature of informating capacity of the organization — measured in the structures of organizations and their relationship to productivity. The specific nature of the dependencies will be determined from the data and regression analysis during the simulated production system.

The variables measuring informating capacity will be initially determined by the beta weights attributed to each sub-component as they were determined in the first stage of the simultaneous method using Ordinary Least Squares (OLS) analysis.

The model will test three hypothesis regarding the inter-relationship among the sub-components, education, information technology and collaborative decision-making (e,t,d) and their relationship to output. Three concepts are introduced mathematically into the model: (1) First a sub component is introduced as a limiting factor where the value of the component is a multiplicand in the relationship — See (11) below. (2) Informating capacity's dependency is hypothesized to be in relation to the scale of the operation, depicted by the use of the exponent -- See (12) below. And (3) informating capacity's dependency on a sub component introduced as a reciprocal, is included — See (13) below.

T=Technology (information) = $f(t_1, t_2, t_3)$

$$T = t_3(t_1 + t_2) \quad (11)$$

E= Education = $f(e_1, e_2, e_3)$

$$E = e_2^{\,2}(e_1 + e_2) \quad (12)$$

D=Decision-making = $f(d_1, d_2, d_3)$

$$D = (1/d_2)*(d_1 + d_3) \quad (13)$$

Table 1: Descriptive Statistics (Log Transformations)

Variable	Mean	Standard Deviation
(L) Labour Hours	11.490	.224
(E) ESOP	7.207	.280
(P^s) Participation	.688	.217
(P^n) Participation	1.27	.526
(LagQ) t-1 Output	9.992	.213
(Q) Output	10.002	.218

Table 2: Regression Coefficients		
	(Q) Output is dependent variable:	
	Equation (1)	Equation (2)
Variable	Parameter Estimate (Standard Error)	Parameter Estimate (Standard Error)
Intercept	-.156 (.406)	-.512 (.542)
L	.460*** (.082)	.485*** (.084)
E	.145*** (.047)	.051 (.066)
P^s	N.A.	-.104 (.053)
P^n	N.A.	.083** (.039)
LagQ++	.383*** (.105)	.352*** (.100)
R Squared	.965	.969
df	34	31
F Ratio	288.21	192.06
Durbin Watson	2.35	2.55

*** Significant to the .01 level
++The lag variable of output was used to reduce the autocorrelation. According to the Durbin-Watson statistic, the Co-efficient of determination, 97 percent, is with relatively little autocorrelation.

References

Baker, D.P. and E. Salas (1992). Principles for Measuring Teamwork Skills. Human Factors, 34, 469-475.
Barley, S. R. (1986). "Technology as an Occasion for Structuring: Evidence from Observations of CT Scanners and the Social Order of Radiology Departments," Administrative and Science Quarterly, 31, pp. 78-108.
Barua, A., C.H. Kriebel and T. Mukhopadhyay (1991). "Information Technologies and Business Value: An Analytic and Empirical Investigation," Unpublished Paper, NSF Grant No. IRI-9012740.

Cable, J. (1988). "A Model and Measure of Employee Participation: Guttman Scale Tests of the Espinosa-Zimbalist Hypothesis," in Advances in the Economic Analysis of Participatory and Labour-Managed Firms, Derek C. Jones and Jan Svejnar (eds.), (Greenwich, Connecticut: JAI Press).

Ching,C., C.W. Holsapple, and A.B.Whinston (1989). "Concurrent Problem Solving and Organizational Learning," Proc 22 HICSS, 3, 483-491.

Conte and Tannebaum, A.J. (1978). "Employee Owned Companies: Is the Difference Measurable?," Monthly Labour Review, Vol. 101, pp. 23-8.

Cooke, W., (1989). "Improving Productivity and Quality Through Collaboration", Industrial Relations, Vol. 28, N0.2, pp. 299-319.

Colling, T. and A. Ferner (1992). "The limits of Autonomy: Devolution, Line Mangers and Industrial Relations in Privatized Companies", Journal of Management Studies, Vol. 29, No.2, March, pp. 209-227.

Cressey, P. and V. Di Martino (1991). Agreement and Innovation: The International Dimension of Technological Change, Herts, UK: Prentice Hall.

David, P.A. (1990). "The Dynamo and the Computer: An Historical Perspective on the Modern Productivity Paradox," American Economic Review, Vol. 80, Issue 2, (May) pp. 355-361.

Denison, E. (1985). Trends in American Economic Growth, 1929-1982, Brookings Institution.

Dennis, A.R., J.S. Valacich, J.F. Nunamaker (1990). "An Experimental Investigation of the Effects of Group Size in an Electronic Meeting Environment," IEEE Transactions on Systems, Man, and Cybernetics, 25, 1049-1057.

Eberts, R.E. and Nof, S.Y. (in press)."Distributed Planning of Collaborative Production," International Journal of Intelligent Systems.

Espinosa, J.G. and A. S. Zimbalist (1978). Economic Democracy: Workers' Participation in Chilean Industry, 1970-1973, New York: Academic Press.

Gallupe, R.B. (1985). "The Impact of Task Difficulty on the Use of a Group Decision Support System," Unpublished Doctoral Dissertation. University of Minnesota.

Gallupe, R.B. (1990). "Suppressing the Contribution of the Group's Best Member: Is GDSS Use Appropriate for all Group Tasks?" Proceedings of the IEEE 23rd Annual Hawaii International Conference on System Sciences, Vol. III, 13-22.

Greenberg, E.S.,(1980). "Participation in Industrial Decision Making and Worker Satisfaction," Social Science Quarterly, Vol. 60, pp. 557-623.

Hammer, T.H. and Stern, R.N. (1980). "Employee Ownership: Implications for the Organizational Distribution of Power," Academy of Management Journal, Vol.XXIII, pp. 78-100.

Henry, J.W., (1989). "ESOPs With Productivity Payoffs," Journal of Business Strategy, Vol: 10, July-August, pp. 32-36.

Ichniowski, C.(1986). "The Effects of Grievance Activity on Productivity," Industrial and Labour Relations Review, October p.77

IDE, (1981). European Industrial Relations, Oxford: Clarendon Press.

Jones, C.J. and J. Pliskin. (1989), "British Evidence on the Employment Effects of Profit Sharing," Industrial Relations, Vol. 28, No.2, Spring, pp. 276-298.
Kleinman, D.L., P.B. Lluh, K.R. Pattipati, D. Serfati (1991). "Mathematical Models of Team Distributed Decision making," In R.W. Sweezy and E. Salas (eds.) Teams: Their Training and Performance, Ablex
Kraemer, K.L. (1991). "The AIME Project," Proc. NSF CTCT Workshop, Washington, D.C. pp.57-61.
Landau, R. (1991). Technology and Economics, National Academy Press: Washington, D.C.
Leibenstein, H., (1981). "Microeconomics and X-efficiency Theory: If there is no Crisis, There Ought to be." In Daniel Bell and Irving Kristol (eds), The Crisis in Economic Theory, (New York, Basic Books
Lewis, F. (1982). "Facilitator: A Microcomputer Decision Support System for Small Support Groups," Unpublished doctoral dissertation. University of Louisville.
Malone, T.W. and J.F. Rockart (1991). "Computers, Networks and the Corporation," Scientific American, pp. 128-136.
Marsh, T. and D. McAllister,(1981). "ESOPs Tables: A Survey of Companies With Employee Stock Ownership Plans," Journal of Corporation Law, Vol. 6, No.3, pp. 557-623.
Mitchell, D.J.B. (1987). "The Share Economy and Industrial Relations," Industrial Relations, Vol.26, No.1, pp. 1-17.
Morgan, B.B., A.S. Glickman, E.A. Woodward, A.S. Blaiwes, And E. Salas (1986). "Measurmeent of Team Behaviors in a Navy Environmnet (Tech. Report TR-86-014). Orlando, Fl: Naval Training Systems Center, Human Factors Division.
Morishima, M. (1991). "Information Sharing and Firm Performance in Japan," Industrial Relations, Vol. 30, No.1, pp. 37-61.
Newton, K. (1989). "Technological and Organizational Change in Canada," New Technology, Work and Employment, Vol. 4, No.1, Spring, pp.40-45.
Norsworthy,J.R. and C. Zabala (1985). "Worker Attitudes, Worker Behavior, and Productivity in the U.S. Automobile Industry, 1959-1976," Industrial and Labour Relations Review, Vol.38, p.546.
Nota, B.C. (1989). "Conditions for Successful Organizational Responses to Technological Change", in American Society of Mechanical Engineers -- The Worker in Transition: Technological Change, New York, N.Y.
Nunamaker, J.F., D. Vogel, A. Heminger, B. Martz, R. Grohowski, and C. McGoff (1989). "Group Support System in Practice: Experience at IBM," Proceedings of the IEEE 22nd Annual Hawaii International Conference on System Sciences, pp. 378-386.
Nuti, D.M. (1987). "Profit Sharing and Employment: Claims and Overclaims," Industrial Relations, Vol. 26, No.1, pp.18-29.
Poole, M. and G. Jenkins, (1991). "The Impact of Profit-Sharing and Employee Shareholding Schemes," Journal of General Management, Vol. 16, No.3, Spring, pp. 52-72

Rajan, V. and S.Y. Nof (1991). "A Game Theoretic Approach for Coopeation Control in Multimachine Workstations," International Journal CIM Special Issue on Intelligent Control, 3, 47-59.
Rouse, W.B. (1991). "Who is Them?" Harvard Business Review.
Shibata, G. and D. Tse, I. Vertinsky and D. Wehrung (1991). "Do Norms of Decision-Making Styles, Organizational Design and Management Affect Performance of Japanese Firms? An Exploratory Study of Medium and Large Firms." Mangerial and Decision Economics, Vol. 12, pp. 135-146.
Voos, P., (1987). "Managerial Perceptions of the Economic Impact of Labour Relations Programs," Industrial and Labour Relations Review, Vol. 40, No.2 (January), pp. 195-208.
Warnken, J. and G. Ronning (199?). "Technological Change and Employment Structures" in a report on a Meta study
Womack, J.P., Jones, D.T., and Roos, D. (1990). The Machine That Changed the World, Macmillan Publishing Company: New York.
Zuboff, S. (1988). The Age of the Smart Machine, New York: Basic Books
Zuboff, S., G.T. Marx, B. Howard and K. Nussbaum (1990). "The Case of the Omniscient Organization," Harvard Business Review, Vol. 68, No.2, March/April pp.12-30.

8. The Possible Roles of Gender and Cognitive Style in the Design of Human-Centred Computer Interfaces

Konrad Morgan[1], Robert L. Morris[2], Hamish Macleod[2] and Shirley Gibbs[3]

[1] Department of Information Science, Portsmouth University, Hampshire UK
[2] Department of Psychology, University of Edinburgh, Edinburgh, UK
[3] Computer Studies Department, Napier University, Edinburgh, UK

Abstract. The`authors review research which has tried to explain and identify the reasons for the differences in attitudes, acceptance and performance with regard to computer systems. The paper covers such areas as individual differences, gender differences, cultural or social class differences, computer attitudes, cognitive style, and psychological differentiation.

Keywords. Interface Design, users and machines, gender, gender difference, cognition, psychology, physical differences

8.1 The role of individual differences in human-centred computer system design

The acceptance or rejection of new technology is often attributed to the quality of the design and implementation process. One of the characteristics of the many 'human-centred' approaches to systems design is the central importance of the user at all the stages of the design process. This is done to increase the likelihood of a sound match between the user and the system when it is eventually implemented. However the very individuality of the users means that the human centred systems designer has to be aware of the differences in behaviour, attribution and attitudes which are likely within the end user population.

Know thy Users... and their Differences!

A slight modification of the once famous delphic inscription therefore seems appropriate as a motto for todays human-centred systems designer, but the wealth of literature on individual differences can appear somewhat daunting to a busy designer with little time to research the field. It is hoped that this short paper will provide a starting point for such an individual and provide references to those areas of the literature which are of most relevance to the current demands of their work.

8.2 Individual Differences

Individual Differences Include:
- Spatial Ability
- Memory
- Mathematical Ability
- Technology Attitudes
- Technological Aptitude
- Age
- Gender
- Cultural or Social Background
- Cognitive Style
- Historical Influences

Over the past twenty years, researchers have tried to explore individual differences, and as a result of this process, have developed several theories and proposed solutions for the problem of individual differences in technology attitudes and computer interface preference. However, some researchers have stated that they felt that many of these findings were descriptive rather than prescriptive [18].

Most of the theories which have been proposed attempt to explain the preferences which different users have for interface types by some form of individual experiential, spatial, psychological or physical difference. Some researchers have declared the goal of being able to isolate the factors responsible for these differences, thereby permitting designers to allow some configurability in computer interfaces, perhaps based on the results of a test [18], or brief inventory of questions [67,1,4,57]. These adaptive interfaces have been the subject of some study, and are still felt by many to have promise in helping to reduce interface design problems [4,58,59].

The individual differences which have been investigated include: spatial ability, memory, mathematical ability, technology attitudes, technological aptitude, age, gender, cultural or social background, cognitive style and historical influences. The paper briefly summarises some of the research which has been conducted in these areas.

8.3 Gender Differences

Gender Differences.

- Aggression (Males more Aggressive)
- Verbal Abilities (Females Superior)
- Visio-spatial Abilities (Males Superior)
- Mathematical Abilities (Females Superior)

Many researchers in the area of HCI have noted with concern that computing is dominated by males [66]. Many of the reasons that have been put forward to explain these differences are identical to the differences that have been proposed to explain the cognitive differences already found between the sexes. These are usually assumed to include: aggression, verbal abilities (some feminist researchers have attacked the theories and research devoted to finding such explanations as being inherently sexist [23]), visio-spatial [36], and mathematical [48,49].

These factors have been difficult to determine, and the exact differences are controversial [5,49,17,10,11,21,28,29,32]. Explanations for these reported sex differences vary from genetic [71,35,6], hormonal [8], cerebral hemispheric lateralisations [9], through to social interaction and role stereotyping [68].

8.3.1 Gender Differences in HCI

It is only comparatively recently that HCI has tried to address this deficit in its understanding of a group that could and should make a larger contribution to computing. Within the past 35 years, only 2% of HCI work has looked at gender differences [34]. Indeed a review of the literature conducted by Fowler and Murray (1987) found that many studies fail even to state the sex of the subject groups. Other studies have been limited to one gender purely by the nature of the task, for example Gomez et al (1984), or Johnston et al (1986). Other difficulties in researching gender problems are that the computer science departments, where most HCI research is conducted, are male dominated. Findings from such studies will obviously be biased towards any gender preferences from that subject population.

8.3.2 Gender Differences in Computer Task Behaviour

Investigations in computer task behavioural differences between the sexes have been limited. One of the earliest such investigations looked at the effects of response time variation [between 1 and 6.5 sec] and list length [4, 6, or 8 digits] in a computer-paced addition task [3]. Males were found to vary their speed of response, to the detriment of their rate of accuracy. In contrast, women only varied their level of accuracy and their response rate remained fairly stable. Subsequent studies confirmed this initial finding, which was not reduced by practice. The authors also investigated the effects of acoustic background noise, and time of day on the S's performance. They reported that noise had some differential effects between the sexes. Females reduced their response rates with noise, while males made more errors. Some cognitive theories have predicted that such task based differences between the sexes would exist [46]. The apparent differences between cognitive strategies adopted by the sexes are discussed separately [see cognitive differences].

Another experiment which investigated the performance variation of males and females on computer tasks looked at the effect of ethanol [0.4g/kg] on a computer video game task [14]. The ethanol reduced the males' 'uncertainty index of discrete-movement', while it seemed to increase the females. It was postulated that these differences were due to the higher levels of stress present in the females, because of their unfamiliarity with videogames. Research into video game playing has found significant differences between the amount of game playing of males and females, with males playing such games significantly more than females [30]. However females may have as much exposure to the skills required in video games.

Instead, the sex differences found in video games may be due to the preference differences the sexes may have in feedback. A study which varied the nature of the feedback from a computer based task to subject [41] found that males performed best when they were given competitive feedback. Females performed best when they were given individualistic [non-competitive] feedback. However, in a study where both sexes used an identical system [receiving identical feedback], males showed significantly more exploratory behaviour than females [56].

In empirical research, heavy video game playing has been found to correlate with developmental problems, particularly with regard to aggression [38]. Frequent players were found to have a lower frustration tolerance than the normal population, although perhaps surprisingly they did not have increased neuroticism, social withdrawal, or increased needs to escape into fantasy. Research has also shown that use of video games does not negatively correlate with overall academic performance [7]. It has been proposed that females dislike the implicit violence involved in many of the video games. Informal studies have found that games which have 'oral aggression', like Pac Man, are much more popular with females [70].

8.3.3 Gender and Cultural or Social Class

Very few studies have really investigated the role of gender and cultural effects on computer use. One of these reported that Ss from a low socioeconomic class (SEC) had lower interest in computers and used them less than Ss from a high SEC [54]. A strong gender difference was found, which suggests that SEC and gender may have to be considered together. However another study found that Ss from a lower SEC showed more interest in computers, and wanted to use them more [64]. This latter study also found that most Ss had little interest in computers, and those Ss who did show an interest tended to have higher interests in intellectual activities. These Ss also had a lack of interest in typical adolescent activities. This trend applied equally to males and females, and over all levels of SEC.

8.3.4 Gender Differences in Computer Attitudes

Some studies have shown that there are no differences in the rates of computer anxiety between the sexes [27]. Instead they found that computer experience was a much better indicator of the level of computer anxiety. Most anxiety was shown by those of both sexes who had less experience of computer systems. Confirmation for this finding comes from two other studies which used computer attitude scales [56,57] for a complete review of the topic of technology attitudes measures.

First was a controlled study in which students who had to use a computer in an assignment were found to develop more positive attitudes towards computers than those who did not, although it is possible that some of these studies could have had their findings affected by expectancy effects.

Second is a study which measured attitudes to computers [45]. However this study also reported that girls exhibited a more positive attitude towards computers than boys. This may reflect a change in attitudes [the study is more recent], or may be a biased sample. A survey showed that the careers advice given to school leavers was highly sex stereotyped where computing was concerned [15]. Some research has also shown that males and females vary in their attribution of characteristics towards computers [74]. Males tend to use more animate descriptions [less mechanical] as they become more experienced, while females tend to show the opposite trend. They become more mechanical in their descriptions as they become more experienced. In a survey of 1,600 students' gender attitudes towards computers and video games [73], both boys and girls rated computers and video games as being more appropriate for boys, and this trend showed as early as kindergarten. The boys in the survey rated their liking for the computer more strongly than did the girls. Both sexes showed a dramatic decline in their reported liking of computers after middle childhood. The second part of the same study compared the computer attitudes of 334 [141 Female, 193 Male] college freshmen. The sex typing found in the school population was found to be attenuated in this group. However one interesting factor did emerge, that males rated their computer expertise as being higher than those of comparably experienced females. This female underestimation of computing expertise has also been reported by others. Researchers who have looked at the subject preferences of the sexes have reported that females were under represented in the sciences overall. This was especially bad in the so called 'hard' sciences, such as physics [16]. Both sexes were equally represented in biology and chemistry, and although females out-performed males, the females rated their performance as lower than the males.

Many researchers attribute the gender differences to the differential opportunities given to the sexes in education [12]. Research has shown that males receive more of the teacher's attention and more computing time than girls in computer based teaching situations [61,24]. This may not be totally due to a selective gender role bias in teaching, since there is evidence that, when girls are given equal access to computers, they tend to use them less than males. However these latter findings have been contradicted in a study which used a large sample size (3,085). In this experiment, females given positive discrimination, were found to adopt the use of computers significantly more than boys [22]. However, the use of positive discrimination would not make these results comparable [69,44,53]. It has being found that students of both sexes who show more realistic and investigative personality types, have more positive attitudes towards computers than students showing artistic or enterprising types [1].

A study which looked at the sex ratio of 5,533 entries to computer courses at US summer camps, found a significant sex difference favouring males [31]. This

3 to 1 difference became larger as the cost and course difficulty increased. The authors postulated that sex role differences in mathematics, the stereotype of computers, male-oriented software, and the symbolic and visio-spatial features of programming were responsible. The last two reasons are particularly unconvincing, since some of the most able programmers have often being women. Indeed research has shown that, while females are less likely to enrol in programming classes, those who do are successful, and make up the majority in groups who are exceptionally talented [42]. Other research by the same author [43], has found that females have different strategies for risk taking, help seeking, and more importantly attributions about success or failure. Other research has shown that when the computer based learning strategies of both sexes are compared, males tended to adopt the more successful learning strategies spontaneously. This was termed the shifting method of cognitive engagement. Females tended to stick to one form of cognitive engagement throughout the task, regardless of its success [50].

8.3.5 Summary of the Review on Gender Differences

As yet there are no universally accepted explanations for the sex differences found in computing. A large non-computing specific meta analysis of 127 different studies with a sample sizes from 7 to 25,000, and ages from 2 months to 30 years found that males were more active than females although age and situational variables seemed to be equally important [20]. The authors concluded that social influences served merely to increase this natural difference. Certainly there is evidence that social and cultural effects play a very large role. Several researchers have surveyed the sex roles portrayed in the mass media [7]. These researchers have found that males are portrayed as being the predominant users, and being in a dominant role in any mixed sex portrayals. One other factor in the lack of females in computing may be the male harassment of females who work in traditional male occupations. Research has found that the rate of such harassment is 75%,compared to 50% in the general population [40]. Sources of such harassment included supervisors, peers, subordinates, and clients. This reflects the existing sexist attitudes that too many men seem to hold, viewing females as 'sex-objects' rather than human beings, or fellow workers. The task of addressing such unfair practices will take considerable time, but it can only be hoped that a time will come when such unfair pressures are removed.

Changing females' attitudes towards computers are among the most important targets for HCI, and there is hope for progress in this direction. While female attitudes are more negative towards computing than those of males, they have more positive attitudes towards writing [13]. These authors have proposed that the use of computer based writing may therefore be an appropriate means of encouraging females to use computers. By trying such measures and giving positive discrimination, it can only be hoped that the male domination of computing can be reduced.

8.4 Cognitive Style

Apart from gender, many HCI researchers have looked for solutions to the problems of individual differences in some kind of difference in the way users think. This is usually termed the user's cognitive style, but is recognised to be the result not just of the inherent characteristics of the user. The cognitive style is influenced by age, education, and the experiential background of the person's life. Messick (1976) defined the cognitive style as being the high level heuristic that organises behaviour. The possible importance of the concept for HCI is shown by evidence that users perform sub-optimally on interfaces that do not match their cognitive style [62,22]. It might be therefore surprising that very few studies have empirically tested the effect of cognitive style and computer use [47], though there are signs that this trend is ending [2]. Such reluctance is due to the disagreement among psychologists whether cognitive style theories have any validity in HCI [33], and even if they do, factors within the task might outweigh the role of cognitive style [63, 72]. An example of the role which individual differences might have has been shown by research which showed that people with high self-esteem made fewer errors, and were more likely to give negative feedback to a computer system which gave simulated human responses when compared to usual computer responses [65]. However this effect was not reversed for those with low-self esteem.

Cognitive Style.

"The high level heuristic that organizes behaviour" (Messick 1976).

Cognitive Style Is Influenced By :
- Age
- Education
- Experience

8.4.1 Psychological Differentiation

One of the most popular cognitive theories in HCI is called psychological differentiation [78,26,77,76]. This proposes two main cognitive styles, field independence and dependence. Field independence is characterised by good analytic and restructuring skills. It is presumed to involve more participatory and hypothesis testing activity when faced with new situations. In contrast, field dependence takes a more holistic approach, which relies upon the inherent organisation of the material. In the face of a new situation, field dependent characteristics are likely to adopt a spectator type approach. The field dependent person would be more person oriented, while the field independent would be more task oriented. There is some empirical evidence that women are more field dependent than men but these tests have been done using an embedded figures test [EFT]. It has already been noted that the EFT discriminates in favour of viso-spatial skills. This would mean that the EFT favoured males anyway, and that any results that used the EFT to discriminate between the sexes would be suspect [23]. Some researchers have speculated that, within computer based tasks, field dependent users would prefer a system guided form of dialogue [39], using a formal language context question and answer systems. The field independent user would prefer a user guided interaction system which encouraged exploration, and flexibility [command line systems, or complex DM environments]. There is some experimental evidence that users performed their tasks faster in environments which conformed to the requirements of their respective cognitive style, however these findings should be taken with caution, since they are based on post-hoc observations [23].

Psychological Differentiation.

Field Independence.
Task Oriented.
Good analytic and restructuring skills.
It is presumed to
involve more participatory and hypothesis testing activity when faced
with new situations.

Field Dependence.
Person Oriented.
Takes a more holistic approach, which
relies upon the inherent
organisation of the material. In the
face of a new situation field
dependent characteristics are likely to
adopt a spectator type approach.
Women may be more field dependent
than men.

If these particular theories have any validity, they should be carried over into computer manuals and on-line help systems. The field dependent user would find manuals which took a cooperative style better to use [37]. In contrast, the field independent user would find a subordinate style preferable. However, it is probably dangerous to make the user models so hard and fast. In reality, it is likely that some form of individual configuration is the ideal method.

Predictions using Psychological Differentiation.
Field Dependent users prefer a system guided form
of dialogue using a formal language context (question and answer systems).
Field Independent users prefer a user guided interaction
system which encourage exploration and flexibility (command line
systems or complex DM environments).

8.5 Summary and Conclusions

In this paper, we have attempted to present examples from some of the types of research into individual differences which has been conducted by the HCI community over the past twenty years. We have primarily concentrated on the possible role of gender differences, cultural or social background, cognitive style and historical influences on interface preference.

Although there is strong evidence that good spatial ability, memory, previous experience and technical aptitude are predictive of good computer based performance [18], there is no consensus about which are the most influential factors in determining individual acceptance or rejection of a computing interface. Instead it is probable that situational and personal differences may be equally influential as any of the other factors which we have reviewed.

HCI practitioners should therefore try to use the research we have reviewed above to highlight those factors which are likely to have the most influence on their target user populations. Once these factors have been identified, it is hoped that it should be relatively simple for the practitioner to apply the research findings to improve the match between their system and the preferences and expectations of their target user population.

References

1. Abler, Rose M., Sedlacek, William E. Computer Orientation by Holland Type and Sex. Career Development Quarterly. (1987) Vol 36(2) 163-169.
2. Austin, Henry Stewart. Associations Of Student Characteristics To Measures Of Introductory Pascal Computer Programming Achievement for Suburban Community College Students (predictors, Michigan). International Dissertation Abstracts (1986). Number 197 AAC8612466.
3. Baker, Mary A., Holding, Dennis H., Loeb, Michel. Noise, Sex and Time of Day Effects in a Mathematics Task. Ergonomics. (1984) Jan Vol 27(1) 67 80.
4. Benyon, D., Innocent, P., Muray, D. System Adaptivity and the Modeling of Stereotypes. 1st Ed. 1 Vol. UK: Elsevier. Proceedings Interact'87. 1987.
5. Block, J.H. Issues and Pitfalls in Assessing Sex Differences.` Merrill Palmer Quarterly. (1976) 22, 283-305.
6. Bouchard, T. J., Mcgeo, M. G. Sex Differences in Human Spatial Ability: Not An X Linked Recessive Gene Effect. 1st Ed. Vol 1. Social Biology. (1977) 24, 332-333.
7. Braun, Claude M., Goupil, Georgette, Giroux, Josette, Chagnon, Yves. Adolescents and Microcomputers: Sex Differences, Proxemics, Task and Stimulus Variables. Journal of Psychology. (1986) Vol 120(6) 529-542.
8. Broverman, D. M., Klaiber, E. L., Kobayashi, Y., Vogel, W. Roles of Activation and Inhibition in Sex Differences in Cognitive Abilities. Psychological Review. 75, 23-50.
9. Buffery, A. W. H., Grey, J. A. Sex Differences in the Development of Spatial and Linguistic Skills. 1st Ed. vol 1. Churchill Livingstone, 1972. in Ounsted, C. Taylor, D. C. (Eds.). Gender Differences: Their Ontogeny and Significance.

10. Caplan, Paula J. Sex Roles and Sex Differences: Introduction. Special Issue: Sex Roles and Sex Differences and Androgyny. International Journal of Women's Studies. (1985) Nov Dec Vol 8 (5) 441-448.
11. Caplan, P. J., Macpherson, G.M., Tobin, P. Do Sex Related Differences in Spatial Abilities Exist? A Multi Level Critique with New Data. American Psychologist. (1985) 40, 786-799.
12. Chen, Milton. Gender Differences in Adolescents' Uses of and Attitudes Towards Computers. International Dissertation Abstracts (1986). Number 210 aac8612723.
13. Collis, Betty A., Ollila, Lloyd O. An Examination of Sex Differences in Secondary School Students' Attitudes Toward Writing and Toward Computers. Alberta Journal of Educational Research. (1986) Dec Vol 32(4) 297-306.
14. Crow, Lowell T., Hirdler, Kathy R. Alcohol Effects on the Variability of Performance in a Videogame Task. Society for Neuroscience Pacific Cascade Chapter (1985, Seattle, Washington). Bulletin of the Psychonomic Society. (1985) Vol 23(6) 519-520.
15. Culley, Lorraine. Option Choice and Careers Guidance: Gender and Computing in Secondary Schools. British Journal of Guidance and Counselling. (1988) Vol 16(1) 73-82.
16. Deboer, George E. Perceived Science Ability As a Factor in the Course Selections of Men and Women in College. Journal of Research in Science Teaching. (1986) Vol 23(4) 343-352.
17. Demo, Deborah. Sex Differences in Cognition: A Review and Critique of the Longitudinal Evidence. Adolescence. (1982) Vol 17(68) 779-788.
18. Egan, D. Individual differences in Human-Computer Interaction. in M. Helander (Ed) Handbook of HumanComputer Interaction. (1988) Elsevier Science Publishers (North Holland).
19. Eastman, Susan T., Krendl, Kathy. Computers and Gender: Differential Effects of Electronic Search on Students' Achievement and Attitudes. Journal of Research and Development in Education. (1987) Vol 20(3) 41-48.
20. Eaton, Warren O., Enns, Lesley R. Sex Differences in Human Motor Activity Level. Psychological Bulletin, (1986) Vol 100(1) 19-28.
21. Elliot, J. Do Sex Related Differences in Spatial Abilities Exist? A Multi Level Theory With New Data. A Comment on Caplan, Macpherson & Tobin. American Psychologist. (1986) 41, 1011.
22. Fisher, Farah Lee. Computer Anxiety in Special and Regular Education Credential Candidates. Dissertation Abstracts (1986) Number: Aac0559808
23. Fowler, C. J. H., Murray, D. M. Gender and Cognitive Style Differences at the Human Computer Interface. NPL Report 90/87 . (1987).
24. Gerver, E. Women, Computers and Adult Education. 1 Vol. University of Strathclyde. in Pilley, C. (Ed). Women and Computing in Scotland. Report of Conference Held by the Joint Working Group on Women and Computers. (1985) 14th June.
25. Gomez, L. M., Lochbaum, C. C. People Can Retrieve More Objects With Enriched Key Word Vocabulary. But Is There a Human Performance Cost?. 1st Ed. 1 Vol. Elsevier Science, 1984. in B.Shakel (Ed.), Human Computer Interaction Interact 84 .
26. Goodenough, D. R. The Role of Individual Difference in Field Dependence As A Factor in Learning and Memory. Psychological Bulletin. (1976) 83, 675-694.

27. Gressard, Clarice P., Loyd, Brenda H. The Nature and Correlates of Computer Anxiety in College Students. Journal of Human Behavior and Learning. (1986) Vol 3(2) 28-33.
28. Halpern, D. A Different Answer To the Question Do Sex Related Differences in Spatial Abilities Really Exist.. . American Psychologist. (1986) 41, 1014 1015.
29. Halpern, D. Sex Differences and Similarities in Cognitive Abilities. Erlbaum, 1986.
30. Harris, Mary B., Williams, Randall. Video Games and School Performance. Education, (1985) Vol 105(3) 306-309.
31. Hess, Robert D., Miura, Irene T. Gender Differences in Enrollment in Computer Camps and Classes. Special Issue: Women, Girls, and Computers. Sex Roles. (1985) Vol 13(3 4) 193-203
32. Hiscock, M. on Sex Differences in Spatial Abilities. American Psychologist. (1986) 41, 1011, 1012.
33. Huber, G. P. Cognitive Style As a Basis for Mis and Dis Designs: Much Ado About Nothing. Management Sciences. (1983) 29.
34. Hudgens, G. A., Billingsley, P. A. Sex: The Missing Variable in Human Factors Research. Human Factors. (1978), 20, 245-250.
35. Hutt, C. Males and Females. 1st Ed. 1 Vol. Penguin, 1972. Johnston, Vivien M. Attitudes Towards Microcomputers in Learning: II. Teachers and Software for Language Development. Educational Research. (1987) Vol 29(2) 137-145.
36. Kaplin, A. G., Sedney, M. A. Psychology and Sex Roles: An Androgynous Perspective. 1st Ed. 1 Vol. Little, Brown and Co., 1980.
37. Kennedy, T. C. S. The Design of Interactive Procedures of Man Machine Communication. International Journal of Man Machine Studies. (1974) 6, 309-334.
38. Kestenbaum, Gerald I., Weinstein, Lissa. Personality, Psychopathology, and Developmental Issues in Male Adolescent Video Game Use. Journal of the American Academy of Child Psychiatry. (1985) Vol 24(3) 329-333.
39. Kupka, I., Wilsing, N. Conversational Languages. 1st Ed. 1 Vol. Wiley, 1980.
40. Lafontaine, Edward, Tredeau, Leslie. The Frequency, Sources, and Correlates of Sexual Harassment Among Women in Traditional Male Occupations. Sex Roles. (1986) Vol 15(7 8) 433-442.
41. Lewis, Mark A., Cooney, John B. Attributional and Performance Effects of Competitive And Individualistic Feedback in Computer Assisted Mathematics Instruction. Computers in Human Behavior. (1987) Vol 3(1) 1-13.
42. Linn, M. C. Fostering Equitable Consequences From Computer Learning Environments. Sex Roles. (1985) Vol. 13, Nos. 3/4, 229-240.
43. Linn, Marcia C. Gender Equity in Computer Learning Environments. Computers and the Social Sciences. (1985) Vol 1(1) 19-27.
44. Lockheed, M. E., Frakt, S. B. Sex Equity: Increasing Girls' Use of Computers. Computing Teacher. (1984), 11, 16-18.
45. Loyd, Brenda H., Loyd, Douglas E., Gressard, Clarice P. Gender and Computer Experience As Factors in the Computer Attitudes of Middle School Students. Special Issue: Sex Differences in Early Adolescents. Journal of Early Adolescence. (1987) Vol 7(1) 13-19.
46. Luchins, A. S., Luchins, E. G. Sex Differences in Reasons Given for Responses To the Water Jar Problem. Journal of Psychology. (1984) 118, 207-220.

47. Lusk, E. J., Kernick, M. The Effect of Cognitive Style and Report Format on Task Performance: the Mis Design Consequences. Management Sciences. (1979) 25, 787-798.
48. Maccoby, E. E., Jacklin, C. N. The Psychology of Sex Differences. 1st Ed. 1 Vol. Stanford University Press, 1974.
49. Maccoby, E. E., Jacklin, C. N. Psychological Sex Differences. 1st Ed. 1 Vol. Heinemann, 1980. in Rutter, M. (Ed.). Foundations of Developmental Psychiatry.
50. Mandinach, Ellen B., Corno, Lyn. Cognitive Engagement Variations Among Students of Different Ability Level and Sex in a Computer Problem Solving Game. Special Issue: Women, Girls, and Computers. Sex Roles. (1985) Vol 13(3 4) 241-251.
51. Messick, S. (Ed.). Individuality in Learning. 1st Ed. 1 Vol. Jossey Bass, 1976.
52. Miura, I. T. A Multivariate Study of School Aged Children's Computer Interest and Use. 1st Ed. 1 Vol. NJ:hilside, Erlbaum, 1987. in Ford, D. H., and Ford, M. E., (Eds.). Humans As Self Constructing Living Systems: Putting the Framework To Work
53. Miura, I. T. Understanding Gender Differences in Middle School Computer Interest and Use. Ca:American Educational Research Assc. Paper Presnted at Symposium Gender Differences in Computing: Policy Implications . (1986).
54. Miura, I. T. Gender and Socioeconomic Status Differences in Middle School Computer Interest and Use. Journal of Early Adolescence. (1987) Vol 7(2) 243-253.
55. Miura, I. T. The Relationship of Self Efficacy Expectations To Computer Interest and Course Enrollment in College. Sex Roles. (1987) Vol 16(5 6) 303-311.
56. Morgan, K., Gibbs, S., Macleod, H., & Morris, R., (1991) An exploration of some possible gender differences in computer attitudes, interface preference and simple task performance : In Lovegrove, G., & Segal, B. (Eds) Women into Computing : Selected papers 1988-1990 Springer-Verlag : BCS Workshops in computing series. pp161-172. ISBN 3-540-19648-X.
57. Morgan, K. & Macleod, H. Technology Attitudes Investigations Paper presented to the British Psychological Society London Conference 1990.
58. Morgan, K., Macleod, H. Results from Exploratory Investigations into the possible role of Personality Factors in Computer Interface Preference. Research paper presented at the second interdiscipinary workshop on mental models, March 1992 (Robinson College, Cambridge).
59. Morgan, K., Morris, R.L., Macleod, H. & Gibbs, S. Gender Differences and Cognitive Style in Human-Computer Interaction Paper presented at East-West HCI Conference, St Petersburg, Russia. 1992.
60. Norman, D. A. The Psychology of Everyday Things. 1st Ed. 1 vol. New York: Basic Books Inc, 1988.
61. Omerod, M. B. Factors Differentially Affecting the Science Subject Preferences, Chances and Attitudes of Girls and Boys. 1st Ed. 1 Vol. Manchester University Press, 1981. In Kelly, A. (Ed.). The Missing Half .
62. Pask, G., Scott, B. C. E. Learning Strategies and Individual Competence. International Journal of Man Machine Studies. (1972) 4, 217 253.
63. Payne, J. W. Contingent Decision Behaviour. Psychological Bulletin, (1982) 92, 382-402.

64. Pulos, Steven, Fisher, Sarah. Adolescents' Interests in Computers: The Role of Attitude and Socioeconomic Status. Computers in Human Behavior . (1987) Vol 3(1) 29-36.
65. Resnik, Paula V., Lammers, H. Bruce. The Influence of Self Esteem on Cognitive Responses To Machine Like Versus Human Like Computer Feedback. Journal of Social Psychology. (1985) Vol 125(6) 761-769.
66. Reznikoff, M., Holland, C. H., Stroebel, C. F. Attitudes Towards Computers Among Employees of a Psychiatric Hospital. 1st Ed. Mental Hygiene. (1967) Vol. 51, 419-425.
67. Rich, E. Users Are Individuals: Individualizing User Models. International Journal of Man Machine Studies. (1983) 18, 199-215.
68. Sharpe, S. Just Like a Girl: How Girls Learn To Be Women. 1st Ed. Penguin, 1976.
69. Sheingold, K. Kane, J. H., Endreweit, M. E. Microcomputer Use in Schools: Developing a Research Agenda. Harvard Educational Review. (1983), 53, 412 432.
70. Shneiderman, B. Designing the User Interface: Strategies for Effective Human Computer Interaction. Addision-Wesley, Reading,
71. Stafford, R. E. Sex Differences in Spatial Visualizations As Evidence of Sex Linked Inheritance. Perceptual and Motor Skills. (1961) 13, 211-214.
72. Van Der Veer, G. C., Tauber, M. J., Waern, Y., Van Muylwijk, B. On the Interaction Between System and User Characteristics. Behaviour and Information Technology. (1985), 4, 289-308.
73. Wilder, G., Mackie, D., Cooper, J. Gender and Computers: Two Surveys of Computer Related Attitudes. Sex Roles. Vol. 13, Nos. 3/4, 215-228.
74. Wise, G, Robinson-Staveley, K., Nelson, L. Report From the Cognitive Motivation Laboratory. USA: Princeton University Newsletter of the Human Information Processing Group at Princeton University . (1987), 3.
75. Witken Et Al. Role of Field Dependent and Field Independent Cognitive Style in Academic Evolution:a Longitudinal Study. Journal of Educational Psychology. (1977), 69, 197-211.
76. Witken, H. A. : Goodeneough, D.r. Cognitive Styles: Essence and Origin. 1st Ed. 1 vol. International University Press, 1981.
77. Witken, H. A., Dyke, R. B., Oltman, P. K. Psychological Differentiation: Current Status. Journal of Personal and Social Psychology. (1979), 37, 1127-1145.
78. Witken, H. A., Dyke, R.B., Faterson, H.F., Goodeneough, D.R. : Karp, S.A. Psychological Differentiation. 1st Ed. 1 vol. Wiley, 1962, Reprinted Erlbaum, 1974.

9. Communication, Learning and Teamwork for Human Centred Engineering Systems Design

James Powell[1]

Graduate College, Salford University, Greater Manchester, Lancashire M5 4WT

Abstract. The scale, complexity and demands of current engineering practice increasingly requires an interdisciplinary team approach. The ability to work successfully in teams and the ability of teams themselves to work well, is now a prerequisite of successful human centred engineering. Learning how to work well in interdisciplinary teams is not a trivial matter. It is a skill that has to be understood, learned and carefully honed. This paper builds on current theories of communication, learning and team building to reveal a good practical approach to improving team communication, operation and hopefully success. Good team practices will lead these operating a simultaneous engineering approach to harness the skills of team members having conflicting personalities who normally come from different disciplines. This in turn should result in creative harmony — where the team effort will undoubtedly achieve far more than the simple sum of the members individual capabilities.

Keywords. communications, learning, informing, team building, simultaneous engineering, complex problems.

9.1 Introduction

In the past, engineering pioneers could work singly on fairly manageable tasks to achieve substantial technological feats. However, contemporary engineering creativity demands more holistic interdisciplinary team work as problems grow in scale and complexity and the demand for greater efficiency and quality burgeons. Most current engineering challenges are simply no longer within the grasp of any one engineer's mind. This awareness is leading many major manufacturing/engineering industries to implement a different approach, known

---

[1] James Powell was formerly Head of Department, Deputy Dean of Technology and Lucas Professor of Design Systems at the Department of Manufacturing and Engineering Systems, Brunel University, Uxbridge, Middlesex.

as simultaneous or concurrent engineering (SE) — the parallel team design/development of new products and processes.

The benefits of successful simultaneous engineering are well documented — reduced time to market, improved ideas, better fit for purpose and higher quality products to meet customer needs. The ideal simultaneous engineering team treats problems systemically where its members, representing two or more different but complementary disciplines, have a close and continuous interactions; disciplines normally chosen to provide the necessary functional capabilities required by a group.

High performance teams portray a holistic and collective intelligence. They impose systemic thinking, not only on problems they tackle as engineers, but on the operation of their own team working. As a result, such teams are proactive in creating a climate of trust and openness, where creative interdependence is built on a recognition of individual team member's personal goals and capabilities. In return for such team support, each team member fully owns the task committed to them by the team because their agreed personal mission simply reflects the shared vision of that team. In such teams conflicts become creative. Differences are seen to be a necessary and valued starting point for a discussion which is then fully resolved through pluralistic negotiation; in other words problems are solved collectively by the whole team 'our way' and not through members giving in, 'your way', or demanding, 'my way'.

Inspired teams have integrating dialogues and share mutual understandings of organisational concepts, methodology, procedures, terminology, data and even epistemology. Diverse views can truly influence team objectives as members suspend their own assumptions and act jointly with their colleagues for the good of the team. To make this possible, the team and each of the members of it, need to have a clear understanding of the performance they are expected to achieve. They also need to feel that the challenge presented to them is creative and properly specified.

This ideal state is rarely reached at the moment, for as Freeman-Bell and Blackwell (1993) and others clearly show, such creative harmony in SE teams is presently more of a wish (and often a marketing ploy) than a reality, at least in the UK. Furthermore, as problems of complexity and scale increase, so does the difficulty of reaching any agreement within a team about issues such as goals, resource utilization and potential solutions. British industrial culture has yet to fully understand this problem and in particular how to engender the beneficial processes of SE teamwork. The present author believes a key to SE success comes from all engineers understanding how they can communicate better and work well in teams with those having differing views to their own.

However, we cannot simply mimic the Japanese way of successful simultaneous engineering, for they have developed a strategy and support heuristics that reflect their own industrial culture. Nevertheless, we can learn a great deal from general socio-cultural theories of learning and team building to develop SE approaches more suitable for British and European Engineering ways.

The remainder of this paper therefore examines two important aspects of improving productive team cooperation. Firstly, it explores peoples' learning styles and suggests how knowledge of them might lead to better communication through active and purposeful listening, and differently focused dialogues/presentations. Secondly, it presents a powerful and well validated team working theory which has been used by the present author to improve the creative design and research within several teams for which he is responsible. The paper concludes by indicating how these two key factors can be brought together, using advanced multimedia, to improve the communication performance within any engineering team, whether it be simultaneous or otherwise.

9.2 Learning Styles and Improved Communication

The work of Thompson (1982) and Newland, Powell and Creed (1987) gives us a strong indication how engineers and others self-inform themselves so that they might operate viably in the real industrial world. Their studies suggest there are four "strategy sets" that allow for both a consistency in engineering design and viability in general engineering. These self-
informing "strategy sets", which the evidence indicates clearly underpin all engineers decision making, was found to be closely related to the way those engineers approached learning. The field of learning has been extensively investigated by Kolb (1976) who summarised the various approaches open to an individual by a learning cycle shown in Fig. 9.1.
Kolb's model portrays an ideal situation where the learner has immediate experience of the world, steps back to reflect on this feeling in context, thinks up an abstract model to explain the phenomenon, which is tested by further active exploration. These doing actions cause the learner to re-sense the world and so begins a new learning style.

My colleagues and I in the Design Information Research Team (the DIRT team is Newland, Hall, Davies, Wright, Rhodes, Powell and Creed) have shown that normal engineering practice places severe constraints on this ideal cycle. To be effective decision makers, DIRT has shown this ideal must of necessity be curtailed — typically, practising engineers operate on far shorter cycles.
The need to make fast decisions causes them to align themselves with a particularly 'strategy set'. These strategy sets short circuit active learning to an arc or quadrant of a circle; some engineers mainly operate within one arc or quadrant; others on a semi-circular arc. For instance in Fig. 9.2, the Design Engineer, Development Group Head and Senior Manager portray similar learning preferences towards 'thinking and doing', shown as a 90° arc in the bottom left quadrant. Other engineers, such as the Development/Technical Manager and the Patents Director, move on an 180° arc between 'sensing, watching and thinking'. 'Sensing' implies an intuitive and feeling based learning preference, and 'watching' indicates systemic observation. These arcs indicate the performance of rapid learning in a decision making situation.

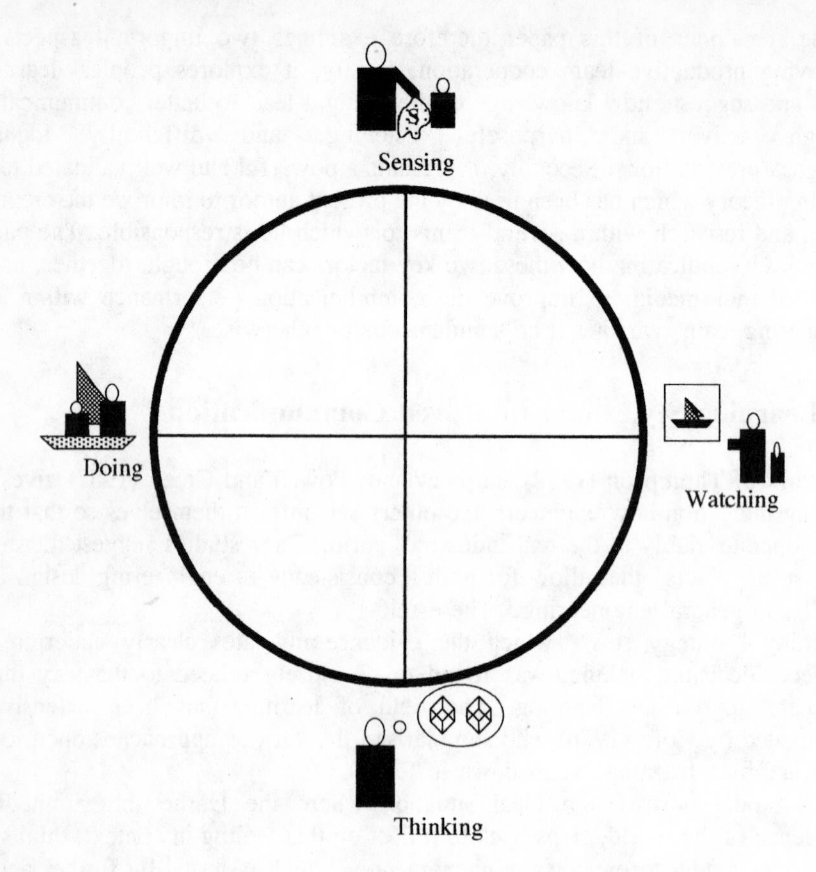

Fig. 9.1. The learning cycle (after Kolb)

It is important to stress that these observations are of engineers predisposition to learning. However, someone who is mainly a 'thinker-doer' is perfectly capable of 'sensing' and 'watching' but normally has to push themselves to learn by this more experiential learning route.

Normally, to cope with resourcing pressures and to keep their operations viable, most practising engineers will 'stick' to their preferred learning approach and corresponding communication style. This gives engineers a secure basis from which to operate as decision makers and observations show they rarely change this approach to learning — it is too much effort and it also drains confidence. It is important to understand these different engineering learning styles if we are to break down the barriers to communications between engineers and others of different personality.

Powell (1987) has shown this is best achieved if we think of engineers as learning using one of four 'Informing Strategy sets', each different, independent and recognisable. He suggests engineers learn in either a Dynamic, Focussed, Rigorous, or Contemplative way; each way represents one quadrant of Kolb

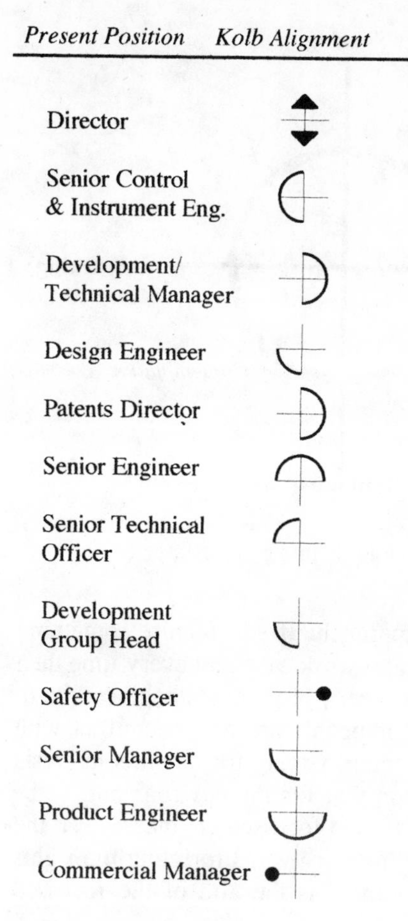

Fig. 9.2. Individual engineers Kolb predispositions/preferences

Learning Cycle as is shown diagrammatically in Fig. 9.3. Let me briefly describe each of these engineers learning styles in turn and the sort of informing communications they prefer.

Dynamic Engineers have an approach to learning which is centred on 'doing and sensing'. They are entrepreneurial and innovative, acting for the moment, sensing a problems potential and doing something about it immediately. It is the dramatic active events in the world which motivate them and allow them to register understanding. To learn, they must be personally involved and if this necessity is satisfied then they are eager for new challenges and novelty. By being assertive and individual in their actions, they can swiftly switch tack. Being entrepreneurial, they can initiate a move to create new profit centres in a moment and thus rapidly create innovative designs. These engineers seek acclaim and their risk-taking attitude makes them good copy for the professional, financial and management pages of national newspapers.

Dynamic engineers have and want attention, they actively manipulate their surroundings as they find this is the quickest way to satisfy their desires. To this end their engineering designs will be unusual and will certainly have novelty value, but they may all too quickly dismiss considerations a customer sees as necessary to the success of the design. These engineering designers are the most aggressive in making any brief fit their present ideas and their customers can easily fall victim to the flavour-of-the month.

To communicate to dynamics requires their complete involvement in any dialogue. This ideally involves them in raw experiences. All forms of experiential learning, role playing and interactive simulation are preferred.

They need to be excited by their communication, asking questions like 'what's in it for me'. They prefer self discovery, using anecdotes, brainstorming and any form of 'real world' challenge. The key to better communication with them is active personal involvement and they learn best about a new idea by sharing it with someone else. Like Winston Churchill, these engineers "play for more than they can afford to lose and they quickly learn the game".

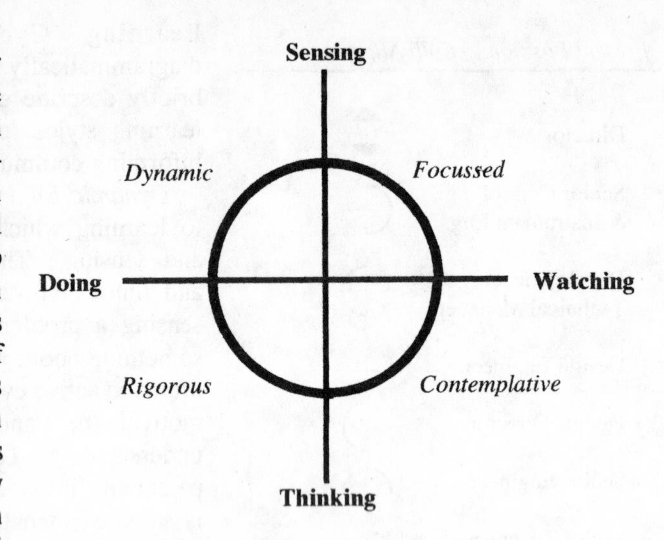

Fig. 9.3. Powell's fourfold of informing strategies

Focussed Engineers concentrate their attention on decisive action. They operate in the world with a down-to-earth approach which is above all practical. Their need to do, can often lead them into being campaigners and expounders of alternative technologies and conservation policies. This 'small is beautiful' philosophy may make them reticent to try untested approaches to engineering. Instead these engineers stay with the 'safe', known approach. If you require something that is tried and tested, a product that will actually work each and every time then these engineers are appropriate for you. The concern of focussed engineers is to ensure products are useful, and if the needs of people are not in conflict with those of nature then they will be taken into account. Caring for nature's interests in general, these engineers look for the solution that fits the environment — the one that gives least distress to nature. For this reason focussed engineers need the values of the customers to be in agreement with their own. Protecting the rights of man and nature, and honing practical solutions, is the aim of the focussed engineer.

Probably known in future as environmental engineers, focussed engineering learners require useful and pertinent information. Communicating with them needs information to be presented in a direct and hard hitting way. Documentary films, practical case studies and example based guide books are extremely appropriate for them. The more practical the ideas, the better they communicate. The focussed need to understand why only change is necessary and have confidence in the information suggesting any change before they will actually alter their perspective.

Rigorous Engineers understand the world by creating abstract models of it. These models give the rigorous predictive power over their world. Through assumed knowledge of the underlying patterns they secure rules that guide them in their engineering. They stand as the guardians of professional standards and aim to produce competent solutions. However, there is a tendency amongst them to give very rigid solutions and this can lead to solutions that are restrictive of human behaviour, placing too much emphasis on unseen control. They will certainly not let a customer down, for they know there is always some kind of technical fix at hand. However, this fix may not always be strictly appropriate. Furthermore, their designs may be fairly standard, lacking any innovative flair.

These engineers are the self-disciplined managers of any task they are presented with — each is given due attention, resulting normally in competent solutions. Complex products like aeroplanes require the abstract modelling skills of these engineers and customers with such complex problems would be wise to have one of these on their ideal SE team.

The rigorous learn best through logical communications. Material presented to them must be well structured and based on a disciplined analytical approach. They dislike subjective judgement, and any sort of frivolity, preferring the cool and calm deliberation of objective reasoning. They relate to complex theories, which seem best to embody their theoretical understanding of the world. They learn well through codes and standards, rule and instruction books, and through traditional pedagogic practices. They also find CBT and programmed learning valuable.

Contemplative Engineers with their emphasis on reflection may feel no great urgency in getting their products into the real world. Their reluctance emanates from a desire to create the all encompassing solution. To this end they will thoroughly analyse all the data which is at hand and then try to retrieve more in an effort to ensure every angle has been covered. Contemplative engineers find it very difficult to reach decisions — the holistic insight they so often seek nearly always eludes them. If someone else makes decisions they can become effective workers, otherwise small commissions with a large time scale are the most they can handle. For the customers with strong ideas and a thorough brief these engineers will be a considerable gain, modifying their own ideas to fit the will of the client.

You communicate best with these type of engineers if you provide them with plenty of original data to mull over and then give them time to explore it in depth. They like to see several approaches and carefully think through their analysis of each approach in turn. Contemplatives like to observe others rather than do something themselves so don't try to involve them in any experiential learning. They would prefer to go to the library and search through a montage of information to develop their own understanding of the world, rather than be guided by someone else.

The ideal would be a sure, fast acting decision maker who can listen, innovate, evaluate and organise, such a person would have to produce a coherent whole that is unique and humanly responsive, they would also need to work selflessly in the optimisation of resources and time. There are some engineers who try to take on this holistic approach to an extreme and use all the strategies identified above. However, Powell and his colleagues (1988) have shown that such a multi-perspective strategy makes decision-making almost impossible in any one individual; so these all-rounded often become ineffectual. However, to achieve an effective 'well-rounded' simultaneously engineered solution, all the above mentioned engineering strategies should be utilised. To successfully stage manage a new product into the real world, many functional skills are also required. The aforementioned studies of Thompson, and Newland and his colleagues, clearly indicate that such abilities, skills and understanding cannot reside, with any quality, in the mind of one design individual. How can this paradox be resolved?

9.3 The Intelligent Engineering Team

As I commented earlier, no one individual may possess all the skills required for creative complex engineering, but a team, acting as a unified entity, certainly can, wielding its joint abilities with strength and acumen. What is needed is an integrated engineering team, possessing the necessary trans-disciplinary skills. But how can such a workable synergistic team be created?

My experiences of a postgraduate course for a Master's Degree in Engineering Design (undertaken over twenty years ago) gave substantial insight into a means of creating the forum for such a team. Those who ran the course envisaged a future where individuals would bring their particular skills together into a 'melting pot' of creative fusion. These individuals would first and foremost recognise the enhanced potential gained through complementing their skills with those of other team members — the goal was a joint pursuit, a joint endeavour. Continued working relationships with colleagues from that course have reinforced my belief that perhaps the rarest design skills of all are those which enable individual designers to overcome the typically individualistic pursuits which are prevalent today. From my continued participation in well balanced teams and considerable observation of other multidisciplinary teams in action, I am convinced that it is such teams, and not individuals acting alone, who can effectively orchestrate the sort of rich and humanly responsive products and processes which society now demands.

As can be appreciated, multi-disciplinary teams do not coalesce by accident; there are two fundamental roles that each member of a team must perform if both the operation of the team and the designs it creates are going to be a success. Only recently has this dual role of team member become apparent from the studies of Belbin (1988 and 1993). He names the roles as functional and team. Let us look at each of these in turn.

Functional Role. The functional role is the most obvious. If a team is to produce novel artefacts, products and processes, solving large scale and complex problems, then there must be substantial expertise and experience at hand. The roles of the mechanical, electrical, manufacturing, or systems engineers must be taken up by competent persons.

The notion of team presents the opportunity to expand the number of jobs usually associated with engineering design. Good simultaneous engineering teams now often include Marketing, Finance and Project Management Skills. Individuals can also be brought in, who have background skills in social sciences, to effectively elicit user needs, or customers might themselves become full players in an effective team. The make up of the team should be eminently flexible — a particular spectrum of individuals being brought together to suit the requirements of a specific brief. Customers should no longer be looking for a particular individual, but the appropriate team, with access to the full range of functional expertise demanded by the brief. However, having the right combination of functional skills does not ensure the individuals making up the team can play the roles necessary to form a viable working unit — the factor of team roles is of equal importance in acquiring a true trans-disciplinary design team.

Team-role. A team that is going to operate with viability needs a balanced mix of personalities. As has been described in the previous section, it is not possible for an individual to exhibit all perspectives and still remain capable of taking effective decisions. A team, however, is an entity that can be more than the sum of the parts. The different parts of its personality can reside in different individuals and each can be called upon at the appropriate juncture. The qualities of drive, prudence, enthusiasm, understanding, opportunism, reliability, all have their parts to play. Nobody can claim to be perfect but a team has the opportunity to emphasise the strengths of each individual and eliminate the weaknesses. Properly orchestrated, a team acquires a mental and emotive strength that provides a significant 'edge' to tackle problems and devise innovative solutions. The team roles are obviously more subtle — they only come into operation when the team begins to form and work together. To his surprise, Belbin found only nine roles were available. When individuals accept the existence of a team then on or more of the following nine roles is open to them:

Coordinators ensure that the best use is made of each member's potential. They are self-disciplined, dominant but not domineering. They clarify the teams goals, promote decision making and delegate well; without them the team quickly losses focus and coordination.[2] *They may be seen as being rather manipulative, off loading work onto others but this is an allowable weakness.*

Shapers look for patterns and try to shape the team's efforts in this direction. They are out going, impulsive and impatient. They often make the team feel uncomfortable but also make things happen. They are challenging, dynamic and thrive on pressure; Shapers have the drive and courage to overcome obstacles. *However they often offend peoples feelings and are prone to provocation.* Lady Thatcher is a shaper.

Innovators, or what Belbin called 'Plants', are the source of a teams original ideas. They are imaginative, uninhibited and often unorthodox. They thrive on solving impossible problems. *However, they are bad at accepting criticism and may need careful handling to provide that vital spark. They may be difficult to get through to as they are often preoccupied and apparent loners.*

---

[2] The sentences shown in italics are what Belbin believes are the allowable weaknesses of any role where a person shows a strong profile in that role. Having a predisposition to act in a particular way is usually at the expense of other characteristics which could become disruptive if allowed to flourish. Team membership helps to contain such disruptive elements.

Evaluators are more measured and dispassionate. They like time to analyse, and see all the options and mull things over. Their aim is accurate judgement. *They do often lack drive and the ability to inspire others. They ensure sensible programmes of action and projects.*

Organisers or *Implementors* turn strategies into manageable tasks which people can get on with. They are disciplined, reliable, methodical and conservative. *However, they are sometimes inflexible and slow to respond to new possibilities.*

Entrepreneurs or *Resource Investigators* go outside the group and bring back information and ideas. They make friends easily and have a mass of contacts. They prevent the team from stagnating by being extrovert, enthusiastic and communicative. *However, they can be over optimistic and lose interest once their initial enthusiasm has passed.* Ronald Reagan was a resource investigator.

Team Workers promote unity and harmony within a group. They are more aware of peoples needs than other members, listening, building relationships and averting friction. They are the most active internal communicators — the cement of the team. *However, they can be indecisive in critical situations.*

Finishers are compulsive 'meeters' of deadlines. They worry about what can go wrong and maintain a permanent sense of urgency which they communicate to others. They are painstaking and conscientious. *They are reluctant to delegate.*

Specialists provide the special knowledge required by the team and the skills that are in rare supply. They are self-starting, single minded and totally dedicated. *But they do dwell on technicalities and only contribute on a narrow front.*

Belbin has shown that to be successful, a group needs to be comprised of people having the right balance of the above role characteristics. Certain roles — that of the Coordinator, Shaper, and Innovator — involve a higher profile in engineering teams than others and apparently carry greater kudos and prestige. However in an engineering context, Belbin's findings repeatedly show that successful simultaneous engineering teams require the right balance of both functional and team roles. For the last eight years I have also used Belbin's team working approach to balance my own interdisciplinary research teams; as a result such teams have become exciting, creative and enjoyable, they have also proved to be extremely productive and have led to the winning of major research awards and funds for large scale and complex problem solving studies.

More recently I have been using Belbin in the education of engineering students on the 'Computer Integrated Manufacturing' and 'Engineering Doctoral' courses at Brunel University. Once again, when student engineering teams have been properly balanced against functional speciality and team roles they become extremely successful.

It is often difficult, in an educational context to test the negative aspects of theories such as those by Belbin to allow students into a position where you knowingly believe they will fail. However, in the last few months some arrogant doctoral students, all Shapers on Belbins analysis, insisted on working together in a team to tackle a major piece of course work. They believed Belbin's theory to be irrelevant and had actually thrown away their notes about his ideas prior to tackling the joint working project. At the start they worked together well on early course work exercises which required them to solve only simple puzzles. However, as the problems became larger and more complex and especially when we asked them to undertake an orienteering exercise, their disharmony and failure to act creatively together showed through. At the end of the course they asked for new copies of notes similar to the ones presented here because they began to see the value of such themes. They are now the greatest advocates of balanced team roles — 'born again' team balancers. This is clearly an example of a team making real use of a constructive alternative theory.

9.4 Learning Style and Team Roles — Tools for Creative Communication Complementary

In the previous two sections, I have tried to present two useful theories to help engineers consider how they might communicate better with each other and secondly to enable the teams of which they are part to flourish. Careful consideration of the descriptions of the people with different learning styles and teamwork roles clearly indicates these theories are closely entwined. Indeed they give a complementary understanding of two aspects of interpersonal communications; it is therefore hardly surprising that they are closely linked. I present them here as two separate analytical human resourcing tools because they should enable easy implementations of different aspects of improved engineering communications and team practice.

Should you wish to understand for yourself your own learning styles or team roles in more depth the references given in the text will provide paper based instruments to enable you to undertake the relevant analyses. Furthermore, if you would like to be part of a small experiment with the present author, he will undertake such analyses for you and give you appropriate feedback; turn now to the Appendix and follow the instructions there if this appeals to you.

Finally, Belbin Associates (1993) now offers a computerised tool to enable organisations to diagnose team roles on a large scale and to help in the selection of 'suitable' rather than 'eligible' team/project personnel. I have found this computerised tool an extremely cost effective and reliable way of undertaking team role assessment. However, if you are a trainer, rather than manager, and are looking for a fun learning way of getting groups to understand the need to work in teams you might consider using a card game, known as *Teams*, developed by HART (1988). HART was one of the research teams (of which I was a member) which undertook its research conforming to Belbin principles. The card game they developed enables a speedy clarification of team roles for individuals and groups in any organisation. The advantage of 'Teams', as a game, is that although simple and enjoyable to play, it provides a context in which complex and emotive issues can be discussed and analysed in a positive and non-threatening way.

9.5 Limitations in the Use of the Theories

Learning

I am the first to admit that there are almost as many learning theories as there are doctoral theses on the topic. The fourfold theory presented here is believed to be as good a summary of learning styles as is possible for those who wish to improve their communication to others. I have found that such a fourfold truly enables informing and communicating processes to be improved. Finer analyses of learning are simply too complex to aid real time human communication. Learning to recognise and send communications messages to the 'four parishes' of learning really does work.

Alternatively, turning the problem round, Thompson (1982) believes human culture constrains individual's perceptions to such an extent that they reject information that is derogatory to the maintenance of their set of agreed cultural values. Thompson goes further by suggesting, like the present paper, that there are only four anthropologically possible information rejection strategies: 'risk absorption', 'cerebral hygiene', 'paradigm protection' and 'foreign body expulsion'. These relate to four distinct cultural biases and their cultures associated information handling strategies. Thompson suggests, just as 'It's the fish that John West reject that makes John West the best', so it is the process of active rejection that actually defines what information is[3]. Relating Thompson's theories to the ones presented here, the rigorous learners in this study 'reject information' to protect their existing paradigm, dynamic learners 'practice cerebral hygiene' in an attempt to leave their minds open to new ideas, the contemplative 'absorb risk' like an 'ever-growing sponge' and the focussed expel information as though it were a 'foreign body'.

9.6 Creative Team Working

As you will quickly understand as you use the Belbin Theory, the nine team roles contain both positive and negative qualities, and team members should be prepared to help contain the destructive side of the roles of themselves and their colleagues. Each role can find active and passive, as well as positive or negative, expression so it also isn't sufficient merely to identify your role. You must be aware of the

[3] John West is the brand-name for a range of tinned fish that is much advertised under this slogan in Britain. The latest television variation on this theme ends with an enormous pile of assorted and unlabelled tins being noisily swept off the table to leave just a neat little array of John West products.

roles strengths and weaknesses and attempt to remedy the defects. Furthermore, most people can play more than one role and can vary their performance to suit the situation. Therefore, team members should therefore try to identify not only their primary role but other parts they may be able to play fairly naturally in a group.

These secondary roles can prove to be valuable if people find themselves in groups where a role is missing. Then, even where it is impossible to fully balance a team by changing personnel, team members can take extra effort to cover for the missing roles. Recognition of the 'missing role' problem can improve team harmony or at least prevent disasters. Furthermore, once a team role analysis has been undertaken the team is ready to ensure new appointments to itself will improve rather than destroy team balance.

Clearly, it is not always necessary to adopt a team-balancing approach. For instance, where routine or repetitive tasks need to be performed by a group of people, it can be unnecessary and indeed often counter productive; some team members, for instance the 'plant', will become frustrated and bothersome in a team which doesn't have creative roles. Team balancing should be reserved for situations where creative engineering is required for complex and large scale projects. Properly balanced teams must be creatively challenged if they are to be successful.

The wealth of studies undertaken by Newland and his colleagues (1984) together with the work of Belbin (1983) observing managerial teams, reinforces the guiding heuristics of this paper — teamwork and communication. When the equal balance of both functional and team roles is respected, the effectiveness of a team far out performs the potential of any individual.

9.7 A Prototype Information System to Improve Team Communication

Based on the preceding ideas, DIRT has developed a working prototype multimedia information system to improve the flow of information between the different disciplines typically represented in a team. This prototype system attempts to match information, and its presentation, to an individual engineer's preferred learning style; in either a rigorous, focussed, dynamic or contemplative way. As an information provider, it presents four alternatives to any discussion and can therefore be used as an interface to aid communication by members of a team having such differing views. The use of multimedia permits images of all sorts — video, graphics, text and sound — to be presented in an appropriate balance to aid learning. In short, it provides a congenial and compelling information transfer environment complementing the normal engineering practices of communication. To help engineers control their access to the different information, the prototype also has a parsimonious interface control mechanism - a refinement of the window-icon-mouse-pointer (WIMPS) environment of an Apple Macintosh. The effectiveness of the prototype as an educational tool has caused much interest from industry, design, commerce and government. The British Sunday Times called it the 'ideal teacher'.

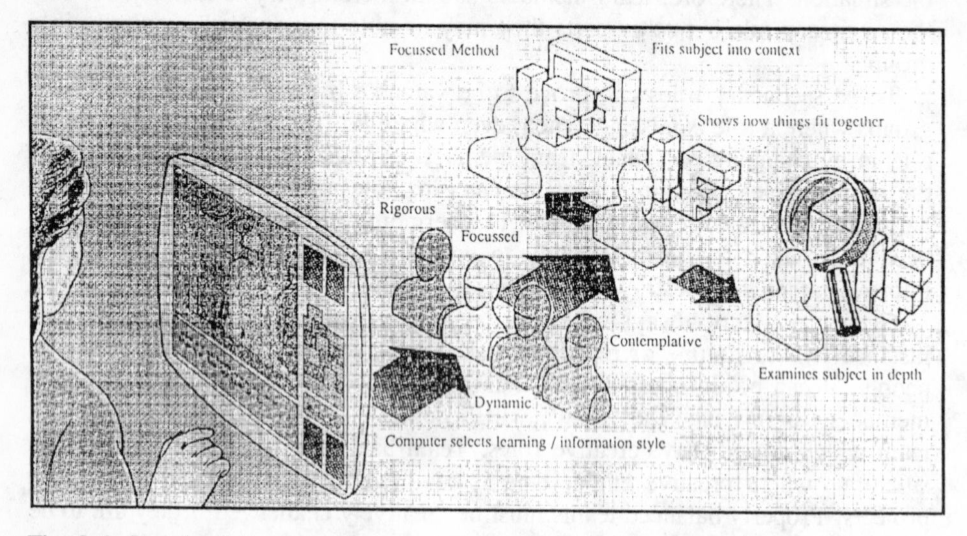

Fig. 9.4. Sketch of the prototype system, taken from the Sunday Times.

Over the last two years, DIRT has undertaken a full validation of this prototype as an advanced technology transfer and communications tool. Such a validation was achieved through detailed long term observations of a representative sample of engineers using a specially developed set of the information system for a short period in their own practices. This system, formed the perfect medium to test our general model of engineers as users of information, since it permitted us to monitor and log some aspects of the actual interactions of participating users with itself.

The whole interaction of the users was videoed to get as complete a picture of the engineers use of our system as possible. Such monitoring enabled me to build up complete records of the sort of information engineers actually prefer to use, rather than records of what they say they like when shown samples of 'good' presentation in a typical psychological experiment.

This validational research showed quite clearly that while limited in present capability, the prototype multi media information system, developed by the author does seem to improve technology transfer in engineering. When an information system exactly matches a preferred style of engagement and interaction it communicates particularly well. The author is now developing more advanced systems taking into account his detailed findings in the validation exercise.

9.8 Conclusion

The paper shows two important aspects of improving productive team cooperation. It reveals how knowledge of team members learning styles can aid the transfer of knowledge those having differing views of the world. It also shows how team balancing can be used to improve creative working in simultaneous engineering. Finally, it brings together ideas from these complementary theories to show how a multi media prototype information system can be used to remove the barriers to communication between these having differing views and to improve general information transfer in human centred engineering.

References

Belbin K M (1983) Team roles at work, Butterworth Heinneman
Belbin Associates (1993) InterPlace - A human resources management system, from Belbin Associates, The Burleigh Business Centre, Burleigh Street, Cambridge CB1 1DJ.
Freeman - Bell, G & Blackwell (1993), Management in engineering, Prentice Hall
Hart, (1988) Teams, Gower 1988
Kolb, D A (1976) The learning style inventory technical manual, MacBer and Company, Boston, USA
Newland, P M, Powell, J A and Creed, C (1987) Understanding architectural designers' selective information handling, Design Studies Vol 8 No 1
Powell J A (1987) Is Design a trivial pursuit, Design Studies Vol 8
Powell J A (1988) Towards the integrated environment for intelligent building Design, in Intelligent Buildings, published by UNICOM
Revans R W (1980) Action Learning - New Techniques for Management, Blond and Buggs
Thompson M. (1982) A three-dimensional model. in Douglas, M. Essays in the sociology of perception Routledge & Kegan Paul

Appendix

Know your Learning Style and Teamwork Role - an Interactive Dialogue

Key ideas in this paper relate to the way peoples' learning styles and team roles affect both the communication between themselves and others in the team and the general effectiveness of the simultaneous teams of which they are a part. If you would like to know more about your own learning style, as predicted by Kolb's theory, please photocopy the pages over, complete the inventory below using the instructions provided and return it to the author, Professor James Powell, Graduate School, Salford University, Greater Manchester, Lancashire, England, M54 WT. He offers to assess your learning style and send you the relevant analysis along with a fuller description of its importance to you as a analysis along with a fuller description of its importance to you as a learner/communicator/team member. He will also then send you another inventory for completion which will enable you to understand your principal team roles. This second inventory, due to Belbin, is too long to be included here. The author would particularly like to use your returns, in a totally anonymous way, to increase his understanding of the relationship between engineering professional groups and their learning/team roles. If you are unhappy for him to do this please tick the appropriate box on the next page.

Learning Styles Inventory - Instructions

This inventory is designed to assess your method of learning. As you fill in the inventory, give a high rank to those words which best characterise the way you learn and low rank to the words which are least characteristic of your learning style. You may find it hard to choose the words that best describe your learning style because there are not right or wrong answers. Different characteristics described in the inventory are equally good. The aim of the inventory is to describe how you learn, not to evaluate your learning ability.

There are nine sets of our words listed below. Rank order each set of four words in each row assigning a 4 to the word which best characterises your learning style, a 3 to the word which next best characterises your learning style, a 2 to the next most characteristic word, and 1 to the word which is least characteristic of you as a learner. Be sure to assign a different rank number to each of the four words in each row set. Do not make ties and write the number in the box provided.

Kolb's Learning Inventory

1.	discrimina-ting		tentative		involved		practical	
2.	receptive		relevant		analytical		impartial	
3.	feeling		watching		thinking		doing	
4.	accepting		risk-taker		evaluative		aware	
5.	intuitive		productive		logical		question-ing	
6.	abstract		observing		concrete		active	
7.	present-orintated		reflecting		future-orientated		pragmatic	
8.	experience		observa-tion		conceptual-isation		experiment-ation	
9.	intense		reserved		rational		responsible	

I do not wish my analysis to be used anonymously for research purposes.

Name of Respondent..

Address to which analysis
is to be sent...

....

....

Profession/Job...

10. Human-Centred Systems: New Roles for Designers, Managers and Employees

Marcin Sikorski

Technical University of Gdansk, Faculty of Management, Ergonomics Dept. 80-952 Gdansk, ul.Narutowicza 11/12, Poland

Abstract. New organizational functions are discussed, related to implementation of human-centred work systems, which integrate computer-based technology, personnel and management. New tasks arising for designers, managers and employees are discussed in the context of preparing people for their new duties in human-centred organizations. The human-centred approach is considered as an alternative for reducing risks involved by introducing new technologies.

Keywords. Computer integrated manufacturing, work systems, management, ergonomics

10.1 Introduction

Recent recession on many markets, paradoxically accompanied by rapid progress in technology, created a difficult situation for many manufacturing and service companies. Because the competition is now very strong, they have to find new ways to discover and satisfy customer needs, regarding quality of the product, its price, design, variability, functionality and delivery conditions. For this reason, large investments have been made into computer-aided manufacturing systems like FMS, CIM, CAE. These systems can help in quickly redesigning the product for specific customer requirements, can optimize the whole production cycle for minimal costs and finally can analyse business effect of these efforts.

Nevertheless, many companies experienced a decrease in sales despite the sophisticated manufacturing systems they had installed. Their case clearly shows that implementing top technology cannot help much if, inside the company:

- people are not able to use these high-tech systems properly
- managers mis-diagnose actual trends on the market
- the way from market analysis to product delivery is too long
- out-of-date management habits block creativity of individuals and cooperation of teams
- cooperative teamwork is not productive enough, despite all available IT (information technology) tools.

Even big companies, if they had focused too much on technological progress but neglected organisational and human factors, now have been losing their position, because huge technological investments did not pay back. In turn, many new enterprises overtake their markets, having even smaller number of staff, who can however fully utilise available technology. Usually for such successful and dynamic companies, the main goal is not gaining a fast and high profit, but primarily building a stable growth, based on moderate but long-lasting income and reliable, job-satisfied staff. It shows that nowadays creating a dynamic and competitive organization is not possible without:

1) putting human resources and management over technology,
2) integrating new technology with human resources and management techniques.

Any technological progress in the company should not result merely in production increase (which cannot all be sold now), but primarily in creating highly flexible work systems, in which:

- dedicated personnel and their unique skills play crucial role in business process,
- all available technology supports people in their work,
- management techniques integrate business process, technology and human resources for better serving customers' needs, building for the company a long-lasting position on the market.

This paper discusses some basic issues, related to design and management of sociotechnical systems in computerized work environment. It refers to the concept of Human-Centred Systems [4], considered as alternative for reducing risks involved by introducing new technologies.

10.2 Modern workplaces and their organization

Each company performs a particular business process, aimed to deliver specific services or products to the market. Manufacturing should be considered as a minor stage of the whole business process, which in the simplest outline (Fig. 10.1) consists of: design, costing, manufacturing, stock, sales and marketing. Performance of business process depends on relations between these stages and some kind of "infrastructure" serving business process (like personnel recruitment or managerial procedures), and also on interactions among many types of workstands involved in the business process.

A typical workplace in modern company consists of five basic elements:

- *hardware:* technological installation, computers, office equipment, communication systems, all kind of technical devices needed to perform the job;
- *software:* not only computer programs, but also all type of instructions, task procedures and knowledge needed to perform the job (they can be located in human minds, computers, manuals, decision support diagrams etc.);
- *personnel (users):* all people involved in the jobs relevant to the business process;

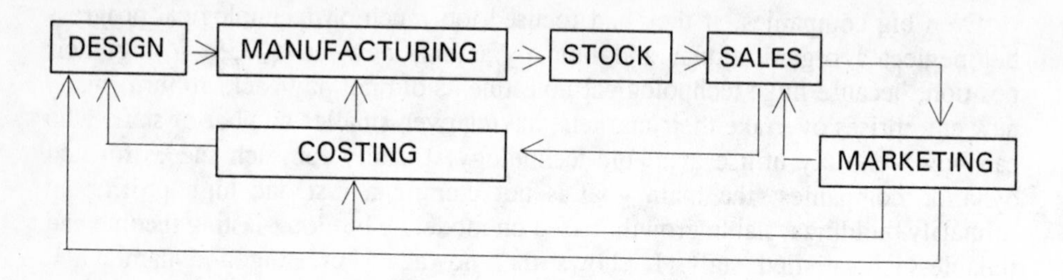

Fig. 10.1. Simplified business process of a typical company.

- *management:* all type of activity aimed to provide maximal performance of business process, including optimal utilization of resources (financial, human, technical), data analysis, costing, planning and decision making, jobs assignment and scheduling;
- *work environment:* surrounding of workplaces, its arrangement and impact on users in sense of health, safety, aesthetics and comfort.

The quality of all five elements and interactions among them are crucial for the performance of the system: humans-technology-environment.

All workstands are captured in a specific organizational structure, designed to serve company goals:

- profit (financial, social, etc.),
- development (technical progress, stronger position on the market etc.),
- usefulness (creating new jobs, activities for local community etc.).

Many companies in today's complicated situation have problems in stating clearly the priority of their goals and the preferred ways to attain them. Moreover, they often have anachronistic organizational structures, based on Henry Ford's division of labour, which fails to satisfy modern requirements. This type of traditional organization is usually represented as a narrow but high organizational pyramid (shown on the left in Figure 2) which:

- has many levels of hierarchy,
- consists of several departments, grouped around specific technologies,
- business information flows top-down, level by level, being often distorted or delayed, horizontal communication among the personnel is minor and usually not related to actual tasks,
- company response to the stimuli from the market is very slow; customers are usually served by anonymous employee of little competence and autonomy.

This type of organization:

- is inflexible, slow and hermetic, departments are often in conflicts for power; any reorganizations or technological changes can be only imposed from outside,
- creates many discomforts to the employed individuals,
- does not explore human skill and creativity,
- people generally do not know each other, team spirit is weak and concentrated on protection of own group position and interests,

- individual prestige is based more on rank and nomination than on real competence,
- everyone is responsible only for his part of the job, not for the results of the whole team, so there is little interest in cooperation, support or learning from others; everyone acts to satisfy the boss, not the client (BOSS-ORIENTED ORGANIZATION).

Such a structure cannot create conditions for stable growth and company development, because it is extremely inflexible, passive and slow. Even if such a traditional company invests substantially into new technology but the old organizational structure remains unchanged, the company will not improve its position. Low-motivated personnel will be not able to manage their new tools, nor analyse properly incoming batches of information. In an extreme case, costly investments into new technology can even 'kill' the company much faster than using very out-of-date technology.

Nowadays, while modern technological systems are very productive but extremely costly, the risk of failure must be maximally reduced. First of all, this can be achieved by careful planning of organizational changes needed by new technology, especially by adapting flexible management strategies. These changes should be focused on keeping the company and its staff customer-oriented:

1) by integration of formerly separated functions: design, manufacturing, sales and marketing
2) by using information technology (IT) for creating multiple links among them for information exchange and action planning (see Figure 1).

Implementing new technology, with extensive use of computers and communication tools, always breaks down the formal hierarchy and hermetic structure of the organizational pyramid. Younger and more dynamic employees enjoy new opportunities for exchanging information and creating new social links. As a result, information flow slips out of hands of old-style managers and messages flow horizontally as well as top-down. Electronic devices become symbols of individual status within the company, but only those who can really use them for the job (or fun) enjoy a real prestige and competence.

For an organizational developer, involved in preparing the changes for technological progress, the most important tasks are:

1) destroying the former pyramid with its departmental structure
2) integration of hardware, software, management techniques, personnel and work environment within business process
3) implementing into the new structure a mechanism for keeping the whole organization market-oriented in all activities, as shown in Fig. 10.1.

The ideal result of techno-organizational changes is represented as the right hand part of Fig. 10.2. Surely it will keep a pyramid-like nature in most of cases but:

- it will be more flat (there will be max. three levels of hierarchy)
- departments are replaced by flexible teams, responsible for specified tasks/areas of consumer service
- team leaders identify needs of the customer and flexibly assign relevant tasks among team members

- teams and individuals communicate, interact, cooperate, exchange information, resources and skills, also across different teams
- informal, task-related horizontal communication is supported by available communication tools and IT
- team leaders create a friendly atmosphere in the group, stimulate creativeness and build a team spirit,
- team members are informed about the current situation on the market and they are encouraged to bring up new ideas, innovations and organizational modifications to improve the quality of their service/product (organizational and technological changes are provoked from inside)
- team members are encouraged to learn new skills and to broaden their interests
- each member's position in the team is based on his/her individual friendliness, competence and contribution to the teamwork, less on age or education
- team members are regularly informed how their work contributes to customer satisfaction (feedback on customer satisfaction)
- team leaders have free access to latest information on sales, which allows them to modify their actions and to coordinate plans with other teams
- team leaders know how to use all opportunities of IT to support team members in their tasks
- for individual employees, not responding to the boss's expectations but first to customer satisfaction is emphasized as a primary goal and as the basis of company profit and existence (CUSTOMER-ORIENTED ORGANIZATION).

In such systems, the technology itself is not crucial but an appropriate management style that can stimulate creative and effective teamwork, which is especially important for such service areas as marketing, advertising, publishing, arts design, applied research, consumer goods manufacturing and many others. Companies where people play really a crucial role, can be recognized by following characteristics:

- the company invests heavily in educating their staff, who are perceived as the most valuable resource and the basis of company future
- personnel fluctuation and absenteeism are carefully analysed as important measures of job satisfaction and of managerial quality
- jobs and work systems are developed around the people, their skills and capabilities; all the technology is designed and arranged to support people in their tasks and to utilise fully their skill and creativity [2].

A term *Human-Centred Systems* [4], recently in use for describing this approach, exceeds the idea of "open management of human resources" [5]. Introducing this approach into business process can give long lasting benefits for company but it requires also new tasks, skills and talents from both employees and managers. This problem will be discussed in the next two sections.

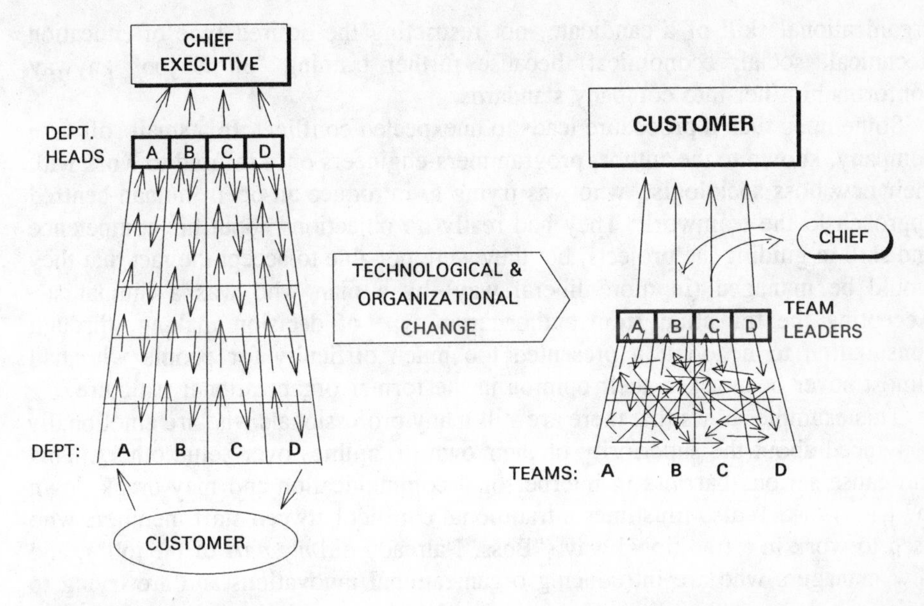

Fig. 10.2. The concept of boss-oriented (left) and customer-oriented (right) organizational structures.

10.3 New duties for managers

The concept of Human-Centred Systems cannot be implemented without active participation of managers, who will be keeping the work system operating in everyday use. A successful manager should be like a team leader described in the former section. His or her effective and flexible management should be based on [1], [5]:

- authority by competence
- creativity, open-mindedness, responsibility, imagination and dynamism
- stimulating various forms of horizontal communication among team members (also across teams), cooperation and social interactions
- ability to use available manufacturing technology and IT as a support in performing assigned tasks
- efficient use of data systems for group decision making and planning
- stimulating leadership style, developing customer-oriented approach in the team
- essential knowledge of design, technology, costing and marketing, needed to cooperate with other teams involved in the business process

Many of these desired skills can be called "META-SKILLS" as they cannot be acquired at business school. They come with professional experience and strongly depend on the personality of specific manager, his or her intuition, temper and manners. Possessing these meta-skills is in many companies even more important than specialistic technical knowledge. For this reason, during recruitment for managerial positions, many companies first test psychological traits and organizational skill of a candidate, not restricting the desired type of education (technical, social, economical) because further training "on-the-job" anyway conforms him/her into company standards.

Sometimes such a procedure leads to unexpected conflicts. In a small software company, known to the author, programmers-engineers once refused to work with their new boss sociologist, who was trying to introduce an open, human-centred approach to the teamwork. They had really no objections about his competence and skill in guiding the projects, but they were not able to accept the fact that they would be managed (in more liberal way) by a man who was a 'humanist'. Accepting the transition from authoritarian type of decision making, through consultation to negotiation presented too much difficulty for people who had almost never been asked their opinion in the former organizational structure.

This example shows that there are still many professionals who are emotionally convinced about the superiority of their own disciplines over some others. This can cause serious barriers in interpersonal communication and may break down the teamwork. It also illustrates a traditional conflict between staff members who used to work in a traditional way ("Boss, I already did *my part* of the job"), and new managers who are introducing organizational innovations and are trying to make people express and exchange ideas. In many cases, by using appropriate team building techniques, such conflict diminishes with time and gradually team cohesiveness and interpersonal communication improves.

For efficient team building some factors are essential but often under-appreciated:

- composition of individual learning styles of team members
- interpersonal behaviour style of team members
- personality of team leader and organizational climate he or she creates. This affects freedom of expressing ideas and information exchange, the contribution of all members to teamwork and their final satisfaction,
- team leadership must be built upon real competence, not on a formal nomination,
- proper role assignment for the teamwork among team members,

Team managers should:

- support learning and team building process
- feel responsible for the balanced team composition and increasing performance and job satisfaction of individual team members
- create multiple feedback with other teams and among his team members
- have a good sense of humour, which helps in everyday duties and breaks down conflicts that appear during the job

It is also the manager's duty to detect existing incompatibilities between personnel and existing job procedures, equipment, software and work environment. If these factors create discomfort or they become sources of human error, the system manager has to propose a solution: to redesign the job, rearrange work environment or re-allocate personnel. This new task requires from the manager a basic knowledge of ergonomics, work psychology and also principles of human-computer interaction. Managers often invite human factors consultants to solve these problems for them but, even in such a case, the final solution must be worked out together with the users, in a participative manner. Team managers should also know what type of work environment is the best for specific activity, because many simple things (like light, colour, arrangement of tables or chairs) may increase or decrease creativity, motivation and dynamism of team members.

10.4 Employees and their new tasks

In many companies, executives proudly claim that people are their most valuable resources. In fact, they mean not all employed staff, but some outstanding teams with their '5I' Ideas — Intelligence, Imagination, Initiative and Information. It's the team leader's task to get maximum from the '5I' dispersed across his or her team, and to combine different complementary talents of the people. It will be however not possible without cooperation and support of all team members: they must know the 'rules of the game' and understand the purpose of organizational experiments they are involved in.

Participation in a good, dynamic team requires from an individual:

- flexibility and readiness to play his/her role in the team
- permanent readiness and interest in learning new skills
- readiness to take part in any type of change (technological organizational, personal) demanded by the market situation,
- ongoing creativity, contribution and delivering new ideas for improving performance of the team
- willingness to express his/her opinion about detected problems in teamwork, or subjective discomforts resulting from assigned job
- proposing changes and being active in implementation stage
- improving personal communication with others

Because in many companies not the educational background but suitable psychological traits are essential for smooth team building, reliable recruitment procedures are essential for selecting appropriate people for specific teams. Training schemes should be oriented not only towards professional development but also on personality shaping and provoking creative thinking. A common mistake is that team leaders and managers often take part in various creativity oriented seminars, training sessions and workshops, but team members who usually do 'the black job of creative teamwork' usually are not invited to go. Human-centred company should provide a number of various opportunities for everybody to select the most suitable form and area of training, education and development.

10.5 Conclusion

In the 20th century, the human is a prisoner of organization, which is technical and cognitive system and includes many spheres of personal life. People usually

join an organization in search for benefits [1]. They agree to lose a part of their freedom and to adapt, because they want to be accepted by the rest of the team and to share profits. However, obtained profits usually are not as big as expected, which causes lasting disappointment. As a result, stress and frustration are inevitable costs of living and working in the organized society.
The organizational structure of a modern company cannot be any longer designed using only traditional, hierarchic approach, based on division of labour, and not taking trouble about expectations, needs and satisfaction of people, who are expected to be for years creative and useful for the company. The Human-Centred approach to organization attempts to achieve a compromise between the demands of modern industry and individual needs of humans, who are forced to live in industrialised society and to perform their jobs.

Human-centredness may now be perceived as a bit idealistic approach, but if we look into the future, probably we have no choice. Otherwise we will have unfriendly high-tech systems operated by frustrated staff, who do not want (or can't afford) to buy the goods they produce. A process of this kind could already have been observed on a smaller scale in post-communist countries after the breakdown of centrally-planned economies. However, perturbances caused by dramatic market reorientation and work-related social frustrations can be much bigger in the future in other countries. A Human Centred Systems Approach can be a realistic way to prevent these problems in newly designed industrial systems and to compensate negative effects on personnel in already existing organisations.

References

1. Baron R.A., Greenberg J. Behaviour in organizations. Understanding and managing the human side of work. Allyn and Bacon. Boston, 1980.
2. Czaja S.J.: Human factors in office automation. In: Salvendy G.(ed.). Handbook of human factors. Wiley, New York, 1987
3. Sharif J., Chang T., Salvendy G. Technical and human aspects of computer-aided manufacturing. In: Salvendy G.(ed.). Handbook of human factors. Wiley, New York, 1987
4. Schmid F., Hancke T., Wu B. The Human-Centred Approach to the Implementation of Computer Integrated Systems. Brunel University, Uxbridge, 1992
5. Torrington D., Hall L. Personnel management. A new approach. Prentice Hall, Englewood Cliffs, 1987.

11. Human-Centred Design, Implementation and Operation of Man-Machine Systems

L. Bálint[1] and M. Iken[2]

[1] Hungarian Academy of Sciences, Budapest, Hungary
[2] Technische Universität Stuttgart, Stuttgart, FRG

Abstract. The present paper is the result of a review, carried out by two team members of the conclusions from the work of one of the teams. It is an example therefore of the type of output which can derive from the intensive work of an interdisciplinary team, over a period of five days. None of the members knew each other before the Institute but the team had gone through the SCANCO process, described elsewhere in this book. The authors introduce the concept of 'ductcess', a mixture of product and process engineering which relies on meta-skills for its implementation.

Keywords. Skills, meta-skills, team-work, CIM, change, education, training

11.1 Introduction

This contribution tries to collect a few important aspects, principles and methods of how to apply human-centredness in the design, realisation, implementation as well as in the everyday operation of complex Man-Machine Systems (MMS). Although it has been attempted to consider first of all large computer-integrated (especially industrial) systems, most of the findings are of a general character related to MMS in a broad sense.

The issues investigated address a wide spectrum of questions. The following list is just a selection of the problems studied by the group:

- Establishing a (new) framework for a multi-disciplinary approach to Human-Centred Systems (HCS)
- Examining and surveying different topics of HCS
- Analysing the questions of different approaches related to systems
  - without humans
  - involving humans
  - integrating humans
  - for humans etc.
- Clarifying and defining what aspects of MMS work are handled well by humans

- Probing and understanding whether machines are in support of or against humans
- Exploring the possibilities, perspectives and probable outcomes of human-machine symbiosis.

All the above subjects receive a certain amount of attention and there are sometimes quite different views, arguments and propositions expressed with regard to the matters selected. However, because of the limited size of this contribution and because of the difficulties arising when widely different viewpoints and principles are to be integrated or at least matched to each other, firm statements and declarations are presented only on some sub-classes of the whole spectrum of issues. It should be emphasised that the findings (especially the final corollaries) are of course sometimes controversial and debatable. This fact is in line with the basic aims of the contribution: the most important goals were:

(1) to collect as many different, even extreme, aspects, views, beliefs and opinions as possible
(2) to extract the common ideas and views
(3) to integrate as far as possible the collected/extracted separate philosophies, beliefs, views and facts into a relatively well supported general scheme

11.2 Refining the Goals

There is a key question which arises during the exploratory and analytical work if an attempt is made to address the above aims: "where might the results of the investigations be used?"

It was decided that the answer should emerge from collecting issues, aspects and views related to and describing the feasible and likely potential applications of the results.

The main practical conclusions and thus, the major potential application areas are related to:

- introducing and developing different associated topics for education purposes
- promoting the exploitation of the new or recollected knowledge about man-machine complexes, human-centredness, team-working etc. in organisations built up on and around the related computer-integrated systems
- initiating and motivating further research with respect to the disclosed but unanswered questions
- providing knowledge and methods stemming from the many disciplines that "have something to say" about HCS
- introducing a framework for understanding the interrelatedness of different disciplines
- providing 'in-width' check-lists of topics related to Computer-Integrated Manufacturing (CIM) in HCS.

The above list expresses the goals of the present contribution and directions described by the inventory of aims and potential results/applications and deduces the need for a well established set of fundamental principles, guiding rules and practical recommendations.

11.3 Targets of the Investigation

The investigation may be characterised by the following objectives:

- Introduction of a taxonomy of HCS-related topics/problems
- Analysis of existing computer-integrated systems (examining success and failure stories and extracting the reasons)
- Classification and characterisation of different generations of man-machine systems (demonstrating the history and the perspectives)
- Outline and illustration of the proposed/projected next generation(s) in HCS and in this manner to:
  demonstrate a long-term vision of human-centred systems
  describe the role of the human (user, operator etc.)
  characterise CIM and the related organisational intelligence
  emphasise and explain the importance of team-building and team-working
  clarify the role of culture (cultural background)
  articulate the necessity of a well-designed decision-making structure and present useful guide-lines
  specify how to allocate functions in a well-working HCS
- Investigation of how to get to the proposed/projected next generation in HCS practice (provision of criteria for successful implementation)
- Development of a glossary and the perspective semantic relations for the above recipes.

The following sections go into some details with respect to the above directions. However, some findings, having been just background information to the final conclusions, have been omitted, partly for sake of purpose-orientedness and partly because of size limitations.

First, a general overview is given by investigating the humans as MMS components, the role of computers in these systems, the overall characteristics of man-machine systems, the generations in the MMS history and the future perspectives for the systems. Next, some specific aspects are dealt with (human skills, CIM and organisational issues). Finally, human-centred creation/enhancement of computer-integrated man-machine systems is surveyed, before summarising the main messages and concluding with the recapitulation of the most important findings.

11.4 General Aspects

This section gives an overview of man-machine systems in a general context. First, the role and characteristics of humans in MMS will be considered then machines (especially computers), as MMS constituents are investigated and finally, man-machine systems as entire complexes are surveyed.

11.4.1 Humans as MMS Components

Humans play a fundamental role in all man-machine systems. Although there are many applications where almost all of the system functions are performed by machines (moreover, fully automated system operation is also often occurring), the significance of human presence, supervision and control is evident. The question is: what kinds of humans are most adequate in the different system categories and system functions/subfunctions. To answer this question, the different classes of human characters and properties will be identified and described and then, these categories can be associated to the different operational requirements.

We have to make a distinction among five fundamental categories of human characters, differentiated in mentality, behaviour, capabilities etc. Although this categorisation results in human types belonging either to real or to virtual/imaginary human characters, it is worth mentioning all five classes because the picture can be made complete only by this full set of categories.

The five classes and their most important properties are listed in the following paragraphs:

- God is capable of performing miracles. This is the 'category' having no real examples among human kind although the quality of human activities or of their outcomes may be sometimes characterised as miraculous.
- Wizards are capable of making magic in the sense that without knowing exact goals (i.e 'what' to do), without knowing 'how' to get there and without knowing 'why' to aim at the very goal and why to take the selected way/method for achieving the very goal, they are able to act appropriately. Typical examples are politicians: controlling extremely complex systems (like large human communities including nations, regions, countries etc). They must act without an appropriate model by which the three questions could be answered. The humans responsible for actions regarding these very complex systems really have to make magic. It is to be added, that these wizards formulate the social embedding of all artists, technicians and scientists (see below) so that they will be able to perform their own tasks.
- Artists (in the widest sense) are humans capable of performing some kinds of art (again in the widest spectrum of meanings associated to the expression), characterised by human activities creating something new, something useful, something original. Artists do know the answers to the question "what" (not an easy question in most cases). Best examples are authors of works of 'art' (in different fields of creative arts in the common sense of the word) and engineers specifying and designing non-trivial works, objects or products.
- Technicians are the experts of procedures, i.e. of how to perform different tasks having been determined by somebody else (of course, an artist). Thus, technicians are responsible for providing the answers to the "how" questions. Characteristic examples are lawyers, farmers, tailors, doctors etc. but process planning engineers as well as performing artists also belong to this character and activity type.

- Scientists answer the most difficult 'why' questions. They are the key specialists of discovering, exploring and/or deriving the models by which artists and technicians can relatively easily perform their tasks. Of course, science is to be meant again in the word's widest sense: from humanities and from social sciences to natural sciences, to life sciences and to technical sciences.

Of course, the above human characters may not be ordered into a priority (order, importance, usefulness, significance). They are all extremely important both in traditional man-machine systems and in advanced computer-integrated systems. They complement each other so they can't replace one another in any specific task or sub-task. The only question is: which character is most appropriate to this or that task or function. This question will be addressed in some detail later in the followings.

It must also be noted that the above character and activity types are not exactly distinguishable and separable. In many cases, people and job functions do not belong to just one of the different classes mentioned but they mix or overlap. However, a dominant class is always selectable and in this way, some important facts with regard to man-machine system operation may be derived.

Finally, it is to be mentioned that irrespective of the above human character types, some important specific properties can be (and should be) recognised. In man-machine systems, tasks are to be divided between man and machine and, as far as human tasks are concerned, between the humans belonging to different character types. The most important such specific properties and capabilities are (with a "+" sign if the property is advantageous relative to the according machine properties and a "-" if the machine is ahead of the human regarding the very property):

- strength in interpreting complex situations (events, data etc.) +
- flexibility and adaptivity +
- aptitude for pattern matching +
- talent for learning from experiences +
- purpose-driven behaviour and activities +
- ability of overviewing and synthesis +
- capability for handling irregular situations +
- proficiency in problem solving +
- talent for self-reflection +
- familiarity with error-handling +
- widespread skills and competence +
- adequacy with respect to handling uncertainty +
- motivation-orientedness +
- ability of own decision-making +
- mastering work with incomplete specification +

- danger of stress and frustration -
- hazard of erroneous perceptions, decisions and actions -
- risk of fatigue, faults and mistakes -

- varying skills, capabilities and performance -
- necessity of rest to recover -

11.4.2 Computers in the MMS

In contrast to humans in man-machine systems, machines are relatively easy to handle, model and to take into consideration. Unlike humans, machines (computers or computerised equipment) are created (designed and realised) intentionally by taking into account human-made specifications. They function deterministically and, in principle, there is no substantial problem in describing their behaviour and operation or in taking into consideration any of their features and characteristics.

The following list presents some of the most important properties and strengths/weaknesses of machines in general and computers in particular. Appropriate signs (+ or -) indicate again whether the related property is a benefit or a drawback of the machine(s) relative to human properties when used in an MMS:

Machines in general

- ability to transfer energy, power and force within (extreme) limits +
- well controllable movement velocities within (extreme) bounds +
- capability of handling objects up to (extreme) mass +
- high efficiency, accuracy and repeatability in demanding precision applications +
- no need for recreation (aptitude of virtually endless continuous operation) +
- limited flexibility -
- requiring complete specification and control -
- finite probability of faulty operation -

Computers in particular

- strength in administrative operations +
- extreme computational capabilities +
- ability of consistency checking +
- superior power in 'data and number crunching' +
- deterministic functions +
- missing ability of self-reflection -
- weakness in handling unforeseen errors -
- limited adaptivity -

The above features of machines/computers and the human properties in the previous paragraph help selecting which sub-tasks or sub-functions of a man-machine system should be (fully or dominantly) performed by machines and/or humans, respectively. The following passage goes into some detail regarding complete man-machine systems.

11.4.3 Man-machine system characteristics

Although the two main 'components' of man-machine systems (humans and machines) have been addressed briefly in the preceding paragraphs, it is to be kept in mind that these man-machine complexes (especially computer-integrated systems devoted for example to industrial production) comprise much more than merely their naked components. If we try to characterise the whole structure, some of the necessary elements may be itemised in the following list (without aiming at a complete and exhaustive directory of the many ingredients):

People

- Appropriate capabilities of staff members
- Motivation
- Innovative personnel
- Preservation of a wide-range of skills and expertise
- Education
- Friendly atmosphere

Physical infrastructure

- Efficient, reliable, accurate (and flexible) equipment for design, manufacturing and testing
- Integrated, networked IT (information technology) sub-system

Organisation

- Innovation-orientedness
- Well established and well working information-policy
- Substantial focus on technological R&D (research and development)
- Well working team structure (mixed, autonomous, cooperative teams)

Input/output relations

Materials-oriented processes
    Quality assurance of incoming parts and materials
    Substantial focus on product R&D
    On-time product delivery
Information-oriented processes
    Market-orientedness
    Early customer involvement in product life-cycle
    Extensive customer support
Money-oriented processes
    Competitive prices
    Cost-consciousness

Starting with the above (although incomplete) set of constituents, the history of man-machine systems is not too difficult to depict.

11.4.4 History and generations of man-machine systems

It is clear that significant differences may be recognised if we split the history of MMS into the following five main periods (or five generations of MMS):

Period 0: No automation — all processes controlled by humans. (This period is not discussed further)

Period I: 'Hard' automation (the period before the emergence of computing machines)

Period II: Automation aided humans (early automation aids humans but humans do most of the jobs)

Period III: Human aided automata (high level of automation takes over most tasks while humans just aid the processes by intelligent supervision)

Period IV: Human/automata symbiosis (optimum task division between man and machine) — the future.

All five periods can be characterised with respect to:

- products/services provided (variety, uniformity, complexity, precision and performance)
- human and machine activity types
- level of machine intelligence and knowledge
- properties of man-machine interaction
- MMS advantages and drawbacks
- typical examples.

Table 1 summarises the results of an effort towards collecting the mentioned characteristics of the above periods I to IV. Again, there is room for much debate but, nevertheless, Table 1. helps in the recognition of what directions are characterising the evolution of man-machine systems and the probable features of future MMS realisations.

11.4.5 Future perspectives in MMS

When looking at Table 1, it must be recognised that Period IV. (the 4th MMS generation, i.e. the age of human/automata symbiosis) is best characterised by the balance between

customisation/mass production
re-usability/creativity
minimum effort/maximum output

which, through the efficient multi-mode and multi-media interaction between human and machine, results in a harmonious co-operation. At the same time, however, a dangerous situation characterised by dependency of humans on their machine partners may evolve.

These are perhaps the main features being characteristic of future (perspective) man-machine systems.

	Period I.	Period II.	Period III.	Period IV.
Product/service - variety - uniformity - complexity - precision - performance	 constrained low small low limited	 elevated intermediate medium limited enhanced	 "unlimited" high high high extreme	 optimum optimum optimum optimum optimum
Human activities Machine activities	 do -	 control aid	 supervise do	 cooperate cooperate
Machine intelligence Machine knowledge	 - -	 "what?" calculus intensive	 "what-how?" procedural reasoning	 "what-how-why?" inferring knowledge & expertise
Man-machine interaction	-	human-to- -machine uni-directional	human-machine bi-directional (sufficiency)	human-machine bi-directional /multiple styles/ (efficiency)
Advantages Drawbacks	friendly limited	hopeful inhomogeneous	productive alienating	harmony dependency
MMS examples	-	NC machine tools calculator databases etc.	nuclear power plant oil refinery space shuttle KBES etc.	???

Table 1.

By recollection from the previous paragraph, the crucial peculiarities may be summarised and emphasised again:

- Optimum variety, complexity, uniformity, precision and performance of the products/services (i.e. neither sub-optimum nor overspecification are occurring: neither disfunctionality nor overburden may turn up)
- Cooperative human and machine operation is evolving by optimum work division and interaction

- Elevated human and machine knowledge and expertise (both theoretical and practical) are to be (and are accessible to be) fully utilised within optimum MMS operation.

A very important aspect stems from the projected benefits and shortcomings. Friendliness is of extreme advantage but dependency is a danger to be avoided by any possible measure. Here, the motivating/organising values are of outstanding significance: personal-, capital- and knowledge-oriented factors are all to be wisely exploited for achieving this crucial target.

11.5 Specific aspects

Now, after a general overview of man-machine systems, some specific aspects are dealt with, namely human skills, CIM (computer-integrated manufacturing) and MMS organisation, as key facets of the parties involved and of the complex structure itself.

11.5.1 Human skills

Human skills are practised abilities directly exploitable by man-machine system operation. Among the many elements of the set of skills characterising any human being, there are two groups which are easily distinguishable: (1) individual skills and (2) collective skills. Individual skills are either physiological/physical or mental/behavioural while collective skills are cooperative/communicative.

The abilities and performance of humans evolved enormously during the history of mankind. Nevertheless, the evolution was resulting step-by-step in more and more types and further and further enhancement of skills, starting from the physiological/physical ones and, through the mental/behavioural ones, arriving at the cooperative/communicative ones. This very process of evolution has been copied by the evolution of the artificial means supporting the enhancement of the related skills in human activities.

As far as the skills, related to the accuracy and precision of human labour are concerned, 'artificial hands' were first introduced tens of thousands years ago, in the form of the early tools. It was in the late eighteenth century when the first 'artificial muscle' appeared with the introduction of the first steam machine. Thus, artificial enhancement of physiological human skills got into its rapidly evolving period. After World War II, the 'artificial brain', i.e. the electronic computer started its revolutionary development, enhancing artificially the mental human skills. And about twenty years later there came the era of computer networking, the 'artificial nervous system' of society, enormously enhancing the human skills of communication and cooperation. And today, all the human skills mentioned, together with their artificial counterparts, do evolve in a rapid course, allowing more and more efficiency, reliability and cost-effectiveness in the operation of man-machine systems, especially of human-centred ones.

All the above processes did lead to a level of progression where it is just a question of decision how to utilise the integrated capabilities of human and machine. Tools and human precision, engines and human workforce, computers and human thinking, networking and human cooperation: these all together serve as a complete set of ingredients by which a virtually infinite palette of opportunities may be generated for achieving almost unbelievable results in creating and operating human-centred computer-integrated man-machine systems.

However, the well known traditional human skills can be successfully integrated into the activities of an organisation only if a set of meta-skills is also present in the staff members (meta-skills are secondary skills which do not directly belong to a specific field of human activities, but which enable people to overcome the problems arising in the early phase when they form just a group trying to become a team). In the following list, a set of important meta-skills are collected:

- Horizontal communication within an organisation
- Elevated authority and responsibility
- Utilisation of information
- Recognition of data relationships
- Understanding the significance of tools
- Synthesis of information and concepts
- Creativity (thinking differently in an active manner)
- Open-mindedness (thinking differently in a passive manner)
- Time management
- Development of team management skills.

The development of meta skills is often neglected and replaced by programmatic announcements on company policy and outline in this respect.

11.5.2 Computer-integrated manufacturing

Computer-integrated manufacturing is one of the key issues in industrial production-oriented computer-integrated systems. The introduction of CIM means, first of all, that:

- shopfloor workers supervise machinery, instead of directly manipulating, operating or controlling the machines
- testing staff take care of production (process) tests instead of product tests (i.e. quality assessment or QA shifts from product level to process level)
- process planning engineers provide NC (numerical control) tools instead of written/plotted documents
- product designers (and their CAD /computer-aided design/ systems) take on process planners' tasks in the case of CNC (computer numerical control) technologies
- logistics and full production-oriented administrative activities are computer-controlled and computerised
- the full sequence of computer-supported production-oriented activities is integrated into a computer-controlled system and thus, product design, process

planning, logistics and administration are all performed under the associated common computer control.

By this way, a highly efficient, reliable and in many cases extremely cost-effective production system can be set up. With applying CIM:

- products get more and more 'variational' and 'parametrised' (being slightly different from each other within characteristic product families and thus easily designed by making selections among variants and/or by setting only a few free parameters)
- processes get more and more 'parametrisable' (i.e. allowing the mentioned variational and parametrised design by the adjustment of just some technological process parameters)
- process planning gets more and more product family-oriented instead of the earlier product-orientedness
- the earlier distinguished role of product design decreases (product design becomes a routine task) and difficult design efforts are more and more associated to designing product families.

Normally, CIM is feasible where, beside the applicability of NC and CNC manufacturing, CAD or DA (design automation) is also well advanced. However, the introduction of CIM itself is motivating the rapid development of these computer-supported design methods, as well.

CIM, as one form (or even one possible constituent) of computer-integrated systems, increasingly requires human-centredness for future implementations. This human-centredness (which will be investigated in somewhat more detail later) supposes, among others, cautious staff selection, personnel education/training and team-working, but also postulates the thorough consideration of some more crucial aspects as well, for example, friendly workplace atmosphere, healthy shopfloor circumstances, special care-taking of staff members etc.

Provided that CIM is applied in those cases only where production efficiency, reliability and cost-effectiveness are enabling and justifying it, computer-integrated manufacturing has a promising perspective, especially if the advanced CIM principles and methods are well combined with the aspects of human-centredness.

11.5.3 The MMS organisation

Every professional person belongs to at least two different activity spheres and in order to develop proper HCS it is of outstanding importance to take into account the total different requirements to which people are exposed in these spheres.

The two most important spheres are the 'social (private)' sphere and the 'business (professional)' sphere. Both of them have different hierarchical levels. At least four distinct levels can be recognised in either sphere, with common top and bottom levels of 'society' and 'individual', respectively. The intermediate levels are depending on whether social or business spheres are under consideration.

The level of hierarchy is accordingly as follows:

- Social sphere
  - Society
  - Neighbourhoods
  - Families/'clubs'
  - Individuals
- Business sphere
  - Society
  - Organisations
  - Teams
  - Individuals.

In both spheres and at all hierarchical levels, there are a number of issues determining how the related structural items function, operate and behave. Again, without aiming at a complete list of these issues, some of the most important ones are cited below:

- Lifecycles (will to survive, expand, strengthen)
- Motivation (of objectives and related operations and actions)
- Missions and tasks (belonging to aims and purposes)
- Authority and responsibility (in task divisions)
- Capabilities and skills (related to functions and tasks)
- Knowledge (related to functions and tasks)
- Information (related to functions and tasks)
- Relation, linking and interaction (between spheres and levels)
- Costs/benefits (of partial and entire operations).

Man-machine systems (as organisations in the business sphere) are to be designed, established, maintained and operated by taking into account the complete set and complex interrelations of the above issues. Special care is to be devoted to the team level because this is perhaps the most important scene of processes related to human-centredness.

	Eastern Europe	Japan	Germany	USA	France
Conformity	+	+	+	+/-	-
Enhancement of individuals' contribution	-	+/-	-	+/-	-
Social responsibility	+/-	+	+/-	+	+/-
Homogeneity	+	+	+	-	+/-

Table 2.

Table 2 is an attempt to assess those characteristics of societies which seem to be important for the successful implementation of human-centred systems. Again, in accordance with the overall viewpoints of the contribution, Table 2 doesn't aim at providing a full picture. It contains just an ad-hoc collection of some characteristic countries/areas having been considered and so the sketch is very coarse.

A plus sign in Table 2. means that the related property is strongly manifested, while a minus sign denotes that the property is weakly appearing in the region/culture under consideration.

The information extractable from Table 2. serves as a good basis for determining specific region-dependent (culture-oriented) aspects of organising HCS.

Team-working is one of the most important features of successful HCS operation. The following aspects should be paid attention to — and if necessary clarified — if successful team-work is to be achieved:

- Although good opportunities to acquire technical skills are offered in most of the industrialised countries, there is a lack in developing meta-skills. Thus, it is important to concentrate on creating these meta-skills. This may possibly be done in traditional institutions of education (schools, universities), but also in the continuing education of adults. It is to be mentioned here that special attention should be paid to the post-communist societies where, because of the restructuring process, new employing schemes and social activities are to be perceived. Note that meta-skills are conditioned by the organisational culture while they in turn inseminate this organisational culture, as well.
- Successful HCS operation supposes not only a multi-language, but also a multi-cultural composition of teams.
- The intellectual property of results produced by team-work should be clarified in advance (note that different law systems are applied with this regard in different countries). The question of 'team ownership' should be addressed.

The process of decision-making is again of great importance for the success of any HCS. This means that an HCS can only work if the people working in the system are encouraged to contribute to the decision-making processes. Such a situation can be achieved if and only if the humans in the HCS identify with the system itself. In turn, identification is only possible if a feeling of being involved in the decision-making can be achieved. Therefore, consideration of the following items is of key importance:

- Concerning the development of negotiation skills and styles, the ability to recognise common interests and the belief that win/win-compromises are achievable must be present. However, this ability and belief are worthless without the conditions for keeping the reached compromise. Therefore, the task of building team relationships is extremely important.
- The development of mediation skills is another crucial factor since mediation is a choice in conflict resolution.
- It should be kept in mind that there are two models of decision-making, namely (1) the consensus-building process and (2) representative decision-making. Although consensus-building is more matched to team-working, both models are to be utilised, depending on the situation.

- It must be taken into account that authority and responsibility are closely linked to each other. If a team is responsible for its action and behaviour, it should have the power to decide what is to be going on and vice versa. (It is worth mentioning that trade unions traditionally require increasing authority without increased responsibility for the workers, whereas management traditionally wants the workers to take more responsibility without more authority).

11.6 Human-centred enhancing of computer-integrated man-machine systems

After having looked at existing systems and at the proposed next generation, the question arises: how can the change be achieved? (i.e., how to get there?)

Optimum (desirable) use of man and machine assumes some important prerequisites regarding the humans involved, the machinery involved and the form and operation of the (computer-) integrated MMS. This part of the contribution goes into some details with respect to (1) the human tasks and skills as well as the wise application of computer-integrated machinery and (2) team-working as a key organisational element in human-centred system operation.

11.6.1 Humans and machines in HCS

Humans (supervisors, operators, users) in a man-machine system should be able to perform:

- efficiently and reliably their routine tasks
- assistance in recovery from system errors (avoidance of disasters) and
- continuous learning (improvement of themselves) as well as innovating (enhancing system operation).

These requirements suppose appropriate human abilities, skills and performance. Some of them will be dealt with later, in relation to team-working, but some others are handled here, in view of how humans may well adjust themselves to the changing circumstances, especially with the evolution of the technology applied.

Whereas the first two conditions are more or less fully met in almost any working MMS, the third requirement is in most cases underestimated and omitted by traditional organisations. This problem is overcome by human-centredness: on the human side (in the interest of developing the system functionality and appropriate human emotions and satisfaction) the constant improvement of personal capabilities and innovativeness is the key element in how to achieve both happy and competent staff as well as successful MMS operation.

It is to be taken into account that with the introduction of CIM, several crucial new problems are arising and these problems must be appropriately handled in order to achieve human-centredness and enhancement in the operation of the computer-integrated system.

Although the scale of the tasks of both the 'white-collar' and 'blue-collar' staff decrease substantially by the introduction of CIM, in general, these tasks get, at the same time, much more demanding. This is the main reason why the problems mentioned arise and why the special handling of these problems is necessary.

The emerging problems can be characterised, among others, by the following contradictions:

- The new supervisory tasks are totally different from the traditional controlling tasks
- There is a tremendous difference between the traditional testing expertise and the new (process-oriented) testing/QA requirements
- The new tasks and skills being supposed by the new process planning needs are totally differing from the traditional tasks and skills
- There is a significant contradiction between the traditional division of work and the new integration of product and process design/planning.

The solution of the problems stemming from these contradictions requires careful system planning and implementation, attentive selection/education/training of the personnel, cautious and selective involvement of the new ways of advanced computer practice and conscientious introduction of team-working in the fully integrated system.

11.6.2 Team-working

As stated above, considering the MMS organisation, one important step towards HCS is the introduction of team-work. However, when creating teams, some important points are worth considering.

First of all it must be recognised that no real change is possible until the management and even the top-management are ready to change their attitudes and behaviour. This means that the management has to accept rules for do's and dont's in order to give the teams the appropriate amount of freedom. Therefore, in an HCS based on teams, the management has to set up clear tasks, goals and targets but should not interfere with the process of the on-going team-work. Thus, one of the most important rules for the management is that they should state 'what' the objective of the team is, but they mustn't prescribe 'how' this objective is to be pursued ('what, but not how'). In order to have a means of control, a reporting system based on milestones is recommended.

If a 'big' team is to be established, it is important to begin with a smaller group (6 to 10 persons). After this group has become a team it is possible to introduce a few new members. As soon as they are integrated, new members can be added again. By this incremental process it is possible to build up big teams. Trying to create very large teams in a single step is dangerous and often results in failure.

Other significant points for the success of a team are:

- Continuity of the team:
- Setting up the team as early as possible during the project
- Let the team work together full-time

- Provide a separate workplace for the team so as to guarantee undisturbed team activities.

The following check-list may help in achieving well established and well working teams as well as effective and trustworthy decision-making:

- diversity (multi-culturalism and anti-conformism)
- team structure (depending on task)
- enhancement of individual contributions
- focus on informal/flexible structure
- common culture of co-operation
- equal opportunities
- principle of representation democracy (when needed)
- principle of consensus building (when needed)
- due processes
- avoidance of 'group-like thinking situations

The last item on the list, 'group-like thinking', refers to circumstances where the urge to conform is of higher priority than the attitude of raising the sometimes inconvenient but nevertheless good and important questions. Special care is to be taken of the skills and meta-skills represented by the team members.

Although it is widely recognised that well-working teams require different skills from the different team members so that these different skills are complementary to each other, it is rarely kept in mind that communication between the team members doesn't allow fully separated skills, i.e. some overlap is necessary between the skills of the participants. However, in a traditional sense, this requirement supposes that each team member is an expert in at least two different skill areas and these different areas are connected within the skill coverage of the related person by meta-skill(s) bridging the gap(s) between the separate skills.

In contrast to this traditional requirement, there is a more appropriate and more effective way of how to achieve effective and satisfactory cooperation within the team: participants need not have more than one skill if their meta-skills overlap with each other, i.e. each skill represented can reach all the further skills by direct or indirect overlapping(s) of meta-skills of team-members (indirect reach means that if the meta-skills of two members representing two different skills do not overlap; there is a chain of pair-wise overlapping meta-skills among the team members that connects the two regarded skills).

The mentioned skill/meta-skill structure can be represented graphically by illustrating the skills by vertical bars and the meta-skills by horizontal bars so that the skills and meta-skills being connected to each other are overlapping. In this way the traditional requirement (the need for at least two different skills and the appropriate connecting meta-skills from each team-member) may be illustrated by Fig. 11.1a. while the new principle (where no additional skill is needed but only appropriate meta-skills are necessary) is illustrated by Fig. 11.1b. Thus, in the traditional case, team members communicate in the way seen in Fig. 11.2a. whereas with the new principle, communication goes on by the way demonstrated in Fig. 11.2b.

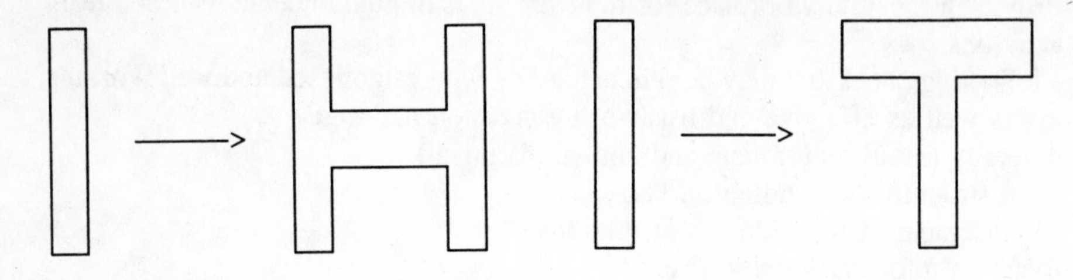

Fig. 11.1 a and b

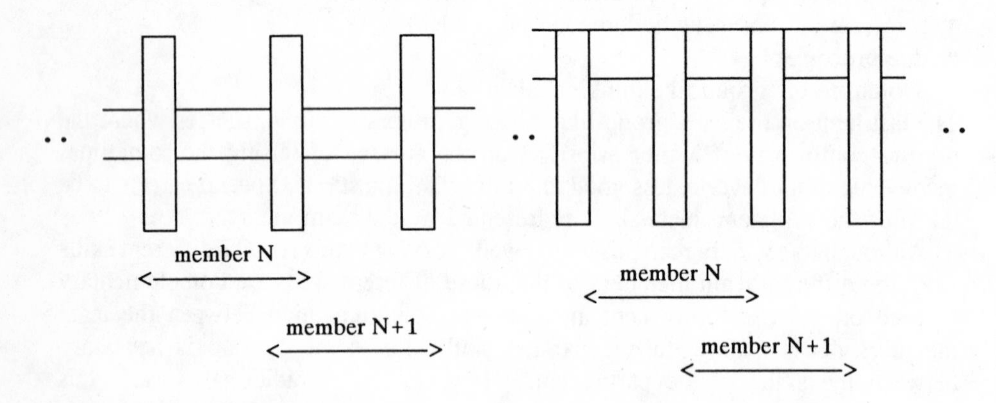

Fig. 11.2. a and b

This new principle means that team members (or prospective team members) need not to get into intensive education for gaining expertise in a totally new skill area. Individual evolution should aim at achieving new meta-skills only. As far as engineering-like activities are concerned, this evolution results in a new model of engineering and thus (in contrast to the traditional product- and process-engineer prototype) a new engineer ideal is emerging. This new ideal may be called 'ductcess-engineer', indicating on one hand that product- and process-orientedness are getting integrated and suggesting, on the other hand, that ductcess-orientedness is the key of success-orientedness.

11.7 Summary and conclusions

Human-centred design, implementation and utilisation of man-machine systems were briefly investigated, by collecting, demonstrating and evaluating some important aspects related to the rapid development of computer-integrated systems.

After clarifying the goals and directions kept in mind during the investigations, general and selected specific properties and attributes of man-machine systems were presented, including humans and machines, especially computers, as well as the systems, themselves. Some practical aspects were also introduced, regarding the exploitation of the findings in establishment and the refinement/development of human-centred computer-integrated systems.

Although a wide spectrum of related questions was dealt with and the conclusions may seem as possible ingredients to a certain kind of a recipe for successful HCS implementation and operation, the content of the contribution is not to be considered either complete, or definite, since the opinions and the corollaries contain many subjective elements. However, the multi-cultural background of the ideas involved obviously suggested that disseminating the collected findings might be of value for a wider community of interested readers.

Thanks are due to NATO (the North Atlantic Treaty Organisation) and LUT (the Loughborough University of Technology) for having made it possible to organise the 1993 Advanced Study Institute on "People and Computers". Special thanks are due to the group members, namely V.Cyras (Lithuania), Z.Fekete (Hungary), J.Hensgens (Holland), S.Kirpich (Belarus), Kate Laskowitz (USA), R.McKelvey (USA) and P.Serrafero (France) who all took part in the team-work, together with the editors of the study, L.Bálint and M.Iken).

12. Integral Communication and Integral Learning

Johannes Ehrhardt

philtec communications, Klostergut Schachtenbeck, 37581 Bad Gandersheim, Germany

Abstract. The author identifies a need for the development of new forms of virtual systems which support the productive enterprise in its changed environment. These systems will use the advanced communication tools and methods available today but they can only flourish in learning which are designed to cope with new developments using an integral approach rather than the classical method of solving problems in small steps.

Keywords. Communication, learning, integral learning, learning organization, meta skills, virtual system

12.1 Introduction

We all know that globalization is no longer just an idea for the future. We know how and where it has become a material fact and we know how practical globalization affects our lives. Our problem is that the general concepts and our cultural patterns do not yet correlate with our knowledge, our reality and our interactions. The functional reality of globalization is growing increasingly abstract and systematic — the human reality trying to cope with it tends to grow increasingly absurd.

Our world is a world of functional systems. We need these systems, which are highly complex, to be incorporated into global systemic interdependence. Yet to handle these systems we have to learn to adapt to new structures and to create continuously new subsystems, combining them with the traditional essence and cultural patterns of our communities. Only if we succeed in building these relationships in a stable and flexible form of interaction, can we hope to live in a 'cité' that can actually cope with global interdependence and global competition. We need new personal and social skills to develop, implement and handle these systems, because, as Lucien Sfez put it:

> *"Pour qu'une cité fonctionne, pour qu'un système résiste, il faut la participation active et l'engagement: sans quoi il n'y a pas identité stable des sujets."* [Sfez, 1993]

12.2 Meta Systems and Interdependence

The meta-systems that foster the practical globalization seem to be out of human reach. The core systems are characterized by highly abstract structures, by regulative process organization and by dense functional relations. A perfect example is the fascinating aeronautic system described by Alain Gras [Gras, 1993].

The formal functionalization of material interdependence creates a layered distribution of goods, competence, financial resources, and services. The regulating instance is of course the added value gained by the interactions. No one is planning the meta-systems and they only work because of the practical subsystems embedded in them — you could also say the meta-systems are the overall generic dimension of systems development. Each system only works because of its regional concretization but their interaction level is a function of the inherent abstractness introduced by the meta-systems. This is the most important point; the abstractness is the material condition of giving flexibility to the basic economic functions. On the application level, the abstraction is the prerequisite of the compatibility that makes practical exchange possible. This practical abstractness enforces business re-engineering. Business re-engineering is the systematic attempt to transform the impact of the globalization of markets into measures to streamline the organizational structure and to redesign the process of systems development.

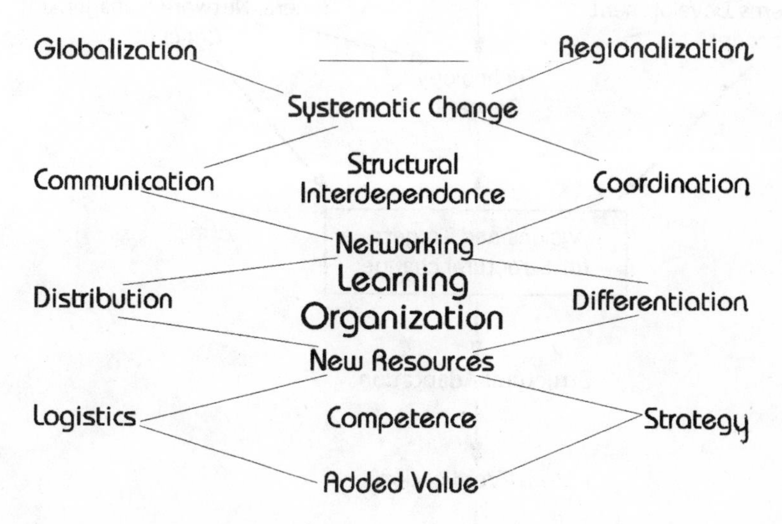

Fig. 12.1. (Source philtec)

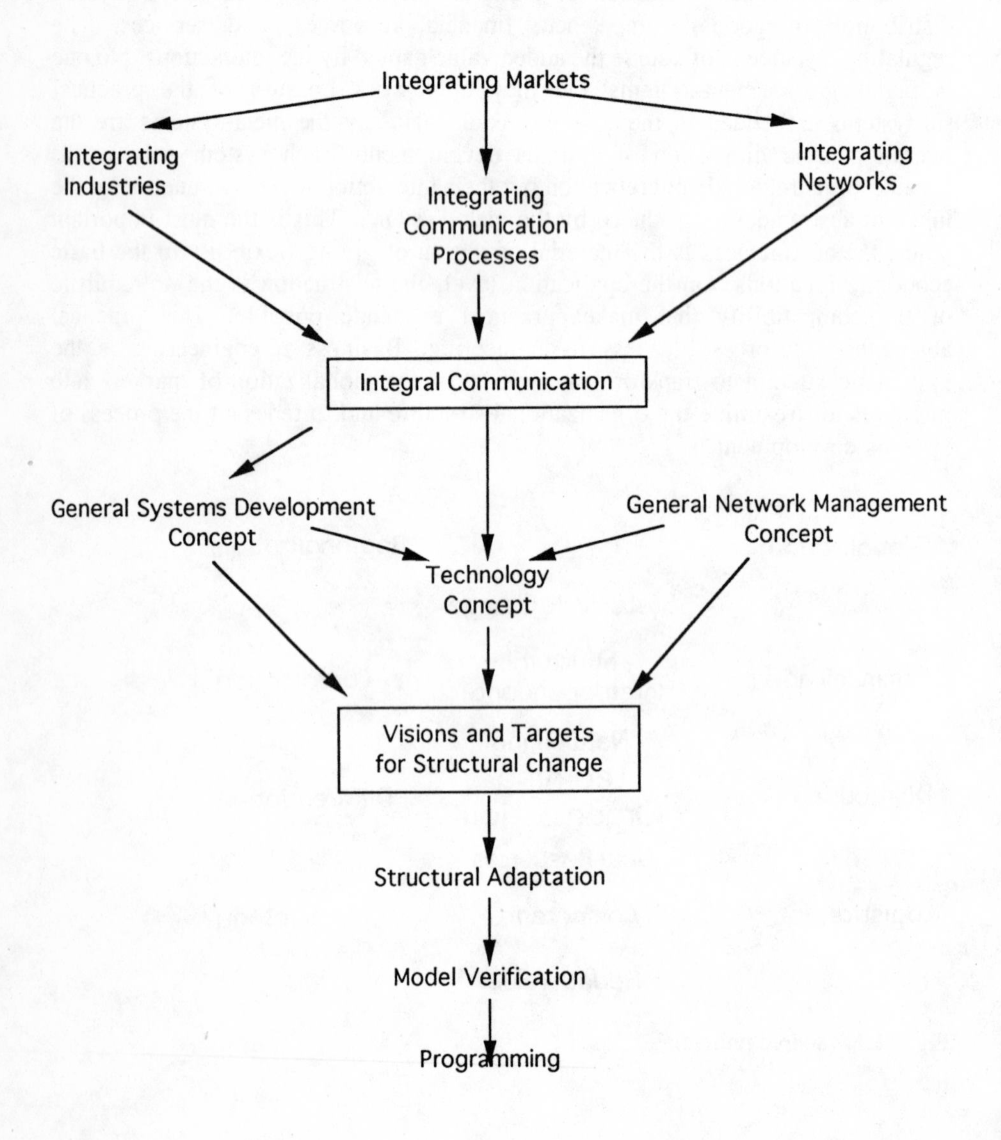

Fig. 12.2. (Source philtec)

The convergence of the communication-related industries, speeded up by the comprehensive digitalization of all economic sectors, provides the technological setting of the dynamic, market-driven global competition.

12.3 Communication in Interdependent and Layered Systems

The technology driven convergence goes along with market diversification, because with the new potentialities, the needs of the consumers can be met in increasingly specific ways. To do this, the diversified markets on the other hand need efficient global structures. To reunite the disintegrating trends, a new integral form of communication is necessary to combine the technical potentialities of the computer and communication industries with new dimensions of understanding.

Of course, the growing global interdependence does not create one single system. The central question is how the emerging structures differentiate into layers of systems development. As the different social, economic, financial, cultural and technological structures are combined into various functional systems, each subsystem is more and more integrated into a 'spider's net' of interdependence. This is why communication is at the heart of systems development.

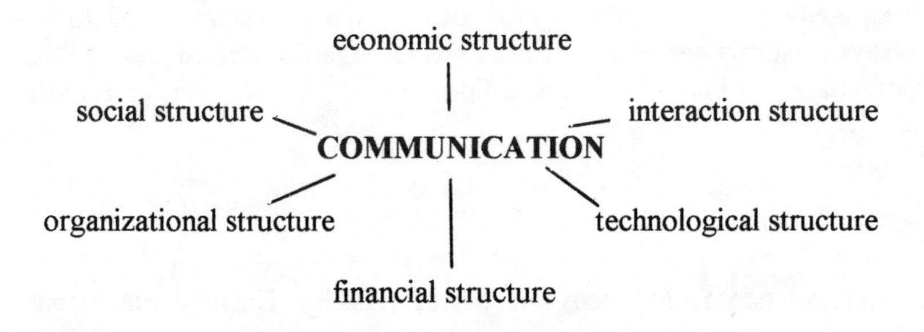

Fig. 12.3.

The dimensions of structural impacts which create layered systems enforce, by this transition, a degree of complexity with which our cultural patterns cannot cope. The complexity in the upper layers is a functional necessity for the forms of interaction coordinating the different structural modes. We all speak of communication and its role for human development but why is communication so important in our situation? The first reason is that we are forced to cope with new definitions of reality and a new scope of action for which we have no model. The grade of complexity and the speed of development with which we are confronted tend to create fear. We need communication.

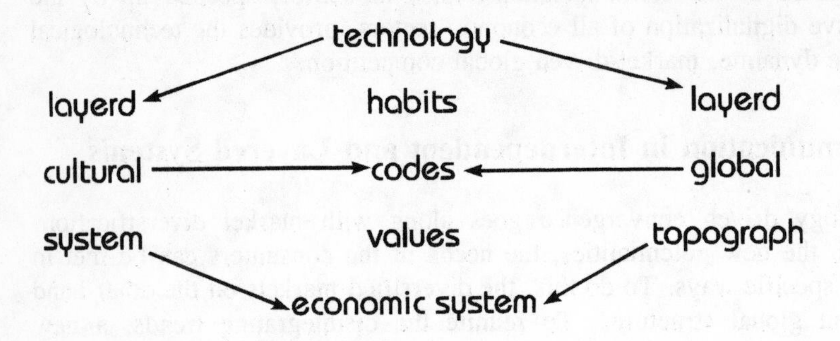

Fig. 12.4. (Source philtec)

The new dimensions of systems development, enforced by:

- global competition in expanding markets for products and services,
- shorter product life-cycles,
- a global financial market working in real-time and
- rising costs for research and development

combine interdependence and competitive challenges. The high frequency of interaction necessary for economic reasons and possible because of the modern communication and transport technologies create a multitude of options that transcend the potentialities of isolated systems. Adequate systems have to be networked systems. Networked systems create virtual organizations to produce the necessary potentials of innovative interaction and to handle the constantly increasing complexity.

12.4 Integral Communications and Virtuality

Increasing complexity needs and breeds improved flexibility. The new dimensions of communication thus propelled are not means in themselves. This communication should be the basis of interaction. Interaction leads to cooperation. In the context of the emerging global economy, communication is not just a means, it is in itself a decisive factor of development. Integral communication uses the diversity of technological possibilities to create an adequate structure to express the need for cooperative interaction. The vision is that this communication could combine the efficiency necessary to cooperate in a highly complex economic development with the responsibility for the changing social and cultural spheres.

The logic of tailored communication structures follows the logic of service customization, but it goes beyond it. The new forms of networked systems deploy virtual networks with the purpose of creating additional capacities, but by doing this they bring about new realms of virtuality. In these new domains of systems development, production and communication are part of one innovative structure of connectivity. This new realm of customised communication-production is a *Learning Organization*. In this organization learning is the cooperative reaction

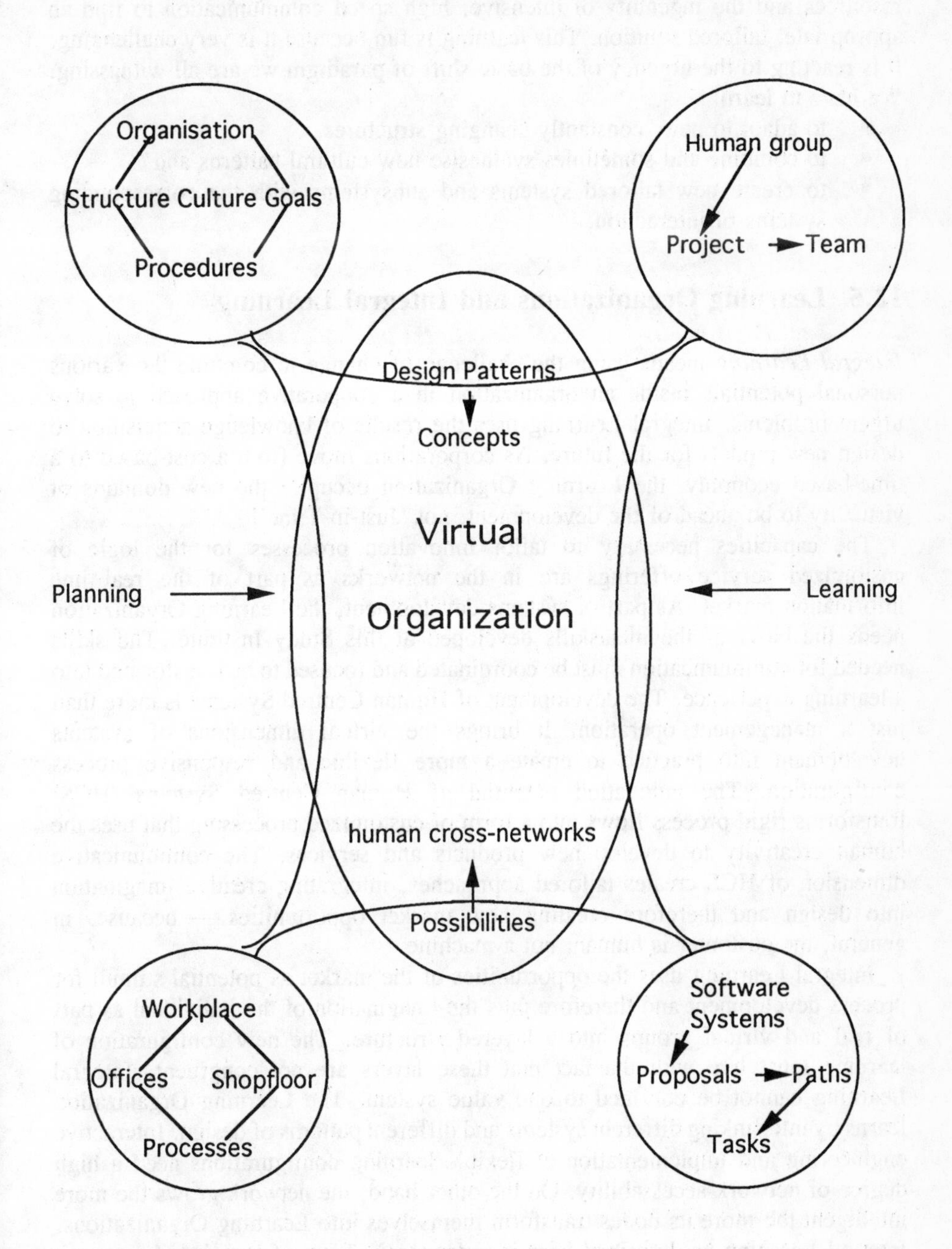

Fig 12.5. (Source philtec)

to the challenges of change. The general orientation is focused on the problem at hand, using knowledge, creativity (that can be learnt!), information, material resources and the ingenuity of intensive, high speed communication to find an appropriate, tailored solution. This learning is fun because it is very challenging. It is reacting to the urgency of the basic shift of paradigm we are all witnessing. We have to learn:

- to adapt to new, constantly changing structures,
- to combine and sometimes synthesise new cultural patterns and
- to create new tailored systems and subsystems with the corresponding systems of interaction.

12.5 Learning Organizations and Integral Learning

Integral Learning means using the challenge of change to combine the various personal potentials inside an organization in a cooperative approach to solve urgent problems. Integral Learning uses the results of knowledge acquisition to design new models for the future. As corporations move from a cost-based to a time-based economy, the Learning Organization occupies the new domains of virtuality to be ahead of the development, not 'Just-in-Time'!

The capacities necessary to tailor innovation processes for the logic of customized service offerings are in the networks as part of the real-time information market. As part of systems development, the Learning Organization needs the basis of the metaskills developed at this Study Institute. The skills needed for communication must be coordinated and focused to be transformed into a learning experience. The development of Human Centred Systems is more than just a management operation. It brings the virtual dimensions of systems development into practice to create a more flexible and responsive process configuration. The innovation potential of Human Centred Systems (HCS) transforms rigid process flows into a form of customized processing that uses the human creativity to develop new products and services. The communicative dimension of HCS creates tailored approaches, integrating creative imagination into design and therefore creating new market opportunities — because, in general, the customer is human, not a machine.

Integral Learning uses the opportunities of the market as potential stimuli for process development and therefore puts the imagination of the individual as part of real and virtual groups into a layered structure. The new configuration of learning must live with the fact that these layers are not congruent. Integral Learning cannot be confined to one value system. The Learning Organization learns by interlinking different systems and different patterns of design. Interactive engineering and implementation of flexible learning configurations need a high degree of network accessability. On the other hand, the network grows the more intelligent the more its nodes transform themselves into Learning Organizations. Integral Learning as described here is a dangerous form of learning, because it only works in the context of real-world virtuality — it is hard to conceive of the normal school as a Learning Organization. This learning puts the security of conventions, the closed circle of all-embracing value systems, the exclusiveness of habits and codes at stake. In a world of real-time access to information and global communication domains, the new learning gives unforeseen opportunities, if the potential of the new spatiotemporal reality that is emerging in front of our eyes is used for the human development.

Bibliography

Gras, A., 1993. 'Grandeur et Dépendance, Sociologie des macro-systèmes techniques', PUF, Paris, 1993.

Sfez, L., 1993. 'La politique symbolique', p.454, PUF, Paris, 1993.

13. Measuring the Cost-Effectiveness of Usability Evaluations

Robbin M. Battison

Nomos Management AB, Stockholm (Note 1)

Abstract. Usability is emerging as the key element in software product quality. The degree of usability greatly influences overall costs and benefits of new software that people are expected to use in their work — especially in industry and business. Usability is measured in terms of performance (effectiveness, productivity, errors, assistance needed) and subjective variables (whether users like what they are using). Several methods of measuring usability are available. One of the most effective is to test representative users performing typical work tasks in a video-equipped usability test lab. Three case studies indicate how costs and benefits of usability engineering can be estimated.

Keywords. usability, ergonomics, human factors, cost-effectiveness, software development, user tasks, usability testing, user testing, productivity, usability engineering, ISO 9241

13.1 Introduction

My aim in this presentation is to examine some of the quantitative issues involved in the human use of computer systems and, in particular, application software (programs that actually do useful work). I will illustrate some of the basic principles and techniques with material from several usability engineering projects. These arguments are intended to demonstrate to industry that usability engineering is a cost-effective way of improving product quality and reducing costs.

Manufacturers and purchasers of complex computer-related systems — whether used in manufacturing, business, financial services or education — have been driven over the years to address the needs of the people who use these tools. The competitive struggle for product quality in this domain is measured against a number of complex dimensions in product use, some of which relate to hardware variables and our human capacity to physically manipulate them. But many relate to information flow and our ability to master and direct work tasks. Others relate to how the tool or system supports a given human organization and task flow.

Within IBM, for example, software quality is not simply determined by examining purely machine-related variables, such as reliability (the availability of the system and its capability of delivering consistent results without errors) and performance (time it takes the system to execute a given task or set of tasks). It is also determined by a number of characteristics relating to the human use of the system to accomplish given tasks: capability (functionality, or what the system allows people to perform), usability, installability, and maintainability, among others.

13.2 What is usability?

Usability is, in a simplified form, the sum of the characteristics that make a product easily understood, easily used, and effective. Since each of these terms varies with the type of population that uses a tool, or may vary from industry to industry, and since 'effectiveness' has different meanings in different organizational contexts, it is clear that usability is situation-specific. (note 2)

Usability is determined by the product's user interface, which in its broadest sense includes more than just the product's method of presenting information to the user and receiving instructions from the user (such as graphic displays, text, keyboards, mouse, voice input, etc.). It includes everything that influences how a user perceives and uses the product, including:

- documentation and online help
- education or training
- user support after training
- the user's experience, knowledge and 'cognitive style'
- the actual work tasks and organizational context

13.3 Why is usability important to individuals and organizations?

Usability is increasingly regarded as one of the most important aspects of product quality, affecting costs of implementation and ultimately affecting whether the system achieves its purpose in an organization. In other words, an otherwise quite usable computer program with an easy-to-understand graphic interface might actually 'fail' if the right training is not provided, or if people try to use it for tasks for which it was not designed or optimized.

What 'fail' means here can vary from organization to organization. It might mean that the organization must double their training time on the new system, with enormous cost consequences. Or it might mean that users will feel unprepared to use the system, and would avoid using it, preferring older, slower, more familiar tools — despite their drawbacks. These and other situations could be judged 'product failures' from the standpoint of the organization that is trying to implement the new system. They can all be avoided with careful planning and usability engineering.

The costs of poor usability are most interesting to examine, since investment decisions hinge on actual costs or perceptions of costs. Some of the costs associated with software products are very well known:

- The development or purchase cost of the program
- The cost of integrating the program with existing computer systems and tools
- The cost of maintaining or servicing the program.

These types of costs are usually very visible and accessible within an organization's cost accounting system, and often within a single department — the department responsible for purchasing, providing, and maintaining computer services. Even here we can note trends that affect usability, since user interfaces account for an increasing proportion of product content (code) and thus development cost: a third to a half of product code may be related to the user interface.

On the other hand, the costs associated with (poor) usability are usually distributed throughout many departments of an organization, and are only now beginning to be identified and quantified. These include the costs of:

- documentation (including 'informal' documentation created by users themselves after receiving the product)
- user support (including the time spent by 'informal' advisors helping their colleagues master a new system)
- users' time (usually the largest cost by far)
- computer-related stress (which affects absences, motivations, attitudes towards work and tools, feelings of self-worth, etc.)
- rework, corrections, and scrap (the cost in labour and materials of correcting mistakes).

A complete usability engineering methodology must be able to take into account these kinds of costs within an organization and show how different types of usability engineering can improve the product or system — and consequently have a favourable impact on these costs.

It is clear that software companies recognize the importance of usability, since they are invoking it in their advertising, and will probably continue to focus on usability throughout the 1990s. It is the competitive edge that users, purchasers, and consumers can increasingly relate to as the 'human variable' in computer usage.

There are other reasons for users and manufacturers to be concerned about usability: standards, regulations and legislation. Here we have manufacturing organizations promoting their own user interface architectures and guidelines as industry standards, and which are adopted, or not, by individual practitioners, groups, and entire organizations.

On a wider stage, EC directive 90/270/EEC has stated a requirement that computer tools have good usability and be adaptable to users' needs, and that they be designed and implemented using software ergonomic principles.

Where will these software ergonomic principles come from? In part they are emerging from the software industry itself, in the form of commonly accepted guidelines backed by available research findings. In part they will be addressed by the international standards being developed as ISO 9241, which covers both hardware and software ergonomic principles. This work is underway and is only partially available in drafts at this time. In addition, several countries are actively addressing the needs for standards in this area, but ISO 9241 is expected to be a 'standard bearer'.

13.4 How to measure and improve usability

There are many different types of methods for evaluating usability, and they are being continually refined due to both advances from the research community and from practising usability engineers. In general they fall into three types, which can be simplified as follows:

User walkthrough — a method for obtaining structured feedback from users at a relatively early stage of design or development. Users are exposed to descriptions of a product, lists of functions, sketches of work flows, pictures of screens or windows, or even a partially functioning prototype (mockup or dummy) in a structured setting. They may be asked to comment on the text, design, or work flow. They may be asked to simulate actual use. Design features and design alternatives can be explored and validated.

Expert review — at any stage of design or development, a usability engineer can judge the appropriateness of a user interface design against a given set of criteria: established guidelines or design principles, pre-established usability goals, or user/task characteristics of a given organizational setting.

Usability test — Given a functioning program and a sample database, a group of representative users can be asked to use the program to accomplish practical tasks that are typical for their organization or field. Interaction can be observed through one-way windows and videotaped in a specially-equipped usability test lab. Other interactions, such as keypresses, mouse movements or references to handbooks can also be observed and recorded. This method is usually supplemented by interviews.

Usability tests are generally regarded to be the best way to evaluate products outside of actual use in the field, since they provide rich sets of data and tend to surface totally unexpected errors based on unanticipated user tasks and reactions.

During a usability test, the following types of measures are usually taken:

- effectiveness — was the task completed correctly?
- productivity — time on task
- need for support — number of times the user sought help or information to complete a task
- acceptance — users' judgments of usability, and how much they enjoy working with the program

Moving from these kinds of test measurements to test findings and recommendations is relatively time-consuming and laborious. Nonetheless it is cost-effective because of the potential gains involved.

The cost effectiveness of usability engineering (or re-engineering in many cases) is a function of several kinds of costs:

- The costs of usability planning and design
- The costs of usability reviews, evaluations and tests that generate findings and recommendations for changes
- The costs of implementing engineering changes and other corrective measures, as well as the costs of their consequences.

Cost-effectiveness also depends upon several kinds of returns or potential gains:

- Increases in productivity or efficiency (more tasks over time, fewer mistakes leading to less rework, less time spent learning, etc.)
- Decreases in expenses (training costs, user support, documentation, etc.)
- Revenue gains (more products sold because they have higher user acceptance and are demonstrably productive and efficient)

Which types of costs and gains are most important will depend on particular organizational contexts, and how particular organizations define and manage product quality.

13.5 Case Studies

Let us now examine three cases where usability testing, in combination with other usability engineering methods, yielded some practical results — as well as the basis for some simple calculations of cost-effectiveness.

Case 1: An administrative application in a medical research and teaching institute

A large medical research and teaching institute had developed a comprehensive computer application (program) that was designed to help staff plan for students, courses, and examinations. It was of strategic importance to the institute's operations. When they installed the program, however, they encountered user resistance to it, and were forced to recall it for rework.

After some considerable rework on the program, they decided to test its usability before actually launching it again (and risking rejection by users). We constructed a set of field interviews and a usability test in our usability test lab to determine whether there were any remaining problems in the application, and whether users would accept the application in its current form.

Three users from the target group were first interviewed and then tested two weeks later. Among these users were those who were most demanding and critical of the application when it was first introduced. We used the interviews to identify problem areas that we could focus the test on.

The results of the test were mixed. Users did like the new system better and judged it to be better and easier to use than the first version of the application that they had experienced. From an organizational point of view, however, their performance was unacceptable. Users completed at best only two-thirds of the tasks correctly using the new application. The test team identified 55 user problems and showed in some specific cases how they were linked to poor interface design and caused poor user performance. The test team recommended that a majority of these problems would have to be corrected before recommending implementation, and advised specific corrections in many cases.

As is often the case in usability testing, many of the problems could have been discovered and identified earlier in the development cycle (and at less cost) by relying on a usability evaluation by an interface expert. Examples of these were inconsistent implementations, misplaced fields, missing instructions and incomplete error messages.

Since the performance results were of such an overwhelming character, no quantitative analysis was performed on the costs involved in re-engineering.

Case 2: A teller system for a national bank

A national bank with 600 branch offices and 1600 tellers (cashiers) had developed and begun installing a new type of PC-based tool to replace their terminal-based system. Since development was continuing on this project even as they installed it in local branch banks, they were interested in knowing answers to the following questions, among others:

- Were there potential usability problems in the new system that would seriously affect user performance (and hence affect the bank's operations)?
- What is the best method for training tellers in the new system? (This national bank had regional training centres with different traditions and different methods).

Rather than taking our video cameras to a local bank office and potentially interfering with bank customers' confidentiality, we constructed a complete bank environment in the test lab. This included a complete teller's desk with computer, printer and other equipment, as well as a supply of bank forms and (play) money.

A total of 8 tellers participated in the usability test, as well as a number of people who played the role of customers. Each teller underwent training in the new system (one of two different methods) and then went through the same 19 financial transactions with these customers. Each test session lasted about 2.5 hours.

As is normal with an untested application, a number of usability problems were revealed. Some transactions were incorrectly recorded, and some teller functions were extremely difficult to use. But in general the system was stable and users were relatively satisfied with it. One unusual finding dealt with the comparison of training methods. Tellers who had undergone the shorter training method performed as well or better than those who had undergone the longer training.

In the quantitative analysis of the results, we made specific engineering recommendations to correct the 62 identified usability problems and recommended they adopt the shorter training method for all their offices. Our estimate of the usability engineering and re-engineering cost was a total of three person-years (including buffer). The potential gain in productivity, decreased errors and corrections, and shorter training method totalled 12 person-years during the first year of implementation alone. Potential gains during following years were not estimated.

We are now in the follow-up phase of this project, and the following items illustrate the potential role of usability engineering in changing both products and organizations:

- The bank instituted a user review council which independently identified additional usability problems in areas which had not been tested.
- The project director indicated that, in her estimation, the usability problems identified during one week of user testing would have taken at least a year of normal field operations to uncover.
- The estimates of re-engineering effort were independently confirmed by the bank's software development team.

Case 3: Military personnel administrative application

Our third example is that of a large application covering administrative and personnel planning for 30,000 military officers and staff. As in case 2, the application was being installed and groups of users had already undergone training. The application had known usability problems, but the client was nonetheless interested in knowing:

- What kinds of problems would a usability test reveal and what impact might these problems have on user performance?
- Was the training program successful and appropriate for two key user groups?

Participants in the test were four civilians employed by the military (all women) and four military officers (all men) who had recently undergone training in the new application. Each group received a set of tasks appropriate to that group; very few tasks were identical. Each test session took 2-3 hours in a simulated office environment in the usability test lab.

Results revealed over 100 usability problems which could in most cases be linked to specific design faults, such as lack of feedback, lack of consistent implementation, inappropriate wording, etc. A post-hoc analysis showed that fully half of these problems could have been identified earlier using an expert review.

The comparative results were also revealing. The two groups used the same interface to perform slightly different tasks, but they differed on rates of successful completion, types of errors, types of assistance necessary, and subjective satisfaction. We thus recommended separate training programs in the future for users who fell into these two categories, and indicated which areas needed to be strengthened.

Our estimate of the usability engineering and re-engineering cost was a total of four person-years (including buffer). The potential gain in productivity, decreased errors and corrections, and less dependence on support totalled 18 person-years during the first year of implementation alone. Potential gains during following years were not estimated.

13.6 Conclusions

Each of the three case studies presented illustrate real-world problems with computer systems which can be solved with usability engineering methods. In each of these cases, product management decisions were made on the basis of usability evaluations using representative users and tasks. In two of the cases, the benefits of making engineering changes exceeded the engineering costs.

Usability evaluations yield tangible results. They may reveal product faults that would cause problems for users. Detecting and correcting them may yield increased product quality and work quality, as well as increased product acceptance and work satisfaction.

When usability faults are identified and corrected at an early stage, before putting the product into the hands of large groups of users, there are several other advantages with usability evaluations:

- The earlier a problem is detected and corrected, the cheaper the solution is.
- The product development team minimizes the risk of later having to rework the product to meet their users' or customers' real needs.
- Those responsible for product development will gain better overall control of project costs, since they will be able to determine in advance, for example, how much effort to put into user documentation, training, and support.

13.7 Why is it so hard to estimate usability costs and benefits?

We have seen how important product usability is to individuals and organizations, as measured on such items as acceptance and productivity, among others. If usability is so important, then everyone should be conducting usability engineering studies. What's so difficult about it?

Apart from the specialized skill that usability engineering requires, there are inherent roadblocks to measuring and improving usability in most organizations:

- Since usability is situation specific, each organization must define its own usability goals and methods. One size does not fit all, although experience can transfer from one situation to another.
- Almost everyone believes in the 'goodness' of usability, but no organization will make an investment in usability engineering unless a business case can be made for that investment.
- Usability costs and potential gains are spread throughout organizations, and may require real detective work to reveal. A given group may have reasons to hide, rather than reveal, their role in overall usability.
- It takes time to reveal real returns on usability engineering investments. It's often a question of estimate now, validate later.
- Part of the real returns are intangible contributions to development processes — better ways of doing things — which themselves have a delayed payoff.

13.8 A closing appeal

What will benefit us all as we move into a more computer-dependent society in the coming decades are more studies showing the effects and costs of usability engineering in actual working situations. Ideally, they should be reported with cost/effort data for:

- usability planning and design
- usability reviews, evaluations and tests
- engineering changes and other corrective measures
- estimates of projected productivity gains
- estimates of projected cost savings
- estimates of projected revenue gains
- followups showing *actual* figures vs. the *estimates* above.

References

1. Nielsen, J.: Usability Engineering. Boston: Academic Press 1993

Notes

1. Much of this work was conducted while the author was manager of Usability Engineering, IBM Nordic, and the author gratefully acknowledges support from NATO, IBM Nordic, and Nomos Management for making this contribution possible.

2. Usability in the software domain is a fascinatingly complex topic, and this short article cannot give a complete accounting of this field. The interested reader should consult one of the many textbooks that have recently appeared in this field, such as that by Nielsen [1].

14. User-Centred Design and the Theory Building View

Roy D. McKelvey

Department of Design, Carnegie Mellon University, Pittsburgh, PA 15213, USA

Abstract. The methodologies by which software systems are developed have undergone an evolution from those aimed at supporting the needs of implementation to those which focus on the experiences of end use. An overview of user-centered design and particularly the area of participatory design is outlined. This is used as a basis for considering Naur's[8] notions of software development and maintenance as 'theory building' as it affects the roles of interdisciplinary design teams. In particular, the notion of a 'theory' of a system design is considered as an extension of Naur's discussions of theory-building in programming practice.

Keywords. software development, interdisciplinary design teams, participatory design

14.1 Introduction

As a field, the area of human-computer interaction is barely 20 years old. In that time, the proportion of a software system devoted to issues of user-interaction has steadily increased, to a point where today, in many applications, the interface code may account for approximately half of the total program. This increase may be attributable to many factors, but it clearly indicates a growing understanding that issues related to fitting a software technology to human use are becoming as important to a system's success as considerations of underlying features and computational efficiency.

In accordance with the emphasis now put on the issues of interaction and man-machine communication, the development of software programs has become the concern of an increasing number of disciplines. To account for the growing number of concerns that now surround the design and development of software products, it has been necessary to
substantially modify the methods by which they have been traditionally produced. Because programming and software design originated as adjunct disciplines of the sciences and engineering, the process of designing and evaluating software

systems has reflected their traditions of emphasizing objectivity and valuing the generalized over the situation specific.
As software systems are increasingly designed with the aim of providing highly interactive environments for an ever-broadening array of users, it has become clear that the issues that will ultimately determine the worth of a program cannot be captured by traditional objective methods. It is also apparent that while generalizeable results may contribute to technological development and the advancement of theory, they provide little insight into designing complex environments for particular user groups.

14.2 User-centered design and design methods

In response to this situation, there has emerged a broader approach to developing software which attempts to account for all aspects of system design from a common perspective. Usually referred to as 'user-centered design,' this approach advocates a highly integrated process of developing software systems, carried out by interdisciplinary teams representing a wide range of expertise. The approach also assumes that a significant role in system design must be played by the potential users of the technology, who hold important information about the work practices that technology intends to augment or replace.
User-centered design has its origins in Scandinavia where it arose primarily to address the social concerns raised by the introduction of automated and semi-automated technologies which threatened to displace high numbers of workers, and in some cases, destroy entire professions. The Scandinavian approach[1] is a method that has as its basis the particular cultural milieu of the Scandinavian countries. Floyd et. al.[5] describe the Scandinavian social outlook on work and quality of life:

> 'An essential feature of Scandinavia is, above all, what appears to outsiders as a far-reaching and widely supported fundamental concern with the building and development of a society in which each individual may live in dignity and in conditions conducive to personal development. This means that, despite existing conflicts of interest, different social groups appear to be pledged to this common goal. A keen endeavour is perceptible to make optimal use of existing material resources, devoting great care to the question of design, in order to achieve a high degree of quality. The combined skills of all members of the society are considered necessary to attain this overriding objective.'

The term "Scandinavian approach" has arisen as a convenient way to broadly characterize a socially conscious attitude towards developing technologies that is most evident in the Scandinavian countries. It is pointed out by Floyd et.al[5]. that the philosophical positions attributed to the Scandinavian approach are evidenced in other cultures, and that within the Scandinavian countries themselves there are a considerable variety of methods lumped into this single catch phrase. Nonetheless, the term has proven useful as a comparative term with other more techno-centric approaches to product development.

The Scandinavian approach has gained steadily in influence over the past several years, especially in the area of human-computer interface design but often in a somewhat transmuted form. While the socio-cultural setting of many counties precludes the easy adoption of the Scandinavian philosophy towards work and personal development, the design methods that were developed by the Scandinavians to realize their vision have travelled relatively well. This design methodology has come to be known as 'participatory design,(PD)' and is characterized by the desire to develop and maintain close contact between developers and user groups[1,3,5]. The participatory design approach acknowledges that all the information needed to develop new technologies cannot be known at the beginning of a project. Instead, design must evolve through a process of mutual learning in both developer and user communities[10]. The emphasis is on

> 'the development of a *shared understanding* of the goals, roadblocks, and accomplishments possible with the new technology.'[9]

The participatory method has been characterized as consisting of six essential components in a paper by Jeanette Blomberg and Austin Henderson[2]. Their analysis provides a good check list of its main themes:

1. Establishment of a common criteria for evaluating the success of a given design by both the developers and users of the technology.
2. Strengthening the character of user-developer interaction — this implies intimate contact between developers and user *in the context of the workplace in which the technology will ultimately be employed.*
3. An aim to improve the quality of work life, to balance the advantages of new technological possibilities with the traditional work practices and skills of the user community — in PD there is a recognition that new technologies may fail for reasons completely independent of the system design or its technological sophistication.
4. Creating organizational structures that support collaboration. This implies the existence of design/development teams representing multidisciplinary skill sets and full participation by users. Participatory design cannot be accomplished without an acknowledgment of the need of on-going and close contact between these groups.
5. Supporting mutual appreciation of each group member's various competencies and ensuring that each perspective is given adequate reflection in the decision making process.
6. Emphasizing design as an iterative process where there is continual negotiation between a wide variety of contingencies related to the problem at hand. This includes technological constraints, communication issues at the interface, work practice issues, and the evolving nature of these concerns over time.

The vision of system design and development that emerges in this approach poses significant challenges to those charged with managing new product development and to those who participate in the team design processes that are required to make it work. Traditional methods of computer programming and software development are having to be considerably rethought so as to allow the flexibility and richness of interaction required by participatory design. The new methods that are emerging emphasize software engineering as a process of *design*. This approach is put forth by Christiane Floyd[6]:

> 'As I see it, software development is, first and foremost, a specific instance of *design*. By design I understand the creative process in the course of which the problem as a whole is grasped, and an appropriate solution worked out and fitted into human contexts of meaning....Software development is an activity of overall design with an experimental attitude.
>
> By design, we mean a specific type of insight-building process that is geared to producing feasible and desirable results within a particular domain. The domains in question may differ widely. We normally only speak of design when there are concerns we wish to fulfil, limited resources at our disposal, and different implementation options to us.'

The choice of the word 'experimental' here is crucial in understanding how software engineering differs from the other engineering disciplines. The nature of designing software is determined by the fact that software is a fundamentally different kind of product from those produced by processes of construction or manufacture:

- In software the means of specification and analysis of a product is the same by which it will ultimately become manifest—through the generation of computer code — to all intents and purposes, the division between specification and production so common to other areas of design is virtually non-existent.
- Programs are inherently complex; it is an observable fact that few, if any, programs of any size can be understood in advance and implemented without significant adjustment.
- Software is made up of an 'abstract' material that is, in theory, infinitely modifiable. This potential for change results in software products going through numerous mutations and extensions throughout their life.

The notion of programming as a process where various things are 'tried out' and evaluated in use describes, at some level, the software development process as it has always occurred. Programming is a process where code is developed, compiled and run to see if it functions as anticipated. In the traditional coding scenario, the programmer *is* the user. A user-centered approach to system development adopts a similar, but broader view of this notion of experimentation. The system design is seen as an experimental apparatus which reflects the current understanding of the technology and its relationship to the concerns of its users. The system, in this case, is developed, given form and used to see if it functions as anticipated. Technical functionality, in this expanded view, is seen as just one aspect of the larger problem.

In terms of design methods, user-centered design requires an approach that supports iteration not only as it pertains to questions of implementation, but also to questions of assessing requirements and monitoring their evolution as various implementation options are tried out by users. A model of software which supports this degree of flexibility in data gathering and experimentation in implementing systems is known as a 'spiral' model. The spiral model is put forward in contrast to the more traditional approach to engineering design, often called a 'waterfall' model. The waterfall model, envisions the design and development process as a series of independent and sequential phases. Sometimes referred to as the 'product view' of software development[4], this approach begins by assuming that some need exists 'out in the world' that will benefit from the development of a certain software package. These needs, it is assumed, can be analyzed and formulated with enough precision such that a set of requirements for the end product can be produced. The requirements are then used to generate a set of specifications which describe attributes and performance criteria that the final product must meet to satisfy the requirements. At this point, a design phase ensues, in which the software, user interface and documentation are produced. Termination of the process is signalled when all of the specifications have been met in some form or another. The design of the user interaction in this approach is often left as a final and separate design problem, one of putting a 'good face' on the technology. The users of the resulting system are expected to adapt to it by a process of training and adjustment of work practice.

The spiral model of system development captures the notion that all phases of the design and implementation activity are in some sense 'mutually informing.' The model assumes that while the various steps that must be taken in order to proceed with the development process occur in some sequence, they are not isolated activities and further, they are likely to be revisited several times during the life of the project. A useful illustration of the spiral model is offered by Austin Henderson[7] in which he breaks down the development process into five distinct areas of activity and characterizes the products that emerge from each phase. The Henderson model is pictured below.

Unlike the linear model, the spiral model allows for repeated analysis of the product in use *as it is being developed.* More importantly, it acknowledges the role that user's growing experience plays in arriving at an appropriate understanding of the technology in question. The Henderson model, it should be pointed out, while getting at the heart of user-centered design principles, does not necessarily represent a process of participatory design. Whether the design method is or is not participatory rests on the question of who is engaged in the activities at each node, and who is empowered to make the important decisions as to how data will be gathered, interpreted and acted upon. For example, it is critical in a PD process that observation happen at the place of work, and that the results of that observation, in the form of say a videotape, are analyzed by all of the team members including users.

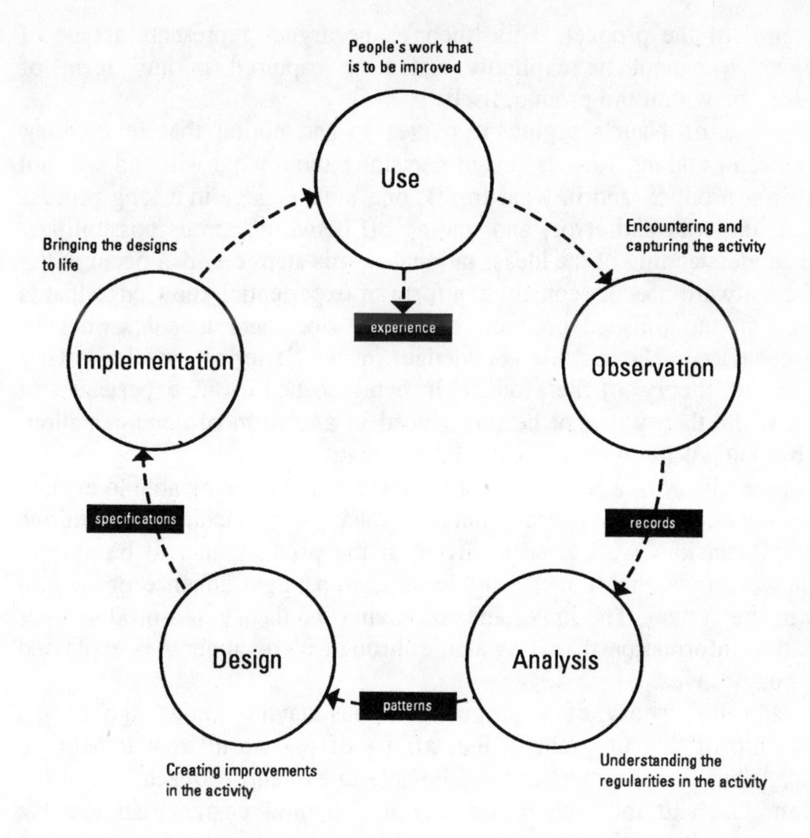

Fig. 14.1. Henderson's representation of the activities and outputs of the development process

14.3 The notion of 'theory building'

Leaving the issue of design methods for a moment, I will now turn to an aspect of software development and production that must be considered in any large-scale programming project: managing the evolution and maintenance of the product. Unlike most products, the design of a software package is not seen as necessarily finalized when it goes into production and distribution. Software products are constantly being revised, extended and debugged as information is gathered from the user community, or as the environments in which they run evolve (e.g. new hardware platforms or processors are introduced). The need to constantly evolve and redesign software products implies that the knowledge of their design must persist in some form for the entire life of the product. Interesting questions about how such knowledge can be captured and maintained over time have been raised by Peter Naur in his paper, 'Programming as Theory Building'[8]. In this paper, Naur proposes that 'design knowledge,' of a product, i.e. the know-how that allows one to efficiently and confidently modify or extend a design constitutes a kind of 'theory' of the product. This 'theory', he argues represents a type of knowledge which cannot be explicitly stated or captured in any form of documentation, or within the product itself.

The essence of Naur's argument relates to the notion that in creating something new, in making various design decisions about what will and will not be included in a product (and in what form), one must engage in a long process of familiarization, trial and error, and trading off between various possibilities. The intimate understanding of the ideas, rationales, mis-steps etc. that occur in the creation of a software product constitute a form of experiential knowledge that is not expressed in the finished product, or in any document that describes its features or behaviour. Having this knowledge, in Naur's terms, implies having possession of the 'theory' of the product. In being so tied to the experiences of human beings, the theory cannot be reproduced in any form of documentation, and therefore cannot live independently of its creators.

Having the theory of a software design means not only being able to explain the results of the development process, but also to have an immediate and intuitive grasp of what decisions were used to arrive at the product, and to be able to anticipate how various alterations to the basic design might enhance or corrupt other parts of the system. The importance of having the theory of a product over having just that information that is available through its documents is explained from three perspectives:

1. Possessing the theory of a program implies having knowledge of the relationship of that program to the 'affairs of the world' that it helps to handle. 'Thus the programmer must be able to explain, for each part of the program text and for each of its overall structural characteristics, what aspect or activity of the world is matched by it. Conversely, for any aspect or activity of the world, the programmer is able to state its manner of mapping into the program text[8].' Having the theory then, means having a sense of not only what aspect of the world has been included in the product, but also what aspects have been rejected, and why.
2. The actual design of the product, the relationship of one form to another, or of one action to another can be explained as to why it is the way it is, to justify it in some form or other. 'The final basis of the justification is and must always remain the programmer's direct, intuitive knowledge or estimate. This holds even where the justification makes use of reasoning, perhaps with application of design rules, quantitative estimates, comparisons with alternatives, and such like, the point being that the choice of the principles and rules, and the decision that they are relevant to the situation at hand, again must in the final analysis remain a matter of the programmer's direct knowledge[8].'
3. The programmer having the theory is able to respond constructively to any demand for a modification of the program so as to support new or changing affairs in the world. 'Designing how a modification is best incorporated into an established program depends on the perception of the similarity of the new demand with the operational facilities already built into the program.

> The kind of similarity that has to be perceived is one between aspects of the world. It only makes sense to the agent who has knowledge of the world, that is to the programmer...[8]' Armed with the theory then, a programmer can alter the program quickly and with little damage to its existing constructs.

Naur's stated motivation for proposing the theory building view of software development is that it provides significant insight into issues relating to the modification of software. He echoes Floyd's view of software development as a process of design, where system requirements are always in some state of evolution:

> "It is invariably the case that a program, once in operation, will be felt to be only part of the answer to the problems at hand. Also, the very use of the program itself will inspire ideas for further useful services that the program ought to provide[8]."

Naur suggests that the theory building view of programming points out some of the most glaring contradictions between traditional software engineering theory and practice. The reasons for this seem to stem from the attempt to consider programming as some objective science and to 'factor out' the role that individual programmers play in the production and maintenance of system designs. Naur points out three areas of software development where the theory building view may have something to offer over traditional software engineering practice:

1. *Modifiability and Cost.* One of the most fundamental concerns of the software engineering enterprise has been to find ways in which software design can be optimized for extendibility. The fact that code will eventually be reused and modified is well understood. Modular programming and various documentation schemes have been forwarded as a means to allow easy and non-destructive alteration to a software program by anyone who studies the program documents closely enough. The insufficiency of these texts to impart an understanding of the design rationale of the program is a fundamental assertion of the theory building view. Modification, it is argued, is a fairly simple matter for the 'theory holders,' but a costly and potentially destructive task for those outside of the project.

2. *Flexibility.* Another fundamental principle of software design methodology is to devise data structures, procedures, and functions that allow for the greatest flexibility of use—to 'build into the program certain operational facilities that are not immediately demanded, but which are likely to turn out to be useful.' To anticipate what will and will not be relevant in the future is not an easy thing to do. As Naur explains, 'Such advice may be reasonable as far as flexibility that can be easily achieved is concerned. However, flexibility can in general only be achieved at a substantial cost. Each item of it has to be designed...implemented, tested and described.' The flexibility that is hoped for by software developers depends upon their ability to impart into the code the necessary information as to when and how it can be extended or modified. 'What is needed in a modification, first of all, is a confrontation of the existing solution with the demands called for by the desired modification. In this confrontation, the degree and kind of

similarity between the capabilities of the existing solution and the new demands has to be determined[8].'

3. *Decay, Death and Revival.* Perhaps the most intriguing and surprising claim for the theory building view is its relationship to program longevity. Since the key information required for modifying a program resides with the developers, it follows that they, and only they, are capable of successfully carrying out its evolution. Naur claims that the modification of a program by those who are not in possession of its theory will inevitably result in its decay— it will lose in simplicity, internal logic and overall performance. The metaphor of decay is extended to considerations of life, death and resurrection: the death of a program results when the programmer team possessing its theory is dissolved; a dead program can remain functional only until it must be modified; a program may be revived by the rebuilding of its theory by a new programming team, but 'the re-establishment of the theory of a program merely from the documentation, is strictly impossible'; the extended life of a program 'depends on the taking over by new generations of programmers of the theory of the program' which can only be obtained from close contact with other 'theory holders.'

Naur's presentation of the theory building view is clearly couched in the issues and practices of computer programming, and the examples he provides are concerned primarily with issues of creating and modifying computer code. In the next section, I would like to return to the question of user-centered design and briefly consider how Naur's theory-building view might be of importance to an interdisciplinary process of designing software with users.

14.4 Theory building and user-centered design

The development of a software system or environment is a large task, involving expertise in many areas beyond those related to the actual coding. The range of tasks indicated in the Henderson diagram clearly make room for the involvement of software engineers, psychologists, social scientists, designers, and users to name a few. The decisions that go into generating requirements for the system, determining what data to gather and how to analyze it, and giving form to the interface and to the underlying technology are all interdependent and equally necessary in a user-centered design process. These decisions are subject to the same evolutionary forces that are assumed in Naur's description of the programming process, and constitute a form of experiential knowledge that exists in individual team members and in some sense 'in-between' them. That is, certain decisions are taken which respond to constraints (or possibilities) that arise from more than one judgment criteria. These trade-offs, or compromises form an essential part of the system design 'theory', but they may not necessarily be wholly held by any one individual team member.

For example, consider the design of the user interface to a system. The interface is where the mapping of system function to the areas of concern that the software addresses is most apparent. The interface is subject to a wide range of concerns:

1) it should express the full power of the technology that it delivers to the user
2) it should be presented in such a way that it is intelligible, pleasing and efficient
3) it should provide users with a tool that improves their situation — i.e. it allows them to get his job done and accounts for the realities of its use context.

The 'theory' of the interface then, involves an accounting of the following areas of knowledge and their interdependency: observational data and task analysis that is derived from the study of the user and his or her environment; the design and development of data structures, procedures and functions that constitute the 'guts' of the system; the constraints imposed by the computing environment on which the system is implemented, including hardware limitations such as processing speed and screen resolution and software-related constraints related to programming tool kits such as user-interface management systems (UIMS); and the 'information design' decisions that constitute the graphic design of the interface. Given this complexity, it is hard to imagine that anyone would argue for the possibility of capturing the critical design information about the system in documentation. Modification and maintenance of the system clearly involves many facets of a 'system theory,' and the participation of many.

The practical importance of the theory building view is what it implies for those who manage the software development process, and those that participate in interdisciplinary design of software products. Most software products are designed with the idea that they will persist in the marketplace for years, and will do so by continually evolving in response to changes in computing environments and to improved understandings of the areas of activity that they intend to support. The theory building view argues persuasively, that software development teams need to ideally persist as long as the product is in active use, providing a continual maintenance/redesign function. The 'theory' of a complex system must express not only the particular decisions made by team members that reflect their distinct areas of responsibility, but also the interdependence of these decisions and their combined effect on the finished product.

That the theory of a system design, on which its future seems so dependent, can only be constituted by the team as a whole implies new ways of working for team members who may be accustomed to contributing to a project at very specific times, and only with regard to a well-defined aspect of the problem . The designer, the ethnographer, or the programmer may no longer be able to work as independent contributors to various projects, but may become permanent custodians to certain products, marshalling them through various phases of development, and managing their transformation into new product lines.

References

1 Bjerknes, G., Ehn, P., and Kyng, M.: Computers and Democracy — A Scandinavian Challenge: Aldershot, England: Avebury 1987
2 Blomberg, J., and Henderson, A.: Reflections on Participatory Design: Lessons from the Trillium Experience. Proc. CHI '90 Human Factors in Computing Systems pp.353-360. New York: ACM Press 1990
3 Clement, A., and Van den Besselaar, P.: A Retrospective Look at PD Projects. Communications of the ACM v. 36, no. 4, pp. 29-37. New York: ACM Press 1993
4 Floyd, C.: Outline of a Paradigm Change in Software Engineering. In: Computers and Democracy—A Scandanavian Challenge (G. Bjerknes, P. Ehn, and M. Kyng, Eds.). pp. 191-210. Aldershot, England: Avebury 1987.
5 Floyd, C., Mehl, W., Reisin, F., Schmidt, G., and Wolf, G.: Out of Scandinavia: Alternative Approaches to Software Design and System Development. Human Computer Interaction v. 4, pp. 253-350. Hillsdale, New Jersey: Lawrence Erlbaum Associates 1990.
6 Floyd, C.: Software Development as Reality Construction. In: Software Development and Reality Construction (C. Floyd, H. Züllighoven, R. Budde, R. Keil-Slawik, Eds.) pp. 86-100. Berlin: Springer-Verlag 1992.
7 Henderson, A.: A Development Perspective on Interface, Design, and Theory. In: Designing Interaction (J.Carroll Ed.). Cambridge Series on Human-Computer Interaction, pp.254-268.Cambridge, Cambridge University Press 1991.
8 Naur, P.: Programming as Theory Building. Proc. EuroMicro '84, Advances in Microprocessing and Microprogramming v. 15. pp. 253-261. Amsterdam: North-Holland 1984.
9 Piela, P., Katzenburg, B., and McKelvey, R.: Integrating the User into Research on Engineering Design Systems. Research in Engineering Design v. 3, pp. 211-221. New York: Springer-Verlag 1992
10 Thoreson, K.: Experiences with Participatory Design. Proc. PDC '90: Participatory Design Conference (A. Namioka, D. Schuler, Eds.). pp.34-35. Seattle, WA, 1990.

15. How Human-Centred is the Quality Philosophy?

Jeremy A. Klein

The Generics Group, Kings Court, Kirkwood Road, Cambridge, CB4 2PF, England

Abstract. Does the drive towards total quality encourage or discourage human-centred systems? The answer to this question lies in the concept of quality being pursued; traditional concepts can impede human-centred production. A post-Fordist quality concept is proposed which acknowledges the heterogeneity of markets. This quality concept implies that 'fitness for purpose' is only possible for a company if its marketing system is also human-centred.

Keywords. quality, quality philosophy, position of humans, total quality, meta skills, core competencies

15.1 Introduction

Few people now advocate Taylor's scientific management or Ford's blueprint for mass production: new business philosophies have replaced them. Yet despite this change in philosophy, humans are still in second place in most production systems. Indeed, human-centred production is not even on the agenda for the majority of industry. Why is the legacy of Taylorism and Fordism so deep that human-centred thinking is still marginalised?

The total quality philosophy is an example of a popular business ethos which might have been expected to lead to greater human-centredness. In this paper we shall show how its interpretation, far from bringing forward human-centred systems, can lead directly into Fordist thinking. The current interest in core competences as an engine of corporate success may, however, act as a catalyst for change.

15.2 Quality

15.2.1 The Paradox

Though advocates of human-centred systems claim improved quality, and though 'Quality' is an increasingly influential business philosophy, the drive for quality has not led to a corresponding drive towards human-centred production.

To understand why this is, it is necessary to trace how the quality philosophy is interpreted in the Fordist framework.

15.2.2 The Fordist Interpretation of Quality

The most common understanding of quality is 'fitness for purpose', but numerous other variants exist, each associated with a with a different author, including 'fitness for use' (Juran) and 'conformance to requirements' (Crosby).

In the Fordist framework, it is not feasible to ask every customer what his or her purpose is. Accordingly, a surrogate is used — a 'product specification'. The customers who will want products with this specification are grouped together and called a 'market segment'.

In this scheme, the quality issue is one of 'conformance to specification'. Provided the product conforms, it is by definition a quality product. The enemy of conformity is variability, so variability must be eliminated. And since humans produce variability, they must be eliminated from the production system. Though this is paraphrased, it represents the dominant mode of thought in industry, and is still implicit in the majority of business literature.

What is not so well understood is that this interpretation of quality contains a major compromise. By substituting a product specification for fitness for purpose, the distinct needs of individual customers are subjugated. The compromise is rarely made explicit, however, because of the language and concepts in use.

For example, the concept of a market segment is universal: market segments exist where collections of customers appear to have similar product requirements. However, market segments do not exist in reality. Markets are collections of individuals which are conveniently *approximated* by market segments. In the standard textbooks, the concept of market segmentation is normally presented as a literal truth.

A related marketing concept is globalisation. In the 1980s, the marketing guru Theodore Levitt wrote that:

"a powerful force drives the world towards a converging commonality" (Levitt, 1983),

and suggested that the future would see global products for global markets. It is little wonder that with such concepts of markets and quality the Fordist view persists.

The Fordist legacy also affects customers. Arguably, customers themselves have been educated to value standardisation as if they, too, saw themselves in terms of segments. And because many production systems and marketing systems cannot cope with anything else, the Fordist mode of production still dominates management thinking. Thus the 'quality' message has no impact on the human-centredness of production.

15.2.3 Towards a Post-Fordist view: the Economics of Variety

One of the barriers to change is the production centred approach to variety. The linkages *Taylor ... Ford ... mass production ... low variety*, and *Post-Fordism ... small batch production ... high variety* are well rehearsed. Taking a micro-economic view, the maximum degree of variety a firm should contemplate is indicated by the intersection of the cost of variety and the price realised for it, as illustrated in Fig. 15.1.

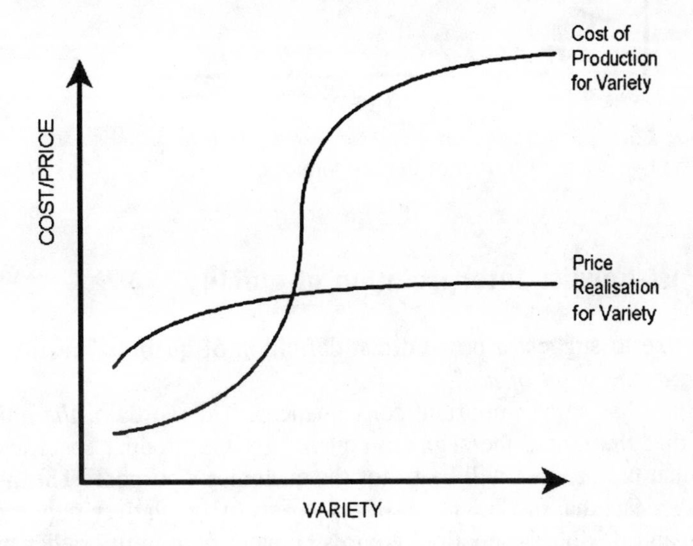

Fig. 15.1. Price versus cost

To the left of the intersection, the realised price is higher than the cost of production: the firm makes a profit. To the right of the intersection, the cost of variety outweighs the price realised for it.

The majority of HCI and FMS literature focuses on reducing the cost of variety. This emphasis is misguided, however, since there are two ways to influence the economics of variety. Either the cost of variety can be reduced *or* the price realised for variety can be raised. These two options are shown in Fig. 15.2.

Taking the option of raising the realised price for variety necessitates a post-Fordist definition of quality, and a new perspective on marketing.

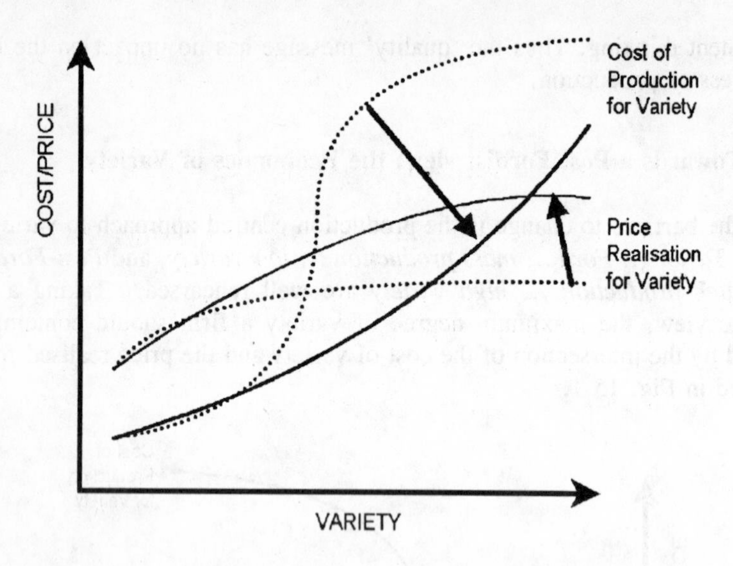

Fig. 15.2 The two ways to influence the economics of variety

15.3 A Post-Fordist Interpretation of Quality?

We would like to suggest a post-Fordist definition of quality: "quality is fitness for purpose *at the point of use*".

This definition has some important consequences. The words *at the point of use* remind us that the larger the segment covered by the product specification, the less likely that the product will be fit for the customer's purpose. This alternative definition suggests that the key to quality is variety. High variety requires flexible production, and flexible production requires humans. Variability rather than being a problem is a virtue.

This view of quality requires a high price realisation for variety, which can be achieved using a *flexible marketing system* and re-educating customers to value customisation over standardisation.

We have experimented in the Generics Group with flexible marketing systems. These have a short chain from production to consumption, a blurred boundary with production, a rich and unconstrained dialogue with customers, and an ability to respond quickly to change. It is interesting to note that these are not generally characteristics of computer systems.

By contrast, the symptoms of inflexible marketing systems are easily encouraged by the use of computers. Using the familiar "4Ps of marketing", typical symptoms are shown below:

Marketing Variable	Typical Symptom
Product	Product choice made using too few variables or unsophisticated decision rules
Price	Rigid discount structure
Promotion	Unselective use of mailing lists
Place	Mechanistic delivery schedule.

15.4 Levers for Change: Corporate Skills and Competences

The concept of human-centredness relates to another current theme in strategy: corporate skills and competences. A skill or competence, as illustrated in Fig. 15.3, is a systemic property involving skilled people, capital resources and organisational culture.

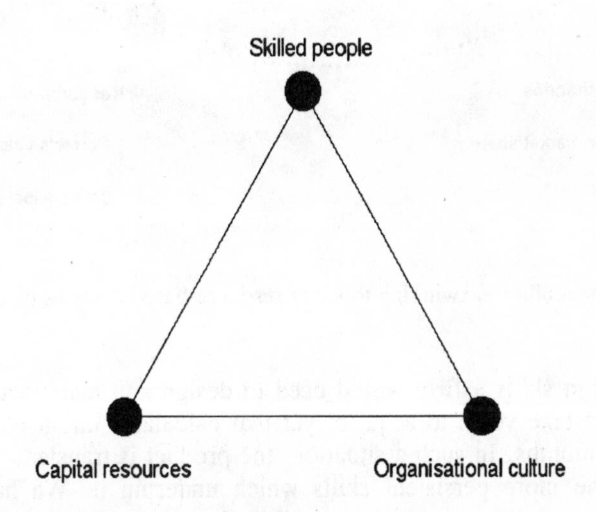

Fig. 15.3. The components of a corporate competence or skill

There has been a swing in recent years towards resource based theories of competition. In the 1970s corporate success was interpreted more in terms of market factors than resources. Market share, in particular, was seen as a determinant of success: this belief was immortalised in the Boston Consulting Group's matrix of relative market share versus market growth. The pendulum still appears to be moving in the direction of resource-based theories (Fig. 15.4).

The swing towards resource analysis was led by Prahalad and Hamel (1990), and has stimulated a great deal of interest worldwide. One of the reasons is that in many industries, particularly technological ones, product life cycles are becoming shorter whereas skill lifecycles are becoming longer. For example, the

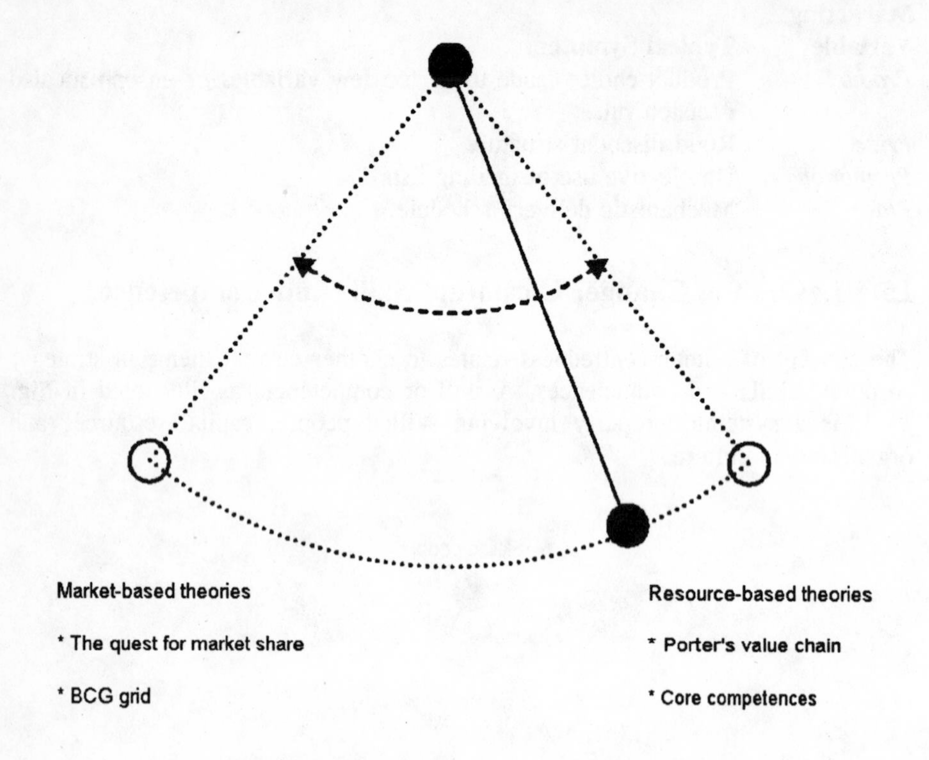

Fig. 15.4. The pendulum is swinging towards resource-based theories of competition

electronics design skills a firm would need to design and manufacture a pocket calculator could take years to acquire; yet that calculator might only be on the market for six months. In such a situation, the product is transient compared to the more persistent skills which underpin it. We have found it effective to conceptualise inter-firm competition here in terms of skills rather than products (Fig. 15.5).

It was suggested in an earlier paper (Klein, Edge and Kass, 1991) that a two stage approach to skills could be taken, whereby a special class of skills called 'metaskills' govern the way in which a firm acquires and deploys skills. The paper asserted that at least four fundamental metaskills exist: learning, innovating, skill categorising and embedding. This approach therefore implies a layered model in which the flow of causality is as shown in Figure 6.

More generally, firms can be seen in their environment as layers of attributes. (The term 'attribute' includes all layers of the diagram - skills, metaskills, products, etc). Each layer affects the behaviour of the next layer in the chain. For example, metaskills affect the way in which skills are acquired. There are additional inputs into each layer, so a firm's metaskills do not determine absolutely the skills it will have, but they do

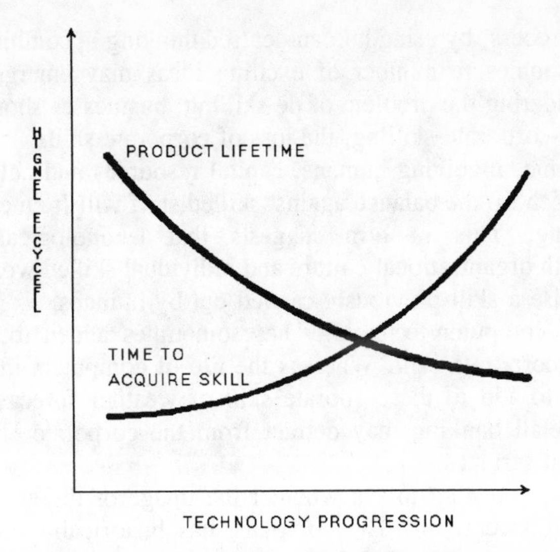

Fig. 15.5 Skill lifecycles frequently dominate product lifecycles

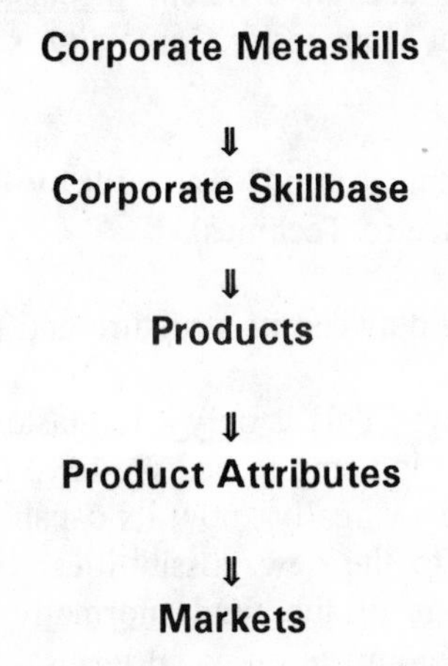

Fig. 15.6 The layered flow of causality

determine the way in which the firm will behave if a management decision to acquire a particular new skill is made.

15.5 Conclusions

We have suggested in this paper that it is not enough to view human-centredness from a production perspective. It is necessary to address marketing systems, quality systems, and strategy with human-centred thinking, and this may involve challenging some of the accepted constructs of business theory.

Out of this process, by using human-centred thinking in combination with other business philosophies, a number of exciting ideas may emerge. For example, instead of considering the problem of de-skilling, businesses should be looking at the threat of de-corporate-skilling: the loss of corporate skills. Because corporate skills are systemic, involving humans, capital resources and culture, technology investments which tip the balance against skilled staff will frequently result in de-corporate-skilling. This in turn suggests that technological systems must complement both organisational culture and individual skilled workers rather than merely mechanise a skill previously carried out by humans.

Empirically, computer technology has sometimes added to, and sometimes detracted from corporate skill. Whereas the use of computers in a meterological office is likely to add to the corporate skill of weather forecasting, the use of computers in retail banking may detract from the corporate skill of providing tailored financial services.

Finally, it is interesting to ask whether the image of the computer is itself a barrier to anthropocentrism. The computer has historically been presented in anthropomorphic terms. The first newspaper reports of the Manchester computer illustrates the point (Times, 1949), with the anthropomorphic terms underlined.

> Experiments ... to produce an efficient mechanical "brain" have been successfully completed at Manchester University, where a workable "brain" has been evolved.
>
> The Manchester "mechanical mind" was built by Professor F C Williams, of the Department of Electro-Technics.
>
> There is a close analogy between its structure and that of the human brain.
>
> Mr Turing said yesterday: "This is only a foretaste of what is to come, and only the shadow of what is going to be. We have to have some experience with the machine before we really know its capabilities. It may take years before we settle down to the new possibilities, but I do not see why it should not enter any one of the fields normally covered by the human intellect, and eventually compete on equal terms".

References

1. Levitt, T. (1983) The Globalisation of Markets. Harvard Business Review, 61(3), 92-102.
2. Klein, J. A., Edge, G. M. and Kass, T. (1991) Skill-based Competition. Journal of General Management, 16, 1-15.
3. Prahalad, C. K. and Hamel, G. (1990) The core competence of the corporation. Harvard Business Review, 90, 79-93.
4. Times (1949) The Mechanical Brain. June 11.

16. Multimedia Technology

Frank Ainscow

Interfacing Ltd. Engineering Design Consultancy, Ravenswood, Park Road, Winchester, Hants, SO22 6AA, UK

Abstract. Whenever there is collaboration to achieve an agreed goal, there is an evident need for the exchange of information amongst the participants; in the context of people and computers, the use of multimedia suggests itself for that purpose. The extension of computer applications to make use of multimedia has become widespread and highly commercialised in recent years and months, and there is a degree of misconception concerning the applicability and capability of the technology.

This paper seeks to identify the main technological components of multimedia, to place them in context with other aspects of computer technology and to give an up-to-date assessment of the state of the art in each area. Where possible, trends are identified, and likely future developments are forecast.

The author has spent most of his professional life working with the technology of human/machine interaction, and takes the opportunity to present a personal view of the nature and goals of this aspect of technology.

Keywords. Information, communication, technology, media, multimedia, visual, audio, aural, tactile, interfacing

16.1 Questions and Definitions

In a strictly one-way medium such as text, the writer must attempt to guess what questions are in the mind of the reader. In the present case, the central questions are taken to be: what is (are?) multimedia – what is it for, why do we need it, and how is it different from other branches of computer technology? Secondly, how are requirements likely to evolve as users begin to understand the potential and find productive uses; and in the light of that, what strategy should multimedia suppliers and users adopt to benefit from its development?

The factor that gives us the ability to analyse the application of multimedia is the realisation – blindingly obvious in retrospect, but often overlooked – that multimedia is all about communication. That is to say, the purpose of what we call multimedia is entirely contained within the activities that we group together as communication. This is really a matter of definition: the media of which we have a multiplicity are in fact communication media, and we use several of them in the hope of achieving better communication than if we used only one. In a sense, using this name is a bit like calling a small radio broadcast receiver a transistor — we are identifying a function by referring to the particular means by which it is performed. No harm in bending words this way, so long as everyone knows what they mean.

So far, we have only a partial definition. To narrow it down to a precise one, we need to introduce two further ideas. First, in the present context at least, we are talking about an aspect of computer technology, and by inference, only those kinds of communication which are, or could be, aided by computers. This is not a real restriction, of course; simply a matter of opinion as to whether the application of computers to a particular process is an aid or an impediment. Second, the distinction between multimedia and other computer communications is the transfer of information in non-textual forms, and possibly the involvement of more than one human sense — normally sight and hearing.

In a nutshell, then, this definition of multimedia is offered: The application of computer technology to support the communication of information in forms other than written words. Note that this excludes non-computer based telecommunications such as telephones and television, non-communication use of computers, and conventional information delivery by computers in the form of text. It does not exclude text as one medium to be used in conjunction with others.

The definition provides immediate answers to all the parts of the first question, except the issue of why we need it. This has to be answered by demonstrating that computer based communications are both necessary and, in the absence of multimedia, in some way inadequate. To people working in a company that uses office automation for all its internal communications, the need for computer based communication technology will not be in doubt; but in a wider context, the necessity for it is based on the mismatch between the ever-increasing quantity of information available and the limited capacity of the human mind to accommodate it. Human nature seems unable to accept limits to what it considers to be a good thing, and humanity is currently engaged in a kind of information gluttony. It falls to technology to find ways of manipulating the vast amount of information to deliver it succinctly and in a digestible form. The inadequacy of conventional computer communications may be demonstrated by comparing an exchange of E-mail notes with a face-to-face conversation, perhaps using drawing, to discuss, say, the layout of the office furniture.

16.2 Interfacing – a Superset of Multimedia

The preceding discussion has implied a definition of communications as the exchange of information, but has carefully avoided qualifying the participants in the exchange. In particular, the question arises of whether a computer may be said to participate in communication in its own right, or must be regarded as purely a channel for the exchange of information amongst people. It is sometimes held that intelligence is an essential precondition for participation in any process of communication, and the Turing test gives us a way of determining whether a machine may be considered intelligent. Although, at present, we have no machines capable of fully satisfying the Turing test, it is certainly feasible to construct machines which give the appearance of intelligence - ability to answer questions and make decisions, for example - within tightly defined areas, for which the machine has been prepared. In the author's view, the concept of participation by machines in communication is valid so long as the subject of communication stays within the predefined area, and it does not imply intelligence in its general sense. The concept is justified on a pragmatic level because it facilitates the study of communication techniques.

As a way to distinguish communication with machines from that between people, as well as to point out its technological nature, the process of transferring information across the human/machine boundary is termed 'interfacing'. Interfacing embraces, as well as traditional text and multimedia techniques for delivery of information by machines to people, a set of methods for information transfer in the reverse direction — from people to machines. Such methods are important because they will eventually lead to the harmonious collaboration of people and machines in improving the quality of life for mankind.

16.3 Varieties of Communication

To get any further with an analysis of multimedia applications, it is necessary to study the various types of communication, whether computer based or not, to see how and whether multimedia may be applied to each. For this purpose, we can usefully identify the following five categories of communication:

1. information: the simple transfer of knowledge, either through a question and answer process or as a straightforward dissertation.
2. education: structured information delivery with the intention of imparting a skill.
3. instruction: the issuing of commands to be carried out by the recipient. (Note the word is not used in the sense of education).
4. persuasion: an attempt to alter the opinions of the recipient to the commercial or political benefit of the initiator.
5. entertainment: the passage of information purely for the amusement of the participants.

We may also distinguish types of communication according to the relationship of the participants: whether peers or superior/subordinate, and according to their number: whether a single individual or a group. Categories 1, 4 and 5 take place on a one-to-one or one-to-many basis between participants who are, at least for the purpose of the communication, peers. Category 2 is generally, but not exclusively, one-to-many and may imply a measure of dominance by the initiator, while category 3 is clearly from a superior to one or more subordinates. Communications involving machines as participants fall generally into categories 3 and 5, especially if we think of a database query as a command to deliver information rather than a question; although it is not hard to envisage machine participation in category 2.

These relationships have a strong influence on the applicability of multimedia technology because the media are themselves characterised in similar ways.

16.4 Categorisation of the Technology

An attempt to categorise communication media according to the human senses to which they are directed is useful insofar as it points out areas where the technology is lacking. There exist, for example, no media which stimulate the senses of smell and taste. The fact that there are many media which present themselves visually, somewhat fewer audibly, and almost none associated with the other senses is to be expected, given the dominance of sight and hearing in human perception. For communication in the human-to-machine direction, it would clearly be beneficial if the machines could comprehend our natural forms of utterance, such as speech and gesture.

Taking a pragmatic approach to categorising the technology, the following types suggest themselves:

A - interactive delivery of stored text/graphics/images with simple animation.

B - as A, but with the addition of stored audio.

C - interactive delivery of stored video (with audio).

D - real time capture and transmission of video and audio.

E - touch.

F - machine interpretation of spoken words, gestures and images of the external world.

These may be broken down further, into their component technologies:

Group A encompasses the traditional media of text and graphics to convey ideas in words and to show spatial relationships. Conventional photography extends this into the representation of real objects by their images. The contribution of computer technology is to allow animation of the graphics, so that the dimension of movement is introduced into the spatial relationships; and, further, to make the delivery of information respond to the expressed needs of the recipient. As a step towards student-pull learning, this greatly increases the effectiveness of the information transfer.

This group is concerned essentially with one-to-many communication, and generally with the delivery of information from machines to people. An important exception is text, which is currently the prevalent means of transferring information from people to machines.

The absorption of graphics and images into the computer domain has made rapid strides in recent months and it is now easy and relatively cheap to produce a multimedia presentation containing high quality images.

Group B extends the power of group A by stimulating (assaulting?) more than one human sense simultaneously. As is demonstrated by the well known techniques of using visual aids in presentation, this substantially improves the level of retention of information by the audience. The manipulation of sound by computers has recently come to popularity, and, by being applied in an inappropriate way, has led some to regard multimedia as a trivial adjunct to the serious business of computing.

The special case of sound, speech, is a clear case of the substitution of an established human mode of communication by a mechanical process. It has application where verbal information must be delivered without immediate human intervention, such as routine public address announcements and telephone services such as Directory Enquiries.

Sound, including speech, is necessarily one-to-many, and, leaving aside purely human interaction, is predominantly machine-to-human. The recognition of spoken words by computers falls, rather arbitrarily, into **Group F**.

In the sense that video is simply the presentation of a sequence of still images in rapid succession, **Group C** is not conceptually different from group B. However, the problems in storing and delivering the sheer volume of data needed have led the technology of video to diverge significantly from that of still images. Ubiquitous television and cheap videotape machines have accustomed all of us to the presence of moving images accompanied by sound, leading us to accept the rather poor quality of the images, as well as the content, and this has set the standard for computer-based video.

To attain even that video quality, it is at present necessary to make use of specialised hardware extensions to a computer to perform the necessary decompression and image manipulation. These are expensive but are now capable of delivering video which is generally comparable in quality with television, and better in some respects. Recent developments in software-only video, while possibly acceptable in specialised circumstances, provide poor quality video except in the most powerful and expensive machines. This is likely to improve with increasing processing power in small computers and with further development of the compression algorithms.

Stored video is applicable to one-to-many uses in presentation and information delivery. In all cases, the information being delivered is no more than a record of events that happened at some other time. True communication requires the addition of other simultaneous media.

Group D is again conceptually similar to group C, but differs significantly in implementation because of technological constraints. In addition to the decompression of the data, we now must capture and compress the video images in real time, and transmit them over data channels of limited capacity. The whole process must be done without introducing perceptible delay to the user.

Although this technology may find use in one-to-many and in many-to-one applications, its strength lies in one-to-one communications between people: video telephones are with us now, and their increasing prevalence over the next few years seems inevitable.

Group E, as a component of multimedia, is conventionally taken to mean the use of touch-sensitive screens as computer input devices. (One-to-one, human-to-machine.) Although this is, strictly speaking, a communication medium, it is barely different from ordinary pushbuttons. Of greater significance is the artificial stimulation of the human sense of touch to simulate gripping an object or acceleration. The first of these is coming into use in virtual reality systems, and has potential application in remote manipulators; the second, requiring that we regard our up-and-down sense as part of the sense of touch, is in widespread but highly expensive use in flight simulators.

Group F is the part of interfacing which is sometimes excluded from the class of multimedia. It is concerned with the transfer of information from human minds to machine memories, and with the perception by machines of objects and events in the real world.

Machine recognition of human speech is feasible, but falls short of the level of usability required to make it a satisfactory interface. Because speech is such an important human communication method, however, it seems very likely that the technology of speech recognition by machines will develop rapidly and will ultimately replace text as the dominant means of human-to-machine communication.

Similarly, vision systems exist which can recognise objects and measure their spatial relationships, but the operation of such systems is primitive and restricted to specially prepared environments. The technology has a long way to go before it becomes a useful human-to-machine communication medium, but such is the need for it that, in the longer term, its development seems inevitable.

For the present, the term 'gesture' has come to be applied to the interpretation of the motion of a stylus on a sensitive surface as input to a computer. This includes not only commands, but also the recognition of handwritten characters as text. Such a system must be regarded as a substitute for a keyboard, and has application where a keyboard cannot be used. If we consider that the ability to write is more prevalent amongst people than the ability to use a keyboard, there is obvious need for it, but the realisation is not particularly reliable, and must be regarded as a stop-gap measure until a better alternative is available.

16.5 Technology and Applications

If we regard the communication types and the technologies as orthogonal, we can conveniently show them in the form of a table and gain some insight by examining the possible combinations as they exist now and as they might come to exist.

The video telephone is a clear cut example of combination 1D: it makes use of real time video and audio to provide peer to peer exchange of information. The other 1X combinations are workable, but justified only in specialised circumstances, because of the time, effort and equipment required to prepare the material.

2C is well established as video-based training or IVD courses, while 2A and 2B correspond roughly to computer-based training (CBT). Interestingly, outside the computer field, 2A and 2B are what used to be called multimedia before we took over the word.

	1:Information	2:Education	3: Instruction	4: Persuasion	5:Entertainment
A: Interactive text/graphics/image with animation		CBT	Manuals	Presentation and point of sale	Games
B: As A, with audio	Announcements		Operating instructions		
C: Stored video with audio		Interactive video			Films
D: Real time video with audio	Videophone Surveillance				News
E: Touch	Feedback and questions; simulators				Virtual reality
F: Speech recognition, vision, gesture			Machine control		

Table 1. Technology/application matrix

3A…3C implementations are coming into use as multimedia reference manuals or as on-line instructions to operators in industrial processes. In places where literacy is not common, 3B and 3C can provide a means of employing people in jobs which they could not otherwise cope with. 3F is potentially a means of controlling the operation of machines by voice commands, but at present its principal use is in computer input for the physically disabled.

Combinations 4A, 4B and 4C are coming into extensive use in presentations and point-of-sale applications — the things we currently regard as mainstream multimedia.

5X combinations are widespread in computer games — it is now almost unthinkable that a new computer game should not embody some kind of multimedia element.

Touch screen function is normally employed in conjunction with other media to provide interactivity with the delivery of information. Acceleration simulators are in widespread use in the training of aircraft and spacecraft pilots, where even the high cost of the simulator is dwarfed by the cost of the real vehicle.

16.6 Trends in Multimedia

Accepting that the commercial development of new technology is driven by profitability and limited by feasibility, to identify the trends, we need to estimate where the demand and financial justifiability for a particular combination exceed the current availability of products, provided that the combination is technically feasible.

The benefits of multimedia to education have long been recognised, and the financial justification well rehearsed. However, this is now a mature market, and apart from specialised training, strongly constrained by cost. Combinations 2A, B and C can therefore expect continuing turnover, but not rapid growth. 2F is probably not applicable, at least in the short term.

The logical end point of increasing machine-based education is the situation where each minuscule facet of knowledge is encapsulated in a standard work by the one expert in that facet, and that work is used by every student. The role of the human teacher would be diminished, and it is arguable that an undesirable uniformity of knowledge would ensue. The counter argument is that the prejudices and misconceptions of individual teachers would have less effect, and the educational information would be of uniformly high standard.

The glamour or novelty value of a multimedia presentation is a great asset in persuading an audience to a point of view and category 4 has been a dominant market for this reason. With maturity, however, comes the realisation that there is no concrete payoff, and the cost and inconvenience of multimedia as compared to, say, a projected transparency presentation make it progressively less attractive. Point of sale applications fall into this group, and rely heavily on novelty value. Although there is a huge number of transactions to which multimedia technology could be applied, and if this were to happen, this market would outweigh everything else, it is only really convenient in a very small subset, so the probability of its implementation is low. While there remain areas of industry and commerce to which multimedia is a novelty, category 4 seems likely to be viable, but again limited in growth potential.

Computer based entertainment, in the form of games, has been and remains a powerful driver of multimedia technology. Whatever we may think of the exploitation of sophisticated technology for pure amusement, we have to accept that the ultimate determinant of the commercial success or failure of a product is how a large number of people choose to spend their money. Currently discernible trends in entertainment amount to no more than better bells and whistles and better video quality, but the genre has surprised us before, and may well do so again. It has already been suggested that 1D is the only widely useful category 1 combination, but that is not to say that it has little commercial potential. The human appetite for information is insatiable, particularly if the information can be presented in a readily usable form. It is likely, therefore, that real time video/audio information transmission will show explosive growth in the near future, and that the demand will be for higher quality video and very sophisticated call handling facilities.

Category 3, the issuing of instructions, is almost virgin territory for multimedia, and ought therefore to offer the opportunity for growth. An obstacle here is that, in most situations, the passing of orders between people would be impeded rather than enhanced by the use of any kind of computer technology. If, on the other hand, we consider the issuing of commands to machines, any improvement in ease of use is valuable. Suddenly the direction of multimedia converges with another fundamental aim of computer technology — that of transferring some of the burden of bridging the human/machine gap to the machine. The use of voice and gestures is the natural medium by which people communicate with each other, and quite rightly, they demand that the machines should fall into line. For this reason, it seems highly likely that, as the technology is developed to allow it to happen, interfacing, in the form combination 3F will be very widely adopted as the means of issuing instructions to personal computers.

To draw these threads together, the discernible trends are that 'education', 'persuasion' and 'entertainment' are likely to provide a continuing but unexciting market for multimedia products, but the real growth will be initially in real time 'information' and in the longer term in voice and gesture 'instruction' of computers.

16.7 Conclusion

To return to the present, the conclusions of this paper and the golden rules for the use of multimedia can be summarised in a few sentences:

- Multimedia is an element of interfacing, the bridging of the communication gap between people and computers.
- The technology is undergoing rapid development and change. Things change from esoteric and expensive to widespread and cheap in a short time.
- A wide variety of techniques is available: it is essential to choose the right one, or combination, for the purpose in hand.
- Rapid innovation brings a share of trendy rubbish. It is important to distinguish value from trivia.
- The preparation of multimedia material consumes far more resources than does simple text, and may be out of reach for some purposes. The cost of preparation must be balanced against the anticipated benefit.

Finally, the reason for its existence: multimedia is a powerful means of communication, and can provide high levels of acceptance of a message by an audience. Let us be sure that the message justifies the medium.

17. The Use of Prototyping in the Problem Structuring Methodology

Nikitas A. Assimakopoulos

Department of Information Sciences, University of Piraeus, 80, Karaoli & Dimitriou Street, GR-185 34 Piraeus, Greece.

Abstract. The Problem Structuring Methodology is used as a design process to identify the different environment levels of a computer development system up to the detail design stage. It covers the gap which (at least in the first stages) the traditional systems development cycle has. To examine the human-computer interfaces, prototyping is used:
- within the Problem Structuring Methodology
- at the early stages of the development cycle to optimise the Data Model for conversion into the appropriate database schema.

The proposed methodology has been tested in practice and its framework can be adjusted to handle different types of system development project.

Keywords. Database management systems, identification, information systems, prototyping, systems analysis

17.1 Introduction

The purpose of this paper is to propose an updated and comprehensive method for the development of small and medium-sized business computer systems, and to suggest how this method could be used as a vehicle for further research into the problems of computer systems development.

It examines briefly the basic principles of two major approaches to computer systems development:
- structured systems analysis with the use of Problem Structuring Methodology (PSM), which has been developed by Panayotopoulos and Assimakopoulos (1987) [11]
- prototyping

The advantages and disadvantages of each are highlighted, illustrating the conflict inherent in the two approaches and stressing the problems that occur when trying to use both on the same system. The paper goes on to suggest a simplified methodology framework, based firmly on structured system analysis with the PSM design, but which is able to release the undoubted potential of a prototyping approach without losing the essential control provided by the structured approach. The methodology put forward is offered as a kind of prototype to be used in a series of detailed tests, run within a number of problems, with a view to proving (and if necessary improving) its flexibility and scalability.

Research is also being conducted into the feasibility of adjusting the methodology framework to suit each individual systems development project put forward, and these tests will be designed to provide information from which a set of guidelines can be identified.

17.1.1 Structured Systems Analysis

Structured systems analysis (SSA) is now being used extensively by organisations, though in many different forms. It can be roughly defined as an integral group of tools and techniques for modelling the required and proposed system, held together by a framework of steps and stages, conditions and checklists, indicating which tool should be used in what circumstances. The tools themselves, which include Data Flow Diagrams, Entity Models and Entity Life Histories are not new. They have individually proven their value over the last decade and many of them are common to all the major SSA methodologies. It is mostly the *framework* which distinguishes the different approaches to SSA and makes a grouping of structured methods marketable as a Methodology, described in Maddison (1983) and Olle (1983) [9 & 10]

The framework is obviously very important because it provides the means of measuring and controlling the project but methodology suppliers differ in their opinions as to the level of control needed. The main methodologies for computer information systems development are presented by Assimakopoulos (1989) [2]. It is observed that one of the problems we face lately in practice is that the structured design methodologies have an initial but quite important problem. This is the direct application to real world problems. The reason for this is that these methodologies do not see problems but they try to apply a process into a problem.

PSM is a new management methodology which was developed to cover this gap and is based on a systematic structure process. The process may be used by managers as well as consultants (system analysts) to help their clients to solve their problems. The product of this cooperation will remain with the client as a tool for further decision making i.e. reorganisation, redesigning, or checking of operations. It goes further than the usual diagrammatical presentations of subsystems and individual elements of a system to determine their positioning and role. To build such a structure process, a researcher needs to have structured thought for approaching the problem. This will help him or her to get into details and also to synthesize all the different parts. The process identifies completely the problem, analyses in detail the structures, procedures, the role of individuals, the flow of information and eventually controls the communications. The terminology of the process is based on definitions, giving also their designs, coding forms and relationships at communication level which are necessary for the problem structuring. This structuring process has the advantage of distinguishing the different levels of organisation and to work in any combination of them. The developing of the process is easier for consultants if they use transparencies for each level of organisation, with different colours for each basic subsystem. The more complex the super system is, the more levels need to be created for a complete analysis.

The main advantage of this methodology is that it is a language for knowledge representation and communication with the client. It identifies exactly the real problem which he or she wants to develop with the information system but it goes up to the detail design stage of the traditional methodology for the physical implementation.

Crinnion (1986) [4] has suggested that it can be a continuum between a 'toolbox' approach, where a loose framework allows the analyst to choose the best tool for the occasion, and a 'cookbook' approach, where the methodology framework is complex and rigid, forcing analyst teams through a rigorous process of definition and specification.

Whereas a simple 'toolbox' approach is ideal for the development of small systems, and works well in the hands of experienced and creative analysts, very large systems need a much more formal 'cookbook' approach. Managers are prepared to sacrifice the small chance of having a short, brilliantly innovative development for the longer, standardised process which can almost be guaranteed to provide a working product.

However, most organisations have projects in their portfolio which vary considerably in size and complexity and therefore require different development approaches. Such an organisation needs sometimes to use a 'toolbox' and sometimes a 'cookbook'. Some of the methodology suppliers are now recognising this need, and are building more flexibility into the frameworks. There is however, a danger in this of losing some of the benefits of completeness and control.

One relatively recent advance in systems development technology has made the use of a cookbook methodology less of an overhead. Automated model-building tools, (like for example *Automate Plus* or *Excellerator*), enable the analyst to record designs directly on to the computer screen. Other automated tools in the analyst workbench, in particular an active data dictionary, can carry out many of the cross-checking tasks which make some aspects of the job of an analyst so tedious. However, some of these tools lock the analyst too firmly into the full methodology, and can make a toolbox approach less possible.

Few people nowadays would deny that structured systems analysis has provided major benefits for those organisations who have adopted one of its many variants. They have experienced greater user involvement in and commitment to the project, a more accurate definition of requirements, a better control of the development process, and ultimately a better system. Moreover, the fact that many of the methodologies base their design approach on the structure of the data of the system rather than on the processes makes the system more easily amendable, and gives it the potential of a longer life.

17.1.2 Prototyping

As well as embracing structured systems analysis, many organisations have also decided to adopt an advanced technique for the programming task, and have progressed from third to fourth generation languages. Grindley (1987) [7] says that there are clear advantages in this as one statement in a fourth generation language can take the place of a number of 3GL statements.

The main advantage however of using a fourth generation language, (more accurately a fourth generation environment), is that it enables the analyst/programmer to use the prototyping technique. Prototyping can be defined as:

Building a physical working model of all or part of the proposed system, and using it to identify requirements.

The major benefit of such an approach is that the users are able to see a version of the proposed system long before it has been fully developed, and are therefore able to correct any misunderstandings at an early stage. They also get a very clear picture of what the system will look like; a much clearer picture than can be obtained from the 'paper' models created in structured systems analysis.

There are two forms of prototyping in common use; they are known as 'Rapid' and 'Evolutionary'. Rapid prototyping involves building a very early prototype of parts of the system, using any techniques available. The quality of the programming is unimportant, because the prototype will eventually be discarded and the true system built properly. The sole purpose of the rapid prototype is to get user feedback on the requirements and proposals.

On the other hand, the Evolutionary prototyping approach involves building a carefully structured working model of the core of the proposed system, with a view to revising and extending it, rather than throwing it away. This type takes longer to build, but because a 4GL is used, it can be assembled and adjusted relatively quickly. It is the facility to write quick and throw-away code, provided by fourth generation environments, which makes the technique of prototyping feasible.

17.1.3 The Conflict

There are however problems in trying to make use of both structured systems analysis techniques with the PSM and prototyping at the same time. These problems stem mainly from the difference in the philosophy of the two approaches. It is true that both can be seen as mechanisms for improving the process of systems development, but both have evolved from different assumptions of how systems development should be done, to such an extent that in some ways they can almost be considered to be incompatible.

Structured systems analysis and design methodologies like PSM use modern effective modelling tools, but base their frameworks on the traditional systems development cycle, which is split into the main stages of: Investigation, Analysis, Design, Construction, and Implementation. Each stage is broken into easily measurable units, and a stage is normally considered to have to be completed before the next stage starts. This provides a clear demarcation between different processes and allows for the use of specialist staff at different stages e.g. business analysis during the investigation and analysis stages, more technical systems designers during the design, and programmers during the construction. The reasoning behind the use of these formal stages is the same as for a major project in any other field, such as architecture or engineering i.e. that each component, once constructed, will underpin the components to follow. The later that an error or misunderstanding is discovered, the harder and more expensive it is to put it right.

This is considered particularly true of the programming task, which can be the most expensive and time-consuming. It is essential that a full and explicit program specification is provided before programmers begin work, as they are only expected to carry out the limited task of translating requirements into a computer language.

On the other hand, the use of a fourth generation environment and prototyping techniques reduce the criticality of this programming stage; much fewer instructions take less time to create, and therefore can be changed more readily. These higher level languages can also be used by less specialist staff, for example the business analyst, and even by the user, cutting down on the need for formal program specification as communication.

The concept of prototyping cuts across the development cycle stages, as each prototype includes elements of all four stages, Investigation, Analysis, Design and Construction. The definition of prototyping quoted earlier would suggest that it should take place during the 'requirements analysis' stage of the project. However, at that point in most structured systems methodologies, no physical design has been considered, so building a physical model should not be possible. Some research has already been done by Dennis (1987) [6] on the attempts to fit the prototyping technique into existing structured systems methodologies without changing their stages and tasks; the evidence suggests that they have met with limited success.

The other important element in the prototyping technique is *iteration*; the process of building part of the system, checking it with users, then altering or even rebuilding, and rechecking etc. until it is considered satisfactory. This again clashes with the structured system analysis approach, where each step is fitted into a dependency schedule, and consists of a sequence of tasks, each of which can be checked and signed off. Here we notice the contrast of design strategy at the heart of the conflict. Whereas SSA methodologies, in general, put forward an one-off constructive view of development, prototyping supports the evolutionary approach, in which modifications are considered to be the norm. Lantz (1987) [8] has proposed this evolutionary approach in design and construction and it is then naturally continued in the succeeding implementation and maintenance stages.

The use of prototyping for systems development has led in places to a change in the users' view of what is required and they are now able to go for a more advanced system with greater functionality and greater user involvement. Fourth generation environments lend themselves particularly to the development of on-line systems, specialising as they do in dialogue design facilities. Also, many fourth generation language routines, after they have been developed, become standard procedures or components in future systems, requiring only slight tailoring to fit the new system requirements. This 'component engineering' approach means that the user can often see at a very early stage, a number of options in prototype form, and make a decision accordingly. Being able to see the system they are going to get it gives the users a much clearer view of their requirements. They are much more able to see the potential of the proposed system in prototype form than in the diagrammatic, text-supported requirements specification provided by SSA.

On the other hand, SSA with the PSM is much better at analysing the 'logical' requirements of the system, providing a much deeper understanding of the business, opening up a larger range of design and implementation options, and giving the user wider choice. Boar (1986) [3] says that there are undoubtedly systems for which a prototyping approach would be unsuitable or unduly restrictive.

The problem remains, how to take advantage of the mature, thorough, risk-minimising approach of SSA, and at the same time reap the benefits of a more quickly produced, and more user-oriented system, as provided using a prototyping approach.

17.2 The Proposed Methodology

The methodology described here has been devised in an attempt to bring together the critical elements of structured systems analysis with the PSM and prototyping. This should provide, in one systems development method, the advantages of both approaches. A minimal tool set has been used, and every attempt has been made to preserve the method's simplicity and the flexibility, placing it towards the 'toolbox' end of the continuum. Emphasis has also been placed on its ease of understanding for the user, particularly in the early stages. An example of this 'toolbox' approach using the PSM is given in a banking application by Assimakopoulos (1988) [1] where the environment of a procedure of an agricultural loan was analysed and designed. Its structuring designs (organizational levels) are presented here in Figs. 17.1a, b, c, d and e which is the matching of all designs. Figure 17.1e is the consultant's model in final form, agreed on by the users, and represents a desirable and feasible design which can be easily verified and validated using cost parameters in links and nodes. The ranking of the results is the decision support information requested to choose the path which it will be programmed.

It is common practice for a methodology to be described using its own tools and models. Such a description exists for this system development methodology but for the sake of brevity, it is described here with the help of, say, a 'road map'. Figures 17.2 and 17.3, illustrate which modelling tools are used and in which stages.

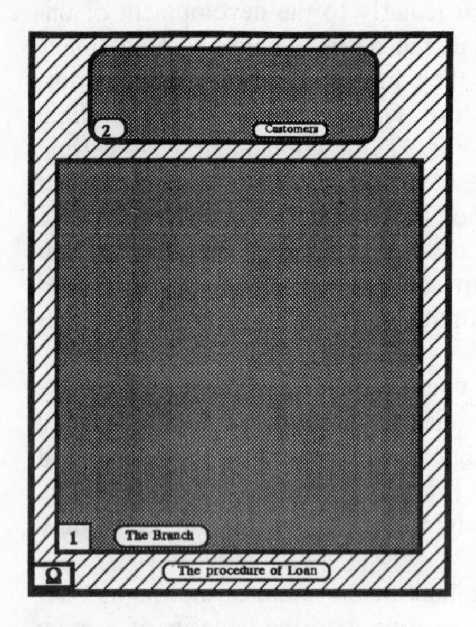

Figure 1a: The basic subsystems of Ω

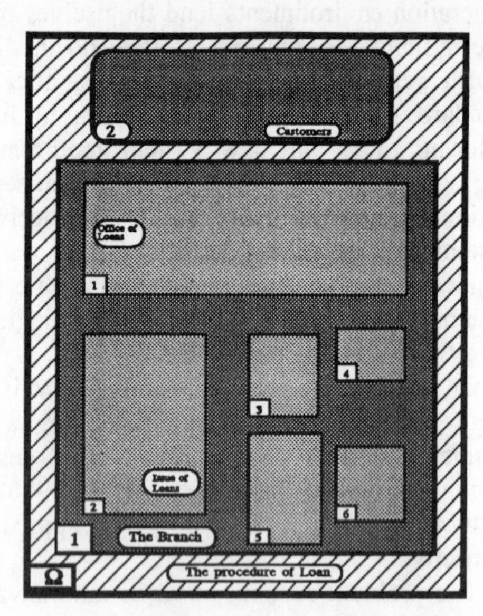

Figure 1b: The main non-basic subsystems of Ω

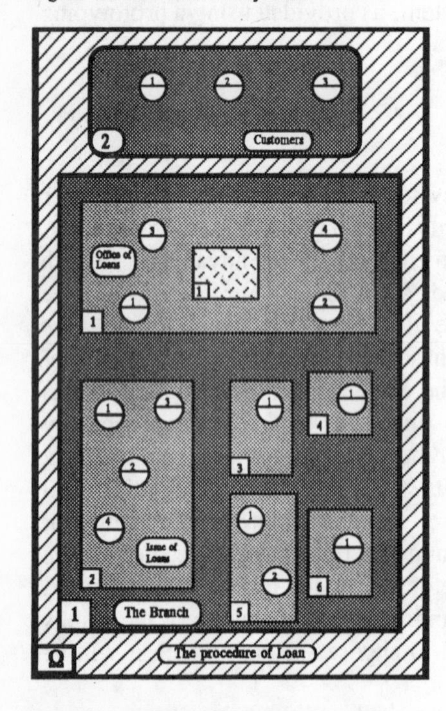

Figure 1c: The main non-basic subsystems of Ω with individuals

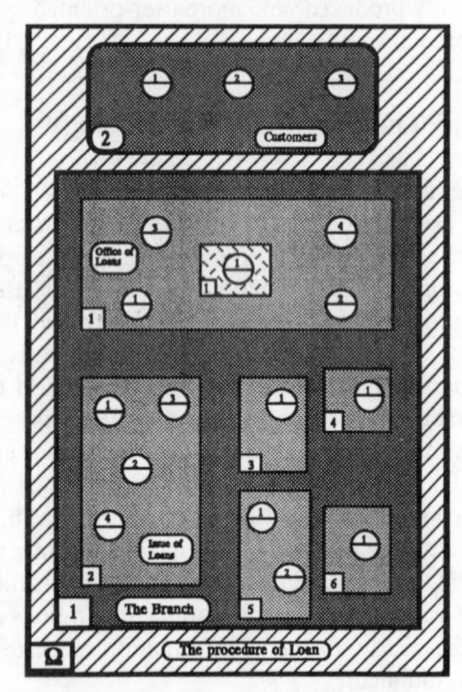

Figure 1d: The main non-basic subsystems of Ω with <u>all</u> the individuals

Fig. 17.1.

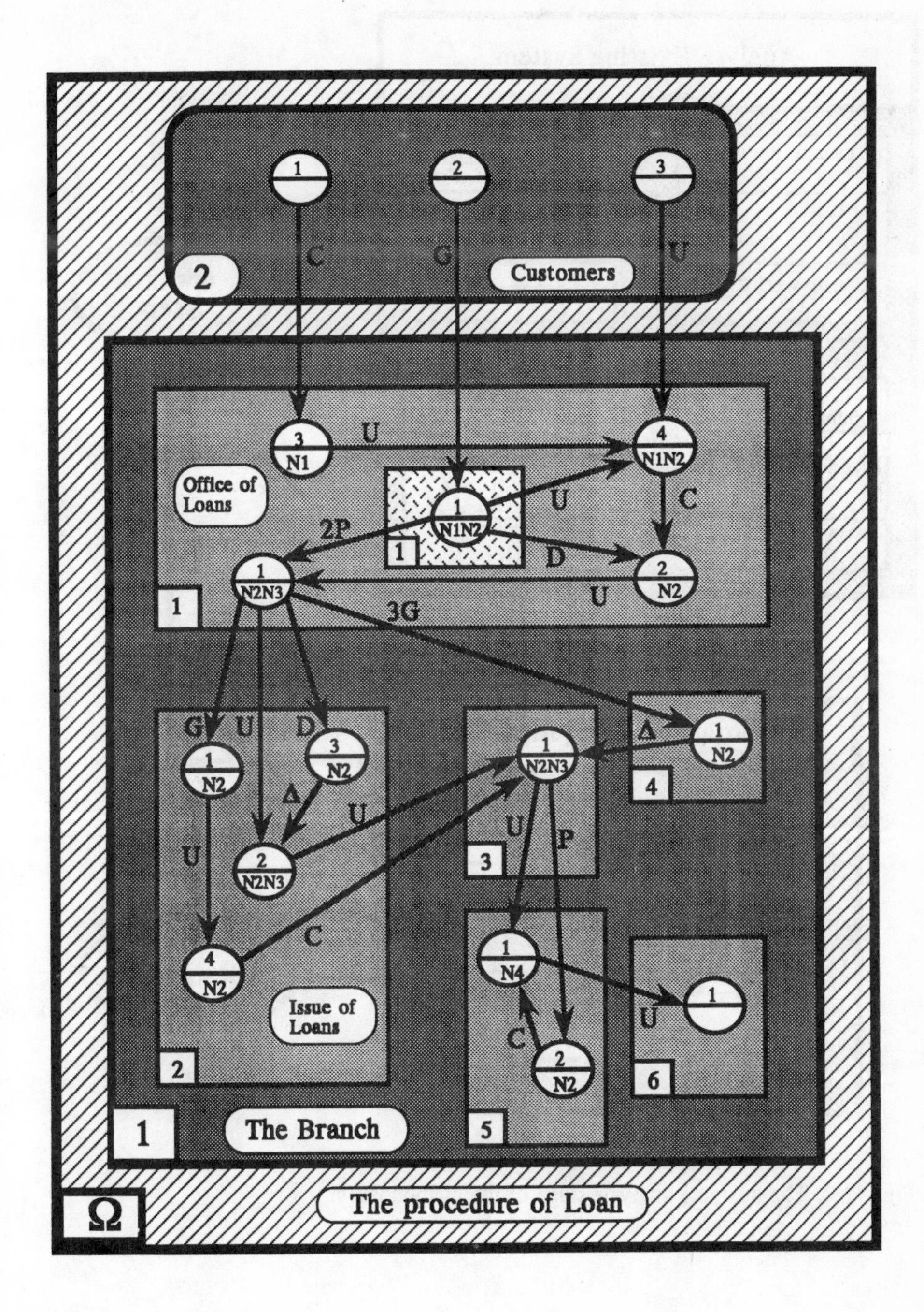

Fig. 17.1e. The matching of levels with link and node parameters

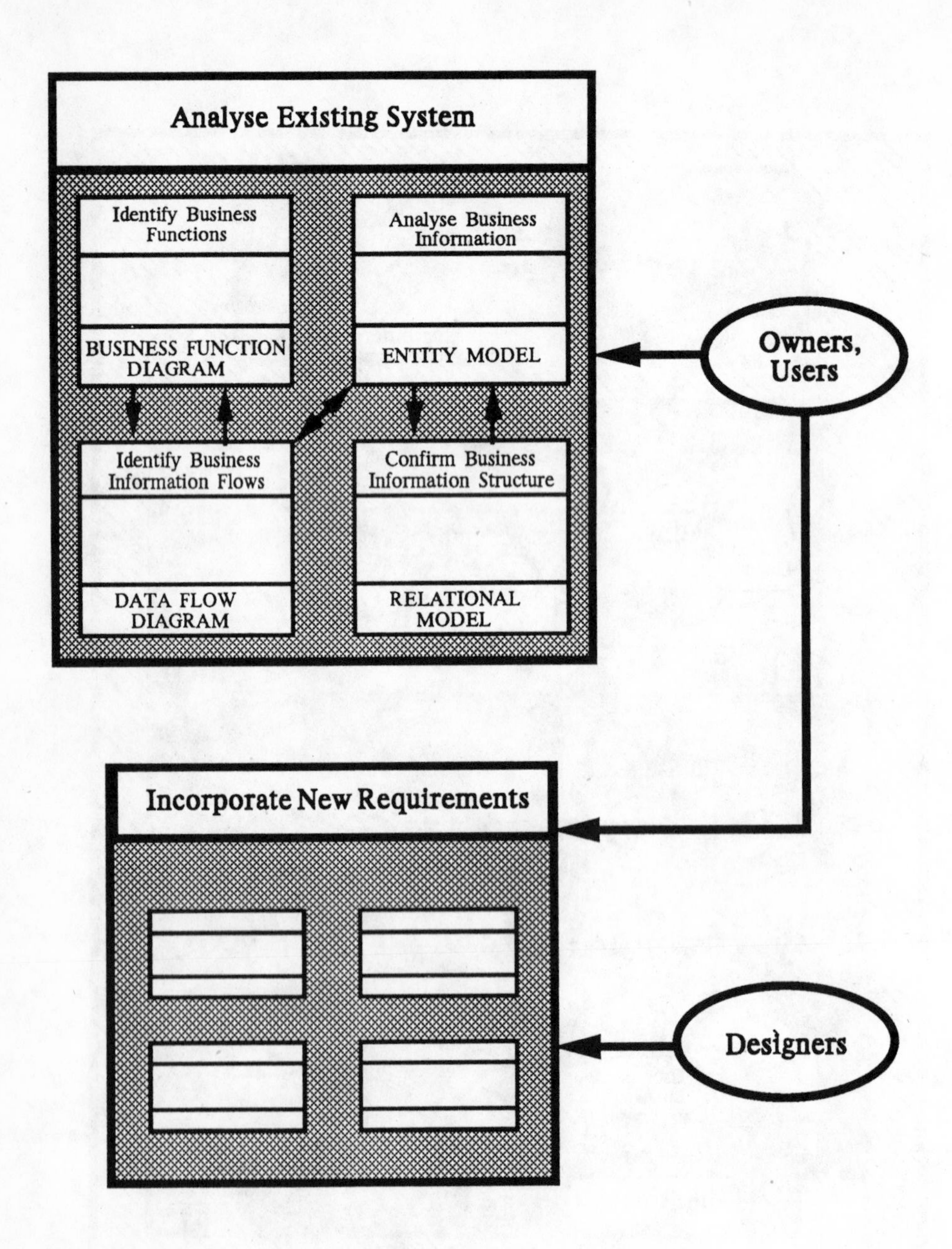

Fig. 17.2. The business analysis stage of the methodology

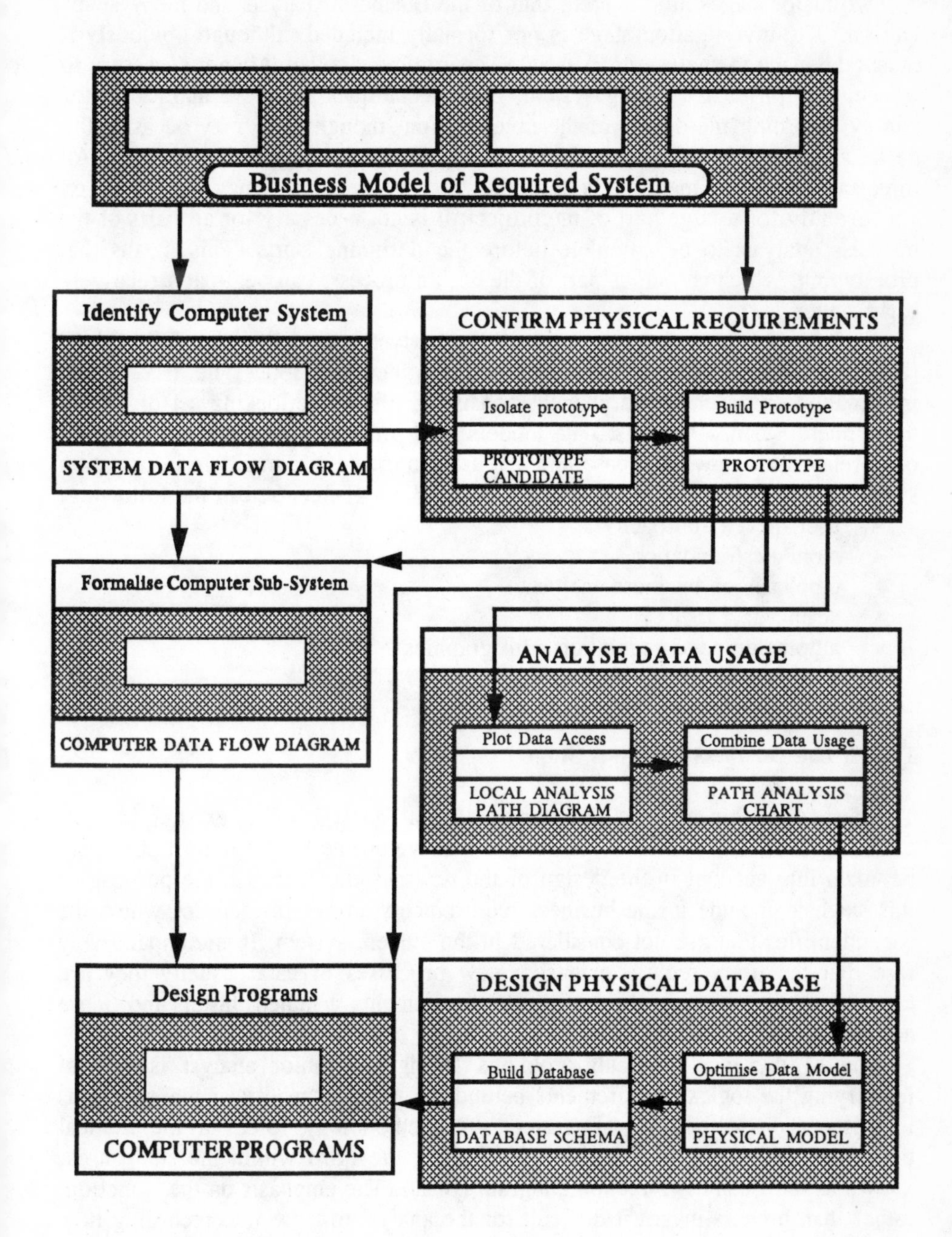

Fig. 17.3. The system's design stage of the methodology

Two major stages are covered, that of the Business Analysis and the Systems Design. The investigation stage is not formally included, although obviously it must take place to analyse its material. The argument is that it is not necessary to 'model' the physical existing system; other techniques are more applicable for simply recording the details of the investigation, though there may occasionally be an advantage in using a model to clarify a complex physical procedure. An important point to mention is that the two major stages may be going on concurrently for a large part of the project; it is not necessary for all parts of the business analysis to be complete before the designing starts. This means that prototyping, which is seen as part of the design process, can begin at a relatively early stage.

We have tested prototyping even in the early stages, using the IEW CASE [Computer Aided Software (or systems) Engineering] tool. The IEW is an information engineering workbench, consisting of an interlocking set of formal techniques. Business models, data models, and process models are built up in a comprehensive knowledge base and are used to create and maintain information systems. The critical characteristics of the IEW may be centred in the following:

- user driven approach
- strategic foundation
- emphasis on business analysis
- strong data focus
- automated code generation with graphics
- a knowledge base.

17.2.1 The Business Analysis Stage

The purpose of this stage is to produce a 'logical' analysis of the existing system, extracting from it the implicit requirements of the business. These must obviously be taken into account in the design of the new system. It is also the purpose of this stage to include in the business requirements any extra facilities which the user identifies that are not considered in the current system. It is comparatively rare that the users require extensive new processes or data; usually they are concerned with getting their current requirements handled faster and more accurately.

One of the most difficult problems facing the junior analyst is that of identifying the logical requirements behind the physical reality of the system as it exists. To make this task easier, the methodology forces a hierarchical decomposition of the business functions using the PSM within the study area, known as the Business Function Diagram (BFD). The emphasis on the 'function' rather than process makes it difficult for the analyst to lapse into recording how processes are carried out. This is carried forward into the next modelling activity, as the functions of the BFD become the processes of the Data Flow Diagram (DFD). The standards used for the DFD are those of DeMarco (1980) and Assimakopoulos (1988) [5 & 1]. With a few minor additions, every attempt has been made to keep these early tools as user-friendly as possible. The two models, the BFD and the DFD cross-check each other, and are iterated until a logically simple and aesthetically satisfying model of the functional requirements is arrived at.

To examine in detail the data requirements, two further models are used; they are referred to here again for simplicity reasons as the Data Model and the Relational Model. The Data Model is basically an entity-attribute-relationship model, arrived at by a pragmatic top-down approach. The Relational Model is built from the attributes identified in the earlier model, and put through the normalisation process. These two models are obviously used to cross-check each other, but they are also integrated with the functional models in that the entity types on the final version of the Data Model become the 'Data Stores' on the final version of the Data Flow Diagram.

It is accepted that these four models alone cannot constitute the full documentation for a requirements specification; they must be supported by explanatory text, data dictionary entries, descriptions of DFD functional primitives, background information etc. The case is put that the level and content of these is a matter of judgement between the analyst, the user, and the project manager. All that the methodology supplies are the essentials to guarantee that a full analysis is conducted.

17.2.2 The Systems Design Stage

Whereas the Business Analysis stage dealt purely with the logical view of the system, never concerning itself with the way requirements might be satisfied, the Systems Design stage involves immediately examining options for implementing the requirements.

The first model used is referred to as the Systems Data Flow Diagram and it is built using the Business Data Flow Diagram as the starting point. Each process is examined in turn and decisions are made as to which parts of the system are to be computerised. The system DFD contains the computer processes and the clerical/admin./operational processes, indicating the location of the data stores. To examine such diagrams, a number of processes need to be split, as they will involve a human-computer interface.

Where such an interface has been identified, it provides an ideal candidate for prototyping. Each of these combined interface-processes can be isolated, together with its appropriate files/entity types, and issued to an analyst/programmer.

The products of the prototyping stage include detailed information on entity-relationship paths used; this is used in optimising the Data Model for conversion into the appropriate database schema.

While prototyping is going ahead, decisions can be made on the grouping of the different programs and modules into sub-systems. This is done using a version of the data flow diagram called the Computer DFD. Again at this stage there may be prototyping opportunities, as menus and control procedures may be involved.

Information from the sub-system design, the prototypes, the path analysis and the proposed database schema, all feed into the final program design and construction process. The form of this will very depending on the hardware and software environment and on the types of prototyping employed.

Again, there is a great deal of supporting information necessary in the systems design stage, but exactly what, and how much, will vary depending upon circumstances; the methodology provides the basic minimum steps and models to carry out the task.

17.3 Further Research using the Methodology

It must be stressed that all the tools and techniques within the methodology are in general use and have proved their value over time. It is the combination of the tools, particularly those from prototyping with those from SSA with the PSM, that make the methodology, in our view, an important source of study. A number of systems have been developed within the Agricultural Bank of Greece using the approach, and discussions are taking place within the Bank with a view to conducting a series of more detailed trials.

The methodology is offered to organisations as a kind of 'prototype' of an approach to combining SSA, the PSM and systems prototyping techniques. The proposal is that more companies and organisations should adopt the methodology, adjusting it and tuning it to their particular needs.

Another fruitful area of research is into the flexibility and scalability of the methodology, observing how its framework can be adjusted in particular circumstances to handle different types of systems development project. It has been suggested that a truly flexible methodology should allow for the use of different tools, tasks and stages depending on the type and nature of system to be developed, but where are the guidelines for such decisions? It is hoped that this proposed research project can provide some of the raw material from which these guidelines can be formulated. Because of the continuously changing nature of systems analysis, there can never be a complete solution to the problem of systems development. It is however suggested that the proposed methodology comes from practice and provides the opportunity to take advantage of the best of modern analysis and design tools. It contains the flexibility necessary to adjust their use to a wide scope of varying circumstances.

References

1. Assimakopoulos, N.: The routing and cost of the information flow in a system. Systems Practice, 1, no 3, 297-303 (1988).
2. Assimakopoulos, N.: Management methodologies for computer information systems. Resource Mang. & Optim., 6(3), 187-204 (1989)
3. Boar, B.: Application Prototyping. Wiley Interscience (1986).
4. Crinnion, J.: Toolbox or Cookbook? An Analysis of Systems Design Methodologies. Proc. of Intr. Con. on Systems & Cybernetics, Vienna (1986).
5. DeMarco, T.: Structured Analysis: System Specification.. Yourdon, New York (1980).

6. Dennis, R.: Phased design: a mixed methodology for application system development. Database Magazine (1987).
7. Grindley, K.: Fourth Generation Languages. IDPM (1987).
8. Lantz, K.: The Prototyping Methodology. Prentice Hall (1987).
9. Maddison, R.: Information Systems Methodologies. Chichester: Wiley Hayden (1983).
10. Olle, T.: Information Systems Design Methodologies: A Feature Analysis. IFIP. Amsterdam: North Holland (1983).
11. Panayotopoulos, A. and Assimakopoulos, N.: Problem structuring in a hospital. European J. of O.R., 29, no 2, 135-143 (1987)

18. A Survey of Current Methodologies for Manufacturing Systems Design

Stefan Fritz[1], Joachim Heinen[2], Felix Schmid[1] and Bin Wu[1]

[1] Department of Manufacturing and Engineering Systems, Brunel University, Uxbridge UB8 3PH, England
[2] Hochschuldidaktisches Zentrum, HDZ-KDI, Rheinisch-Westfälische Technische Hochschule Aachen, Dennewartstr. 27, D-52068 Aachen, Germany

Abstract. In 1992/93 a research team from the Department of Manufacturing and Engineering Systems at Brunel University, undertook a survey of manufacturing industry and researchers in the UK and other European countries on the topic of Manufacturing Systems Design (MSD). It was the aim of this study to identify current best practice and the emerging theories of MSD, and to investigate the level of adoption by industry of advanced methodologies for the design process as applied to MSD. The research was planned to generate accurate data on the use, problems and benefits associated with the application of MSD methodologies. Key topics of systems design included the degree of consideration of people and organisation related aspects, in contrast to merely technology based approaches. The authors brought together some of the results established in this field so far and put them into a logical context to form a basis for further investigations. This paper reports the analysis of current literature of MSD methodologies, as well as the results obtained through a survey of manufacturing companies. Finally, developments required for the future are discussed.

Keywords. manufacturing systems, systems design. human centredness, survey, Europe, methodlogies

18.1 Introduction

It is widely recognized by industry that markets, products, technology and methods are changing at a faster rate than ever before. The shortening of product life cycles and rapid advances in innovative technologies demand that companies should be able to change rapidly. To reduce the time to market, under the twin pressures of achieving cost reductions and highest quality, is one of the challenges which today's manufacturing organisations face.

One of the major tasks in the process of bringing a product to market is the design and implementation of the manufacturing system. The typical shortcomings of traditional Manufacturing Systems Design (MSD) approaches are the long lead time, the poor quality of systems designs, and an 'over the wall' mentality — resulting in mis-investment and inefficient manufacturing systems.

In the past, manufacturing companies tried to meet the challenges of introducing new manufacturing technology on its own. In general, there was a tendency of companies to introduce new technology without making significant changes to the organisation (Schulze-Dieckhoff 1990, Gerwin 1992). Little attention was paid to organisation and people as inherently important resources in manufacturing systems. Manufacturing companies overlooked that the successful operation of the majority of manufacturing systems depends upon an appropriate work organisation and the workers' skills and motivation. They thus missed out on the opportunity to improve their manufacturing performance by reorganising production and changing work practices, instead of purchasing expensive production equipment (Kidd 1990).

As a result of focusing too much on technological aspects, the investment in advanced manufacturing technology often did not yield the expected improvements in productivity and quality. Womack (1991) stated in a survey of automotive plants, that the plant equipped with the most sophisticated manufacturing technology was one of those with the poorest quality and productivity.

To find out why many manufacturing systems do not perform to their full potential, more knowledge is required of the way manufacturing systems are designed. In this context, it is of particular interest to find out whether the application of formal design methodologies is an appropriate means to overcome the problems stated above.

Methodology of Research

The overall objectives of the research project undertaken at Brunel University were to investigate the current best practise in MSD and to identify research areas which would produce results to assist the MSD process.

In this context, a comprehensive literature research of methodologies for the purpose of MSD was undertaken. The aim of this task was to identify methodologies currently available and to define an outline of requirements which an MSD methodology should satisfy to support the designer or design team during the MSD process. This outline can be used to evaluate proposed methodologies for the suitability of an integrated approach — considering people, organisation and technology aspects in a balanced way. The questionnaire based survey undertaken addressed issues such as the level of adoption of formal methodologies, problems encountered and cooperation in the MSD process.

18.2 Discussion of Current Methodologies

To investigate the methodologies currently available within the public sector, a literature search was carried out. The analysis was concentrated on particular aspects of MSD such as, to what degree the methodologies allow the consideration of 'human factors' in the design process. This term includes, according to the definition proposed by Kidd and Corbett (1988), issues such as work organisation, allocation of functions, hardware and software ergonomics and environmental working conditions. Furthermore, investigations undertaken in this report consider the extent to which these methodologies could assist the design team in the design process.

Despite the uniqueness of each design process, there is a belief that the use of formal design methodologies is likely to improve the result of the design as well as facilitate the planning process itself. Many authors on the subject note that methodologies serve as a guide to the design of the manufacturing system and make the task somewhat easier for the designer. According to Wallace (1991) a systematic approach provides: a starting position, a frame of reference and a means of communication. The major benefits arising from the use of a methodology outlined in the literature are a decreased effort for design in terms of cost and time and an understandable, reproducible planning process. A further advantage noted is that the use of a methodology can ensure that all aspects which require consideration for the successful design of a system are given that attention (Wu, 1992, Aggteleky, 1987). Nadler (1981) argues that a methodology is necessary to handle continuing change and Davis (1982) noted, that effective organization design is a learning process that must be pursued systematically.

There are some reservations in current literature, however, regarding the application of methodologies for manufacturing systems design. Critics of methodologies point out that they have a narrow focus of attention on specific issues and therefore involve the risk of sub-optimisation. This view is confirmed by Havn (1992), who noted that methods, as we know them now, are developed to deal with one layer of a system or only a few. Some of them do quite well within this limitation. The methods for the design of technology usually ignore problems of people and organisation, and Socio-Technical methods ignore problems of the design of technology.

The rigid structuring imposed by some methodologies is seen as a further problem because it is likely to impede the designers' creativity (De Vries 1992). In a DTI brochure[1] the following statement concerning the approach towards MSD can be found,

> 'it should be noted that mangers and engineers cannot expect to rely too much on design methods to guide them through the area of interdisciplinary design'.

Havn (1992) concludes that the methods swell monstrously in the attempt to cover all aspects of manufacturing, and that they are difficult to apply in practice. DeVries (1992) states that, too often, simplified models of the design process have been frustrated by the complexity of practice.

---

[1] This booklet entitled 'Organisation, People and Technology' is one of a range produced by the Department of Trade and Industry (DTI) for it's 'managing into the '90s' programme.

In summary, one can say that in recent literature doubts are expressed about the suitability of currently available design methodologies for the purpose of MSD. Some authors even argue that the use of methodologies is, in general, not the approach to manage change within manufacturing systems. A contrary view sees the necessity to develop new methodologies. The latter view is supported by the group 'Socio-Technical-Design'[2] who noted:

> 'when facing the task of organising manufacturing it becomes more and more important to search for a comprehensive process of design and introduction, which uses social-technical methods to improve the cooperation of the employees in a production company'.

Throughout the literature review, which was carried out by means of database searches and book reviews, the research team encountered difficulties in identifying suitable MSD methodologies. Because of these difficulties, the majority of the methodologies had to be compiled out of reference lists in books or articles. Consequently the findings form an arbitrary extract rather than an exhaustive representation of available methodologies.

The scope of the material identified ranges from a list of design principles (Cherns 1976, Trist 1981) to a description of a methodology covering a three volume textbook (Aggteleky 1987).

To establish which of the approaches identified can be classified as *methodologies* the following minimum specification for a methodology has been defined.

'A methodology for MSD is a structured and generic way of designing manufacturing systems. It comprises a defined sequence of phases or tasks to be undertaken within an MSD process'.

All the approaches identified were assessed against this definition. In the table shown in the Appendix, all those approaches are represented which are considered to be a methodology. For the analysis of methodologies a *Set of Requirements* has been compiled out of literature to evaluate the advised methodologies against its criteria. This set of requirements has been applied in the following section to two case examples of MSD methodologies.

18.2.1 Set of Requirements for MSD Methodologies

Wu (1992) identifies a means of evaluation of the completed design as an essential element of a methodology. He criticises the common belief that the application of a methodology is sufficient to ensure a high quality design. In this context, Symon (1990) noted that formal evaluation procedures are required to ensure the user orientation of the system. Furthermore, the author noted that the design process

---

[2] The group 'Socio-Technical-Design' at the Department for Systems Planning at the 'Institute für Produktionsanlagen und Konstruktionstechnik (IPK) Berlin' is an interdisciplinary team consisting of engineers, computer and social scientists. They develop methods and concepts for advanced human oriented manufacturing structures.

has to be iterative and has identified the following three principles which a methodology should incorporate:

- interdisciplinary design teams
- a parallel design process, where consideration is given to human, organisational and technical issues concurrently.
- user participation

Kidd and Corbett (1988) noted that the formulation of a set of values to inform the design is a prerequisite for the development of human-centred production systems.

Brandt (1991) outlines the requirements of a methodology perused in his 'Dual Design Approach' as follows: a set of principles to ensure the appropriate development of both technical and human aspects of man-machine systems.

Marks (1991) advocates the OSTO-approach which does not focus solely on the system itself but also takes into consideration the inter-dependencies with society. The author advocates the consideration of the value system of society when designing a manufacturing system. Any company has to compare regularly the environmental and social future directions with its current practice and must change designs accordingly.

In summary, the methodologies are evaluated against the following criteria and, therefore, a formal methodology should encompass:

- a clear set of objectives or a specification of the MSD project
- a formal evaluation procedure or its development
- the process should be iterative incorporating interdisciplinary design teams and
- simultaneous consideration of people, organisation and technology
- user participation and coordination of involvement at different stages and
- sufficient consideration of the systems environment and inter-dependencies with society

18.2.2 Detailed Analysis of Two Design Methodologies

In the next two sections of this paper, two case examples of design methodologies are analysed in more detail. One approach represents a methodology developed and applied by a UK consultancy, the second one is the Davis approach, 'Comprehensive, Integrated Organisation Design Process (1982), an approach representing a more theoretical methodology.

Description of the Practical Approach

This methodology, developed by a consultancy firm, focuses on the design and introduction of cellular manufacturing. The overall objectives of the methodology are to provide a structured approach to carrying out the design of manufacturing system incorporating the following features:

- The design should be targeted at enabling manufacturing to fulfil its strategic role for the business.
- The key design elements in achieving this are
  - physical restructuring/design of the manufacturing architecture
  - detailed operational design based on defined principles such as Total Quality,
    Systems Engineering and Japanese methodologies
  - business case evaluation
- Achieving a balance of strategic and detailed activities using a holistic design approach

The methodology consists of five phases, of which the first one deals with the consolidation and completion of the business guidelines. The second phase comprises the collection of data for concept definition and the detailed design. The third phase is concerned with data analysis for the detailed concept definition. The fourth phase forms the actual design stage and the fifth phase is a consolidation stage which audits the technical and financial side of the design proposal. The final deliverable is a design proposal for management discussion and approval. The step-by-step methodology is supported by a comprehensive set of techniques and checklists, etc., to be used for individual stages of the MSD process.

Analysis of the Practical Approach

The framework devised stresses the strategic implications of the design or redesign of manufacturing systems. The consideration of the business strategy at an early stage of the design process is vital since a new technology's potential is almost never realized if the strategy is inappropriate. The approach starts with the business objectives and constraints to find out the requirements the new system has to fulfil. The methodology considers the relationship of the company with society as a whole only by means of a market analysis which focuses on the demand for certain products. No effort is made to take the changing values of the company environment into consideration. Consequently, the approach disregards the environment's impact on the organisation and its members.

The methodology follows a sequential approach for the design of a manufacturing system. For example, a task called 'job design' is accomplished after the completion of the physical design which implies that this task is concerned with adjusting people to technology. Thus the approach does not fulfil the requirements of the simultaneous consideration of human, organisational and technical issues postulated above.

People (Workers) are considered as necessary elements of the design but the approach does not provide any principles or criteria to guide the designer towards a manufacturing system that satisfies human requirements. Furthermore, aspects such as qualification, payment schemes and career path systems are not addressed within the methodology.

The methodology does not cover the composition and structure of the design team. The participation of the operators is also not explicitly mentioned. This implies the risk that companies which follow this approach might not regard participation of the shop-floor employees as an important issue.

A further criticism of the methodology is that it regards the process of MSD as a project which ends with the preparation of a design proposal for management discussion and approval. Although the methodology includes a rough plan for the implementation the implementation process itself is not covered. It misses out on the chance to make improvements to the design during the implementation phase and does not encourage the setting-up of a continuous improvement process.

To sum up, one might say that the methodology described is very practice-oriented. It is detailed enough to guide the designer through the complete MSD process. It defines stages and the respective tasks, and advises on tools and techniques for the individual stages. The strongest criticism of the approach is that human factors are considered insufficiently and too late in the design process. Furthermore, changes of society's value system are not considered at all. The methodology does not serve as a coordinating and moderating mechanism to facilitate the communication throughout the organisation of an MSD process. No procedure is incorporated to involve the end-user of the system in the design process.

However, the research team felt that this methodology serves as a good basis for further development to a methodology which combines all the requirements stated above.

The Theoretical Approach

The approach analysed is the 'Comprehensive, Integrated Organisation Design Process' by Davis (1982). Davis developed a list of 21 principles or guidelines for the design of organisations. The principles are listed in four groups titled: 'systems', 'organisational structuring', 'organisational functioning', and 'support systems'. In general, Davis advises development of small 'self-maintaining organisational units' in an iterative way leaving enough freedom for a flexible development of these units. The author emphasises the multi-disciplinary nature of these units and the definition of their boundaries.

The methodology provides a procedure to guide the process of 'Creating the Temporary Design Organisation', which comprises a steering committee, manager, the design team, technical sub-teams and consultants as needed. Davis puts high importance on the dynamic re-configuration of the design team during the MSD process.
The body of the Davis methodology is divided into four phases, each consisting of several steps. The scope of applications reported in literature ranges from the design of a manufacturing unit to that of a complete manufacturing plant (Gerwin and Kolodny, 1992, Trist, 1981).

Before embarking on the design of the organisation, the methodology plans the development of an organisation philosophy to guide the design of the technical systems, social system, structure of the organisation, role of its members, social support system and relationships with society. Davis emphasises the continuity of

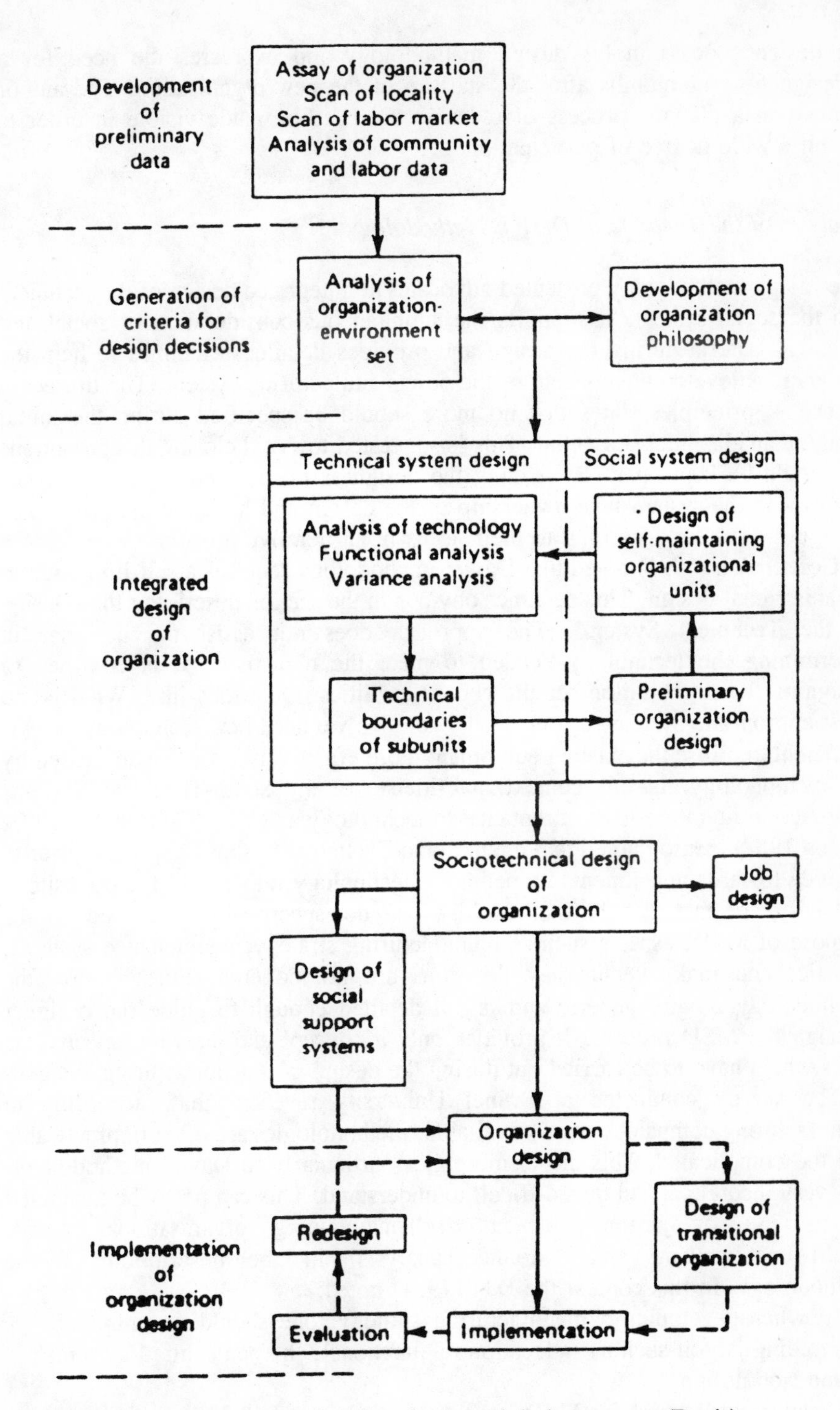

Fig 18.1. Phases of the comprehensive, integrated design process (Davis)

the design process in his design methodology and expresses the need for a redesign 6 to 12 months after the start-up of the new organisation. The author thinks that a planned process of redesign needs to be made visible in order to permit a wide degree of participation.

Analysis of the Theoretical Design Methodology

The design methodology presented advocates an integrated design of the technical and the social system. It supports the simultaneous consideration of social and technical criteria during the design and provides detailed principles to help the designer to develop the concept of the new manufacturing system. The thirteenth of Davis' principles states that no more should be specified during the initial design than absolutely essential. This is suggested to avoid closing design options that could be kept open. By leaving the design as open as possible, the people working in the system take ownership of the design and have the opportunity to change the system according to their needs in an iterative process.

Gottschalch (1991) noted that Davis' methodology requires a self limitation to organisational design. This becomes obvious in the section describing the 'Design of the Technical System'. The approach does not assist the designer in determining the technology needed to meet the objectives. It is confined to designing the organisation for the chosen facilities. Questions like 'What is the most appropriate system for our needs?' or 'Do we need new technology or is it sufficient to utilise the existing equipment more effectively?' are not addressed by the methodology. In this context, a criticism of the Socio-Technical Systems approach in literature is its acceptance of technology as given (Gottschalch 1991, Mason 1988). Mason noted that the in Socio-Technical-Systems approach priority is given towards adjustments by people to technology rather than the opposite.

Due to the fact that the methodology was not specifically developed for the purpose of MSD, aspects such as manufacturing strategy, maintenance systems, logistics and make versus buy decisions are not covered. Furthermore, the methodology is very generic and is not detailed enough to guide the designer through the MSD process. It provides only a concept and does not specify the tasks which have to be carried out during the design of a manufacturing system.

The survey conducted at Brunel University revealed that, according to manufacturing companies' views available, methodologies are often impracticable and too complicated. This criticism applies particularly to Davis' methodology. It is very theoretical and thus difficult to understand. This can partly be attributed to its use of jargon such as 'self-maintaining organisational units', 'multi-functionalism' and 'variance analysis' in the description of the methodology. In this context the DTI (1991) noted:

> "...when developing a manufacturing strategy, one should be pragmatic, avoiding jargon such as 'allocation of functions', 'human centred systems' and 'job design'"

This statement is valid for MSD in particular — a methodology should serve as a means of clear communication between the different functions participating in the design process. Since technical systems designers, social scientists and machine operators are using different technical languages and terms it is important that the language used to describe the methodology is easy to understand, unequivocal and intelligible to all. This view is confirmed by the Brunel University survey, where a considerable number of respondents identified the lack of a common language between the different business functions as a major obstacle for MSD related to cooperation (for references to the survey results see Chapter 3).

The design process described by Davis is based on participation of a wide range of the organisation's members from machine operators to senior managers. In general, this is a desirable feature of a design process because the people involved can make important contributions to the design process. However, cooperation including a large number of functions and individuals with a different background results in slow design processes (Symon 1990). Davis advocates broad participation and presents a procedure to 'create the temporary design organization' but he does not provide any methods to handle the participation of a large number of people to ensure a fast MSD process. This is a major hindrance to a widespread use of Davis' design methodology, since one major requirement expressed by most survey respondents was to reduce the lead times of MSD projects.

Further criticisms of Davis' approach which can be found in literature include that it has too narrow a focus on the system to be designed and thereby overlooks the inter-dependencies with other departments or units in the company, such as marketing, design engineering and that there is no emphasis on continuous improvement.

The approach described thus incorporates many of the characteristics which were identified as problems with the application of methodologies, by the respondents of the survey. It is too complicated, very abstract and difficult to understand. Furthermore, the approach does not provide guidance to the designer for the complete process of manufacturing systems design because of its focus on organisation design. Altogether, those characteristics identified in the previous section indicate that the methodology described is not able to meet the requirements for a practical approach to carry out the design of manufacturing systems. Nevertheless, the principles and the process developed by Davis can serve as a base for the development of the concept of an MSD methodology since it combines most of the requirements identified.

18.2.3 Summary

The two case studies of methodologies presented above demonstrate the gap between approaches developed by social scientists such as Davis and those used in industry such as the consultants approach. The former excels by a high degree of consideration of human aspects but is too theoretical and impractical. The latter provides a practical framework to guide the designer but disregards important aspects with regards to human factors and the wider social context of manufacturing systems which may ultimately lead to success or failure.

Neither of the two approaches provides methods to facilitate the participation of end users in the design process. This observation suggests that a need for further research in this area exists. In a survey conducted by Ingersoll Engineers (1992), managing directors were asked for their view about the best approach to change. According to the results of this survey, most companies prefer to approach change through continuous improvement.

Both approaches discussed fail to consider the implementation process as a major activity in the design process. Industrialists and academics are adamant that the major difficulties in MSD do not lie in the design but rather the successful implementation of the concept. Frequently conceptually good designs were implemented unsuccessfully and resulted in poor systems performance, due to problems encountered during the implementation. As a result, changes must be made to the design and the resulting system does then not conform to the initial design specification.

A further criticism which applies to both methodologies presented is that they focus solely on changes in the systems being designed and disregard the opportunity arising from changes in other units. For example, a product redesign which aims at eliminating unnecessary operations and facilitates manufacturing should be considered during the MSD process. Dertouzos, Lester and Solow (1989) cited experiences from the 'Proprinter project' at IBM. By reducing the number of components of the printer, the assembly operations were eliminated so that investment in unnecessary equipment was avoided. This example suggests that a methodology should include the possibility of product redesign.

18.3 Survey Results

This chapter reports the main findings of the report concerning the use of methodologies in MSD and the problems with the approaches manufacturing companies pursued.

The survey[3] conducted by the Brunel University research team addressed 640 manufacturing companies (75% of them in the UK) and 100 UK manufacturing consultants. Of the sample, about half of the companies were small and medium sized enterprises and half were larger organisations. The survey achieved a rate of response of 11%.

Achieving Performance

To obtain an overall view of the company culture a set of questions asked for the importance of three different success factors for the company. 98% stated that organisation is of high importance to them, 89% see the People related issues,

---

[3] A full report of the survey results can be obtained from the authors.

such as work place design and worker motivation and satisfaction, as being highly important and 77% view Technology as high in importance. This shows that companies have realised, in general, the importance of incorporating people aspects in their strategic planning as well as looking at the organisational implications.

Consideration of Different Aspects in MSD

To investigate to what degree manufacturing companies succeed in incorporating the aspects mentioned above into their approach towards MSD, manufacturing consultants were asked to assess current practise in industry. Fig. 18.2. details which aspects are considered during the design process and those which are overlooked according to the consultants' response.

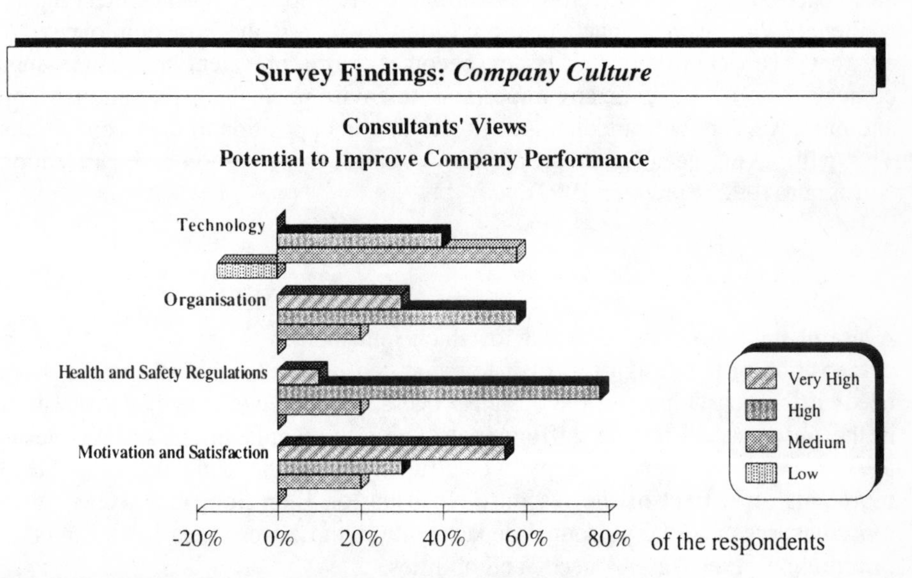

Fig. 18.2. Degree of factors considered during the MSD process

The consultants' view reveals an obvious gap between the aspects companies see as important and what they actually take into consideration during the MSD process. Aspects like personnel skills, psychological human factors, such as motivation, satisfaction etc., and physical human factors, which include ergonomics, health and safety regulations etc, are taken into consideration, in the consultants' opinion, with a low priority.

Summarising the results, one can say that manufacturing companies still do not take into account the operators' skills, well being and personal feelings during the design process to a sufficient extent. As a consequence of this, they encounter greater difficulties during the implementation process and the initial production stages. Furthermore, production systems which do not take into account human factors result in boring, monotonous and machine-paced jobs. These job characteristics lead to physical and health problems, increased labour turnover, absenteeism, accidents and mistakes. In disregarding aspects such as employee motivation, companies miss out on the opportunity to release the potential of their employees to increase productivity and quality (Kidd and Corbett 1988, Osborne 1987).

According to the respondents' answers, environmental considerations seem to have only a minor influence on decisions made during the design process. This is not surprising since an earlier question in the survey ascertained that environmental friendliness was not considered an important competitive factor. Manufacturing companies seem to disregard the increasing importance attached by the public to these issues. In future, environmental considerations will have an increasing influence on the customers' buying patterns. Furthermore, a manufacturing company's reputation concerning environmental issues will have an impact on their attractiveness as an employer. Those companies meeting this challenge will be in a much better position to recruit the best employees. As awareness of environmental issues becomes more prevalent and since most companies do not attribute any importance to environmental considerations, more and more workers will find themselves working in opposition to their convictions. This will have a negative effect on the workforce's motivation and satisfaction, (Birnkraut 1992, Sprenger 1992).

Participation in the MSD Process

A useful indicator for the extent to which human factors are considered is the composition of the design team, since the system is more likely to suit the users' needs if they participate in the design process. To this end, one of the questions in the survey asked for the staffing contribution to manufacturing systems design projects made by various departments/functions in the company. Fig. 18.3. represents an extract of the response, focusing on shop-floor employees, union representatives and the personnel department, as those were seen to be important in representing end-users' needs and abilities.

In a considerable number of the responding companies, shop-floor employees are not involved in the design of new manufacturing cells. Obviously, this number decreases further for design projects of a larger scope such as the design of a production unit or a complete factory. These figures suggest that many companies still disregard the opportunities arising from employee involvement at an early stage of the planning process. Firstly, the employees' knowledge can be utilised to improve the quality of the design, and secondly, the employees will be more supportive during the course of the project if they have already participated in the initial design stages. Concerning the first issue one can say that it is vital to involve shop-floor people, because nobody else has their knowledge and experience about the production process. The people involved in shop floor operations, either directly or indirectly, are generally the only people who are aware of the differences between the way the organisations is working and the way it is supposed to work. Participation is the only way to make use of the

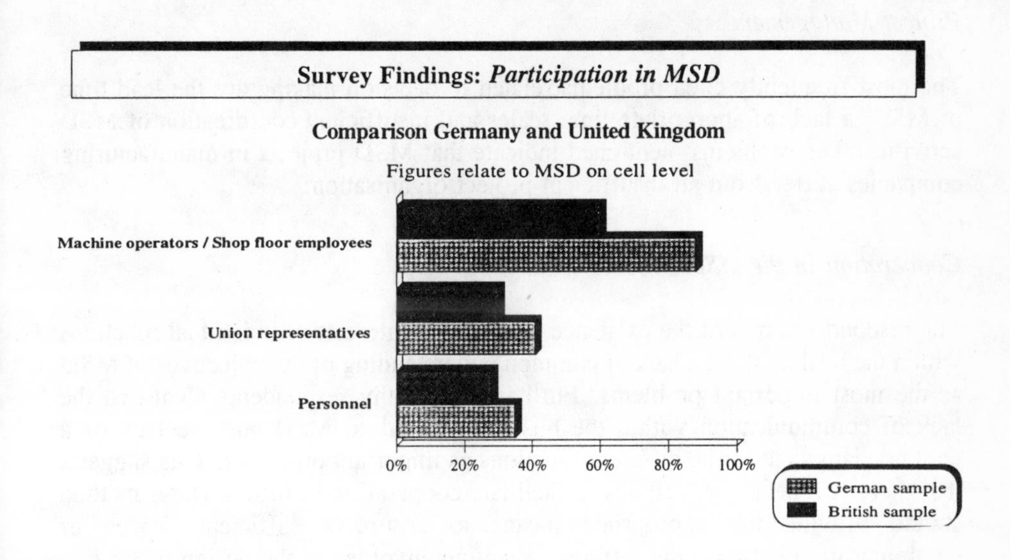

Fig. 18.3. Participation in the MSD process

employees' tacit knowledge, since this information is not available from other sources.

It is of particular importance that those affected have an understanding of the objectives and the background of the changes planned to avoid resistance to these changes. This issue must be viewed against the backdrop of fear of many employees that MSD projects only aim to substitute technology for human skills and thus decrease the size of the workforce. This fear comes from the experiences that many employees have made already with preceding rationalisation measures. (Therkorn 1991, DTI 1991, Sievers 1980, Rieckmann 1982).

18.3.4 Problems of the Design and Implementation Process

To be able to establish manufacturing industry's needs concerning the design of manufacturing systems, it is necessary to gain some knowledge about the difficulties they encounter during the design and implementation process. To this end one section of the questionnaire entitled 'Problems with MSD' investigated various aspects of such problems. The questions were split into four sections, addressing project management, cooperation in MSD, the approach to MSD and the implementation process.

Project Management

The most frequently cited problems related to decision making are the lead time of MSD, a lack of appropriate time scales and insufficient coordination of MSD activities. The problems mentioned indicate that MSD projects in manufacturing companies suffer from an insufficient project organisation.

Cooperation in the MSD Process

The respondents regard the existence of different interests of individual functions within the business and a lack of common understanding of the objectives of MSD as the most important problems. Furthermore, many respondents identified the lack of communication within the business related to MSD and the lack of a common language of the different functions as important problems. This suggests that there is a need for methods to facilitate cooperation in MSD. These method should provide the appropriate means to ensure a sufficient degree of communication between the different functions involved in the design process.

18.3.5 Approach to MSD

A high percentage of respondents stated that the evaluation of concepts is a major problem. The great importance attached to this issue by the respondents suggest that there is a need for methods to facilitate the evaluation of alternatives. In particular, methods are required to quantify the benefits arising from the consideration of human factors during the design process, since it is very difficult to assess the costs and benefits arising, for example from different organisational concepts or increased qualification of employees. Further problems, quoted by a considerable number of respondents, included: a lack of understanding during the conceptual stages, a lack of emphasis on the ongoing improvement process and insufficient definition of the objectives as well as the tasks in MSD.

18.3.6 Implementation Process

The next question investigated the problems arising during the implementation process. The most notable feature is the overall high rate of respondents who encountered problems. Difficulties can be attributed largely to the lack of consideration during the design process. For example, 40% of the respondents attached high importance to the problem of resistance of affected functions. This can be taken as an indication of a lack of information and involvement of these functions during the design process, as well as an insufficient consideration of their specific needs. 36% of the respondents complain about insufficient support during the implementation from other business functions, indicating that MSD is undertaken as an isolated process within one department of the organisation.

In summary one can say that almost all the problems defined in the questionnaire seem to be relevant for a considerable number of respondents. This result suggests that there exist serious deficiencies in the way companies design their manufacturing system. The nature of many of the problems mentioned by the respondents of the survey suggest that the cause for these problems lie within insufficient organisation and guidance during the planning process.

18.3.7 Managing the Change Process

To find the reasons for the difficulties which manufacturing companies encounter with the planning of production systems, more knowledge about the approaches towards MSD was required. In particular, it was of interest to discover whether the use of structured methodologies for the design of manufacturing systems is an appropriate means to overcome the deficiencies discussed in the previous section.

The Use of Formal Methodologies

Manufacturing Companies were asked whether they adopt structured, formal methodologies or whether they employ an informal approach to MSD. Figure 18.4, which illustrates the response, provides evidence that the majority of manufacturing companies do not use any formally defined methodology for the purpose of Manufacturing Systems Design.

A comparison of these results and those received from the consultants revealed, as expected, that amongst the latter the application of formal methodologies are more widespread.

To find out how comprehensive the methodologies are, the respondents were asked to specify the ones they used by assigning them to a possible three choices. 17% had adopted a 'complete framework' consisting of a sequence of stages with defined tasks, tools and techniques recommended for each task and a list of information required as well as its source. The majority of the responding companies use less detailed methodologies which include either a sequence of stages and a list of tools and techniques (32%) or only a set of tasks (36%).

The second question went on to ask those who had referred to the use of a methodology where it came from. Whilst the majority described their methodology as an in-house development (66%) or an in-house development with the help of consultants (26%), only 4% had adopted one from the public sector, from conferences or literature. During the literature research, various descriptions of methodologies used for the purpose of MSD indicated that they were not developed originally for this purpose but rather that they were altered in order to be suitable for MSD purposes. Thus the second part of this question asked for the purpose for which the methodology had been developed originally. 28% of the respondents use a methodology developed for product design, 26% use a project management methodology, while only 15% used a specific development for MSD and 13% used a methodology to guide the design process of information systems.

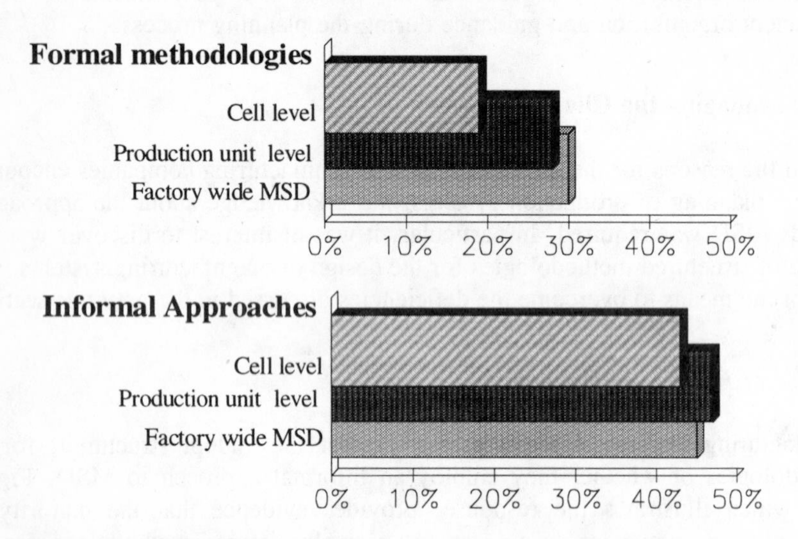

Fig. 18.4. The use of formal and informal approaches to MSD

Problems with the Use of Formal Methodologies

The last question of this section aimed at establishing the problems existing with the use of methodologies for MSD, according to the respondents' view. The response shown in Fig. 18.5. indicates the most frequently cited problems as that of known methodologies being either too specific or too generic for industrial practice and that following a methodology may be too time consuming.

Further problems mentioned concerning the application of methodologies were:

- *'impracticlal, too theoretical'*
- *'Too complicated'*
- *'We try to tailor methods from many areas to produce our own system which we own'*
- *'Horses for courses, need to maintain flexibility'*
- *'Lack of proper, well-developed tools'*
- *'Our people lack skill in methods other than HELIX[4]'*
- *'Suitable interest and general training understanding benefits'*
- *'There are no specific problems with MSD methodology'*

---

[4] HELIX stands for the 'helical project life-cycle design approach' developed by Human Centred Systems Ltd.

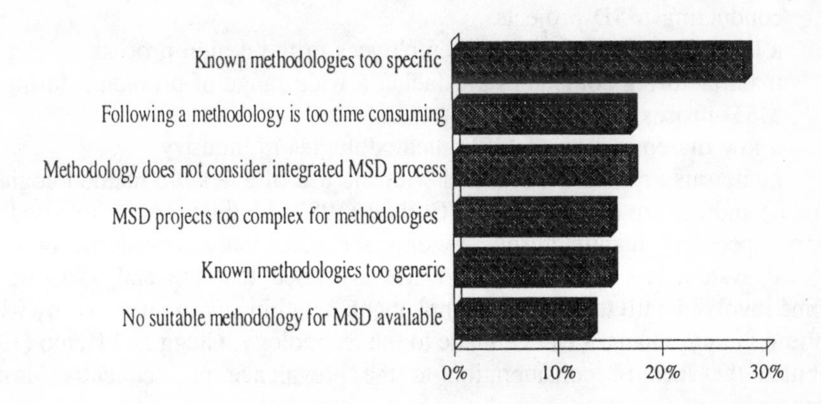

Fig. 18.5. Problems with the application of MSD methodologies

The last question in this section asked whether a methodology, once it had been developed, was used several times in the same way. 40% used the principle of the methodology but changed details according to the problem, 38% are still developing the methodology. Only 13% use the methodology more than once.

This indicates that only a minority of companies have an established methodology which has been proven useful in an application.

In analysing the results of the section covering the use of methodologies, one can say that, in general, there is a low rate of adoption of methodologies for MSD amongst manufacturing companies. Nearly all the methodologies used were specifically developed by manufacturing companies. Correspondingly, the penetration of methodologies from the public sector is very low. There are two possible explanations for this state of affairs: firstly, the lack of awareness in industry of the existence of such methodologies and secondly, as seen in Section 2, there is a lack of availability of methodologies which are considered by manufacturing companies to be suitable for their needs. The latter view was confirmed by several manufacturing companies and consultants during the follow-up interviews which were conducted additionally to the questionnaire survey. The respondents stated that it is very difficult to get hold of appropriate methodologies and tools for MSD. Some pointed out that every MSD project depends on its own specific constraints and concluded that methodologies available are not flexible enough to cope with these varying conditions.

Manufacturing companies see a wide range of problems with the applicability of available methodologies. This raises the question whether the use of a methodology, in general, is not appropriate for MSD projects or whether the difficulties identified by the respondents can be attributed to the nature of the methodologies used.

The concluding key points of the analysis conducted in this report are:

i.) a lack of consideration of human aspects in manufacturing industry when conducting MSD projects

ii.) a lack of participation of the employees in the design process

iii.) manufacturing companies are facing a wide range of problems during the MSD process

iv.) a low dissemination of MSD methodologies in industry

v.) numerous problems associated with the use of available methodologies

Points i.) and ii.) are emphasized by Corbett (1987) findings where he noted that human aspects of manufacturing systems are often only considered once the technical system has been developed. He criticised that the end users do not become involved until the system is implemented within an organisation, by which time few, if any, changes can be made to the technology. Clegg and Kemp (1986) attributed the lack of consideration to the prevalence of 'sequential design' processes.

Corbett advocates a 'parallel design' approach which involves the incorporation of human and social considerations as early as possible in the design process. He concludes that it is necessary to develop a methodology for the simultaneous consideration of social and technical criteria during the design process. In this context, Symon (1990) has noted:

> *'The means of achieving outcomes often dictate the outcomes that are achieved; therefore particular human-centred design methods are necessary to achieve the goal of human-centred technology.'*

The opinions of people involved in research in MSD cited above express the need for the use of a methodology in MSD to ensure the consideration of all important aspects. The results of the survey confirm this point of view and lead to the following key points. These should serve not only as indicators of current concern but also as pointers to future research opportunities.

i) A clear classification of available MSD methodologies is not available. The methodologies should be tested for their suitability on a range of different MSD cases.

ii) New design methodologies need to be developed suited to the design of advanced manufacturing systems. The methodologies should have guideline character and should explicitly advise the use of computer tools and manual techniques at various stages in the MSD process. The balanced consideration of all aspects of People, Organisation and Technology needs to be incorporated in these methodologies.

iii) A classification of reported MSD cases according to the type of manufacture and the organisational structure as well as the scope of the MSD process is required. This case base could provide the foundation for an example based approach incorporating knowledge-based methods. Furthermore such a case base could work as a mechanism for a unified terminology for the MSD field.

iv) An effective project management technique suited to MSD needs to be introduced alongside the MSD methodologies. The involvement of people of at all levels of the organisation and at different stages in the design process requires a systematic management of MSD projects.

v) The dissemination of available MSD tools and techniques needs to be improved. A classification of tools and techniques available and an evaluation of their useability for different MSD cases could encourage a wider use of advanced tools and techniques.

vi) The UK is lagging behind in the use and development of advanced computer tools and integrated systems for the purpose of MSD. Research and development needs to be encouraged and coordinated.

vii) The authors of this paper support the introduction of MSD development centres in the UK, supporting industry in MSD and particularly focusing on small and medium sized enterprises which do not have the resources to invest into advanced MSD approaches.

The MSD development centres would function as a means of technology transfer. Short courses in MSD and a demonstration facility for available computer tools and manual techniques would provide access to better practice for industry. The centres could act as a coordinating body in the research field and would initiate collaboration with various research institutes. A consultancy service provided would offer advice to industry and enable a feedback mechanism into research. It would be important that the same people who are involved in the research activities provide consultancy service, using their own developments. Close links to universities could involve staff of MSD development centres in teaching; in return student participation on a small scale in active MSD research would enhance the students' skills in MSD.

18.4 Summary and Conclusions

This paper has presented the analysis of a survey undertaken by Brunel University investigating various aspects of MSD. The results show that many manufacturing companies employ a trial-and-error approach to reach gradually a satisfactory state of systems operation. Only a minority follow a systematic approach when designing their manufacturing systems.

A major criticism resulting from the project was the lack of simultaneous consideration of people and organisation related aspects during MSD. The fact that designers disregard important aspects and, as consequence, face a wide range of problems during the design process, suggests that this approach is no longer feasible. It is vital to design a system which takes care of the needs and experiences of people in the system.

In general, the formalised methodologies identified by the authors can be divided in two major groups. On one side there are approaches which are too theoretical and do not meet manufacturing industry's need for a practical framework to guide the designer through the MSD process. In contrast, the methodologies of the other group offer a highly practice-oriented approach, but they are not suitable for ensuring that human related and organisational issues are effectively incorporated. Neither of the approaches offered mechanisms to facilitate communication and cooperation. Furthermore, they do not provide methods to ensure end-user participation in the MSD process.

In its conclusion, the research team suggests testing out the validity of other methodologies as listed in Appendix 5.1. It would be valuable for manufacturing systems designers to apply these and other methodologies available in a range of MSD projects in practice. Such investigations would provide information about the suitability of these methodologies for the purpose of manufacturing systems design. Managers would also gain an insight into the robustness, the time scales of applications and the practicability of such approaches.

The future needs concerning the use of methodologies for manufacturing systems design depend on the results of these investigations. If methodologies available can be proved to fulfil the requirements identified in this report, information about these approaches must be made available to manufacturing companies. If not, future research should focus on the development of suitable MSD methodologies on the basis of existing approaches and the experiences gained during their application. This methodology for future research is presented in Figure 18.6.

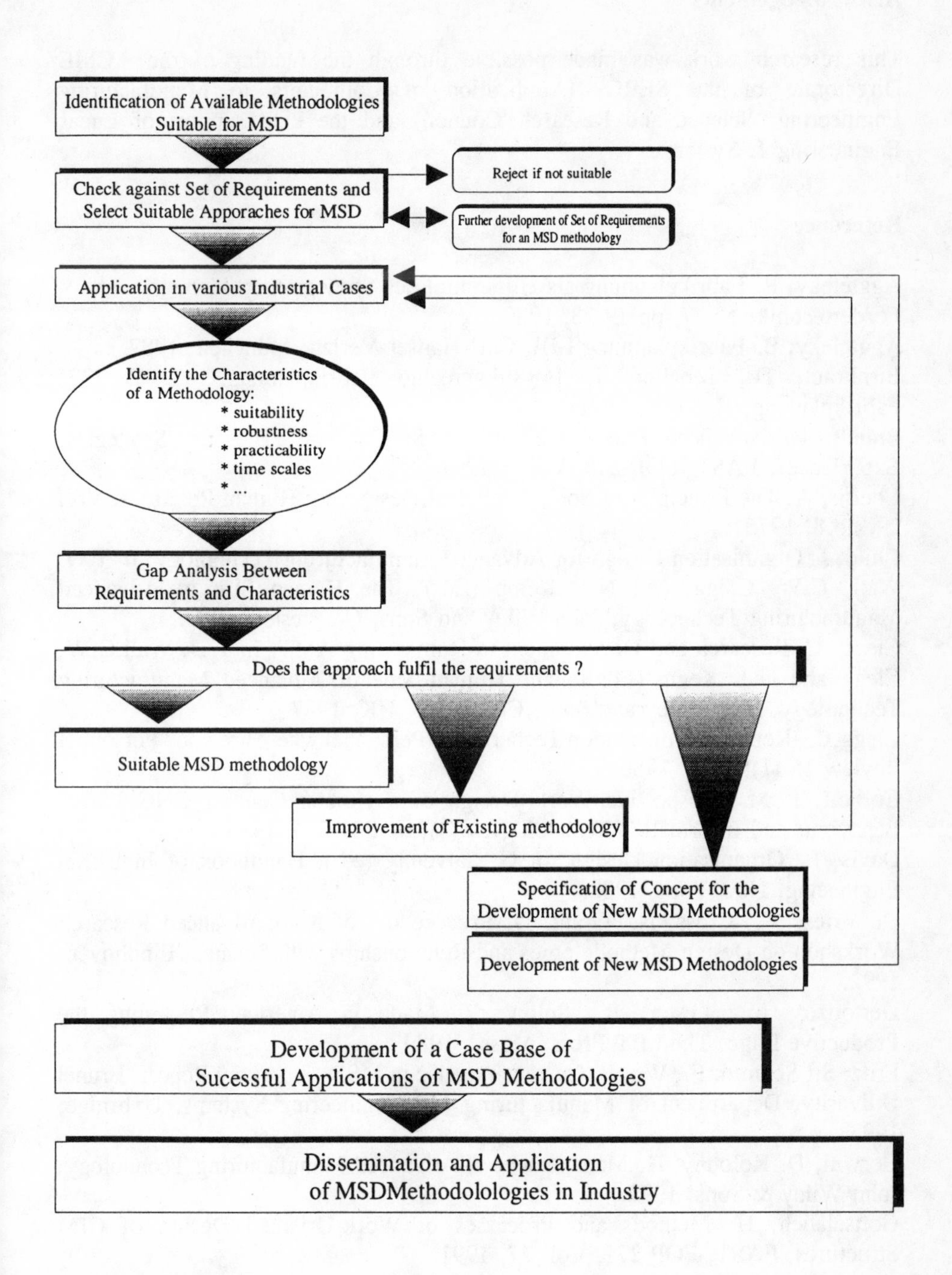

Fig. 18.6. Outline for future work on MSD methodologies

Acknowledgements

This research work was made possible through the funding of the ACME Directorate of the SERC, (Application of Computers to Manufacturing Engineering, Science and Research Council) and the kind support of Lucas Engineering & Systems.

References

Aggteleky, B. Fabrikplannung als Hilfsmittel des Strategischen Managements, Fördertechnik, Nr. 7, pp.19-23, 1989.
Aggteleky, B. Fabrikplannung I-III, Carl Hanser Verlag, München, 1987.
Birnkraut, D., Moeller, J. Logstikgerechte Fabrikplanung, VDI-Z 133, Fabrikplanung, Hanover, 1991.
Brandt, D. Advanced Experience with APS: Concepts, Designs, Strategies, Experiences, FAST, FOP 246, Vol 2, 1991.
Cherns, A. The Principles of Socio Technical Design, in: Human Relations, Vol, 29, no.8, 1976.
Child, J. Organisation Design for Advanced Manufacturing Technology. In T.D. Wall, C.W. Clegg, and N.J. Kemp (Eds), The Human Sise of Advanced Manufacturing Technology, John Wiley and Sons, Chichester, 1987.
Clegg, C. Research and Development in Humanising AMT. In T.D. Wall C.W. Clegg and N.J. Kemp (Eds.), The Human Side of Advanced Manufacturing Technology, John Wiley and Sons, Chichester, UK, 1987.
Clegg,C., Kemp,N. Information Technology: Personnel where are you? Personnel Review 15 (1), 8-15, 1986.
Corbett, J. M. Prospective Work Design of a Human Centred CNC Lathe, Behaviour and Information Technology, 4(3), pp 201-214, 1985.
Davis, L. Organisation Design, in G. Salvendy (ed.): Handbook of Industrial Engineeing, New York, 1982.
De Vries, M., Cross, N., Grant, D. Proceeeding of Nato Advanced Research Workshop on Design Methodologies and Relationships with Science, Eindhoven, 1992.
Dertouzos, M., Lester, R., Solow, R. Made in America: Regaining the Productive Edge, The MIT Press, Mass., 1989.
Fritz, S., Schmid, F., Wu, B. Current Practise in MSD. A Survey Report, Brunel Univerity, Department of Manufacturing and Engineering Systems, Uxbridge, 1993.
Gerwin, D. Kolodny, H. Management of Advanced Manufacturing Technology, John Wiley & Sons, 1992.
Gottschalch, H. Methods and Processes of Work-Oriented Design of CIM Structures, FAST, FOP 271, Vol. 27, 1991.
Havn, E. Questionning Analysis and Design Methods, in: International Journal of Human Factors in Manufacturing, Vol. 2, Part 3, 1992.

Ingersoll Engineeers Survey 1991. Change, The Good, The Bad and The Visionary, Ingersoll Engineers Limited, Rugby 1991.
Ingersoll Engineeers Survey 1992. Commitment, Implemeting the Change, a Survey of the Managemant of Change in Manufacturing Businesses, Ingersoll Engineers Limited, Rugby 1992.
Kidd, P. Organisation, People, and Technology in Europe Manufacturing, FAST, FOP 247, Vol. 3, 1990.
Kidd, P., Corbett, M. Towards the Joint Social and Technical Design of Advanced Manufacturing Systems in: International Journal of Industrial Ergonomics, 2, 1988.
Marks, S. Gemeinsame Gestaltung von Technik und Organisation in Soziotechnischen Kybernetischen Systemen, VDI-Verlag, Düsseldorf, 1991.
Maton, B. Socio-Technical-Systems: Conceptial and Implementation Problems, in: Relations Indsutrielles, 43(4), 198, 868-888, 1988.
Nadler, G. The Planning and Design Approach, Wiley-Interscience Publication, New York, 1981.
Osborn, D. Ergonimics at Work, 2nd ed. John Wiley & Sons, Chichster, 1987.
Riekmann, H. Auf der Grünen Wiese, Verlag Paul Haupt, Bern, 1982.
Schulze-Diekhoff, M. Integriertes Systems zur Ablauf Orientierten Fabrikplanung, München, Hanser Verlag, 1990.
Sievens, B. Das Phasenmodell der Organisationsentwicklung, in: Management Zeitschrift io 49, no. 1, Verlag Industrielle Organisation, Zürich, 1980.
Sprenger, R. Mythos Motivation, Campus Verlag, Frankfurt, 1992.
Symon, G. Human-Centred Computer Integrated Manufacturing, in: Computer Integrated Manufacturing Systems 3 (4), 1990.
Therkorn, U. Ein Betrieb denkt um: Die Dualitische Fabrikplannung, Springer Verlag, 1991.
Trist, E. The Evolution of Socio-Technical Systems, Occasional Paper, Ministry of Labour, Ontario, Vol 2, 1981.
Wallace, K. Some Observation on Design Thinking, in: Research in Design Thinking, Proceeding of a Workshop Meeeting, Delft, May 29-31, 1991.
Womack, J., Jomnes, D., Roos, D. The Machine that Changed the World, New York: Rawson Associates, 1991.
Wu, B. Manufacturing Systems Design and Analysis, Chapman & Hall, London 1992.

Appendix

MSD Methodologies Identified

Methodology	Source	Origin	Year	Purpose
Design methodologies compiled from recent literature				
Systems Engineering - Methodik und Praxis	Dänzer, W. Huber, F.	CH[10]	1992	MSD
Design and evaluation methodology	Wu, B.	UK[11]	1992	MSD
Ablaufphasen der Fabrikplanung	Pröll, E.	D[12]	1992	MSD
Dyn. Groblayoutplanung	Brinkmann, M.	D	1989	MSD
Fabrikplanung	Aggteleky, B.	D	1987	MSD
PadeS[13]	IPK[14], Berlin	D	1992	CIM-Design
Framework for Design and Evaluation	Clegg, C Symon, G.	UK	1989	CIM Design
Parallel design procedure for human-centered AMT[15]	Besant, C.	UK	1988	Design of AMS[16]
AMS design methodology	Doumeingts, B.	F[17]	1987	Design of AMS
Comprehensive, integrated design process	Davis, L.	US[18]	1981	Design of STS[19]
Engineered organisational design	Jenkins, D.	D	1982	Design of work organisational arrangements
ETHICS[20]	Mumford, E.	UK	1979	Design of STS
DRAMA[21]	Bennett, D.	US	1989	Design of Assembly systems

Framework for systems engineering design	M'Pherson, P.	UK	1981	Design of Engineering systems
Systementwicklung mit strukturierten Methoden	Raasch, J.	D	1988	Design of systems
Vorgehensweise der Systemplanung und -realisierung	Patzak, G.	D	1982	Design of systems
Planning and design approach	Nadler, G.	US	1981	Design of systems
Soft Systems methodology	Checkland, P.	UK	1981	Design of systems
SADT[22]	Cane, C. Sarson, T.	US	1977	Design of systems
XSpec[23] design process	Judd, R.	US	1990	Design of mechanical systems/ software control
SSADM[24]	Ashworth, C.	UK	1981	Design of computer systems
MSD methodology	Lucas Engineering & Systems	UK	1990	MSD
Helical project life cycle	Human Centred Systems Ltd	UK	1992	Development of systems/ software

[10] CH: Switzerland

[11] UK: United Kingdom

[12] D: Germany

[13] Participative design of decentralised Structures

[14] Institut fuer Produktionsanlagen und Konstruktionstechnik

[15] Advanced Manufacturing Technology

[16] Advanced Manufacturing Systems

[17] F: France

[18] US: United States of America

[19] Socio-Technical Systems

[20] Effective Technical and Human Implementation of Computer-based Systems

[21] Design Routine for Adopting Modular Assembly

[22] Structured Analysis and Design Technique

[23] executable Specification

[24] Structured Systems Analysis and Design Method

19. Developing an Anthropocentric View of Modern Manufacturing — A Case Study Approach

Felix Schmid[1] and Stephen Evans[2]

[1] Department of M&ES, Brunel University
[2] The CIM Institute, Cranfield University

Abstract. The SCANCO Case Study approach is a well defined and extensively tested tool for the development of systems awareness and team working skills in the context of business systems redesign. The paper describes the structured approach used and relates the process and the results of an application of the tool as a team development activity during the NATO ASI on 'People and Computers'. The authors highlight the possible application areas of the approach and place it in the context of the concept of 'People, Organisations and Technology' (POT). There are some cautionary remarks — the approach requires experienced, skilled and motivated leadership.

Keywords. People, organisation, teamwork, motivation, systems design, organisational change, information systems

19.1 Introduction

There are a number of key areas of engineering involvement where it is essential that staff be able to work in teams and where such an ability has to be created very quickly. Three generic situations which often result in the need for effective teamwork and for new approaches in creating teams are outlined below. The context in which the situations are discussed is that of People, Organisations and Technology.

19.2 People, Organisations, Technology (POT)

In the past, the world of engineering was dominated by technology issues. Improved machines and processes were perceived as the solution to most problems in manufacturing industry. Depending on whether a company was based in a continental European or Anglo-Saxon country, people were considered either as essential to the running of a plant or as a necessary evil. In either case their role was not discussed. The method of organisation of production was often not judged important and was therefore left to *ad hoc* decisions.

The increasing use of very expensive advanced systems, requiring better management and a far more qualified work force, resulted in the realisation that all elements forming a manufacturing entity had to be considered together. Very soon this new paradigm was shown to be applicable to more conventional environments as well, particularly as a result of commercial pressures. The importance of people and of the method of organisation is now held to be on a par with that of technology. The current world recession may have increased the availability of qualified staff — but a holistic view of POT is still essential.

The concept of POT is closely linked to that of Human Centred Systems Design, where the organisation is set up to use people and technology optimally, according to their respective capabilities. However, most existing businesses are not yet able to translate such ideals into *real* performance change. Creating the necessary understanding and commitment across all contributors may be the key which unlocks the potential of the company. This paper describes a case study based approach which attempts to improve understanding and commitment. It clarifies the integration issues of people, organisation and technology, highlights implementation pitfalls and so improves plan quality. Lastly, it demonstrates to the contributors that individuals with different skills and experience levels can and should work together to meet a challenging, common goal. The approach is suited to solving problems in a number of situations common to engineering companies.

19.3 Typical Situations

Situation 1: Strategy Development and Implementation

At various stages of a company's development, it can be necessary to develop new strategies. This can come about as the result of market or technological change (outside pressure) or of a desire to re-orientate the company (inside pressure). In most sizeable organisations, the creation of a new strategy involves people from many different functional areas and with a wide range of technical, scientific and managerial backgrounds. For a strategy to be coherent and supportive of the company's mission, it is essential that cohesion within the group designing the strategy be achieved quickly.

A specific pressure achieved to devise new strategies exists where commercial advantage can be gained from new computer and information systems. Throughout the period of the computing revolution, companies have tended to assemble different and often incompatible systems to carry out particular tasks. However, at some point it becomes necessary to move towards integrated systems which will support collaboration between functional areas.

It is relatively easy to assemble a group of engineers and managers from a wide range of disciplines and to set them the task of strengthening the company's performance by devising better ways of using existing and new information systems. Most likely, such a group will put forward, after a relatively short period of time, a convincing and costed compromise proposal. It is also likely that the proposal will be functional and static. Functional because group members represent their function and obviously seek solutions which meet their needs, with much less concern over other functions' problems. Static because an (unstated) constraint is that the current organisation structure and methods will remain — the new strategy is for Technology only and any change in Organisation or People will be minor and restricted to individual functions. Such a solution is suboptimal by nature. The working group with its wide range of targets must therefore be turned into a team with a common goal. A group whose members were focused on the specific problems experienced by individual business functions must re-orientate itself to satisfy the needs of the company as a whole. This may well be the most difficult task in introducing the changed approach to information management and is typical of situations where the Anthropocentric approach can be of value.

Situation 2: The Management of Engineering Projects

The management of substantial engineering projects and large scale production systems requires a wide knowledge base and a range of skills which can only be acquired through many years of experience. However, rapid technical advances and social changes mean that such abilities become out of date very quickly. One of the solutions adopted by industry for the problems of operating a complex and dynamic systems is the deployment of multi-skilled and multi-functional teams. Typical examples can be found in production environments where products and processes change frequently and unpredictably. Projects such as the construction of the Channel Tunnel require closely knit teams, working effectively virtually from day one. Such semi-permanent teams again require the benefits of integrated understanding and purpose sought for in the Anthropocentric Case approach.

Situation 3: Engineering Education

New education and training approaches, for example, those aiming at a reduction in formal teaching, require teamwork involving students of varying levels of ability and different interests. In terms of creating a functioning team out of a group of people, this is a most challenging situation. Although there is usually a commonality of purpose (pass an exam) and a relatively homogenous mix of backgrounds, there are none of the pressures which can be applied in industry to motivate people into a desired behavioural pattern. Students can rarely be encouraged to perform in a particular manner through an offer of better pay or promotion. Time is usually more limited and more rigidly controlled than in industry, not all subject areas lend themselves to the same approach, exams tend to be immovable and any tasks are both temporary and part-time.

Since most engineering and management students will ultimately be working in industrial teams, it is important to develop an awareness and some of the relevant skills during their studies. Whilst it is possible to impart some of the skills in lectures it is more appropriate to achieve this objective through some form of team work approach, even though there are a number of constraints militating against this, in particular the time limits.

In all the above cases, a process of change must be established quickly, a process which improves both commitment to a common goal and shows how to integrate P/O/T to get there.

19.4 The Case Study Method

19.4.1 Background

Staff at The CIM Institute, Cranfield University have developed a case based approach to the creation of effective working teams. The technique is based on the setting of a realistic task to a group of people, who may be working together for the first time. The method has been used in many different settings, including all the scenarios described above, in industry and education. It was also used during the NATO Advanced Study Institute 'PEOPLE and COMPUTERS - Applying an Anthropocentric Approach to Integrated Production Systems and Organisations' with the twin objectives of creating an awareness of the need to transform companies with human factors in mind and of developing strong teams. The latter was a necessity arising from the structure of the Institute where large periods of time were used for team based development of concepts.

The NATO ASI offered an ideal opportunity to test and demonstrate the way in which the method works. It involved the transformation of a set of individuals from a wide range of occupational and cultural backgrounds first into working groups and then into teams. The Institute had members from Western Europe, the USA, Russia, Turkey and other countries. Their job descriptions ranged from academics in sociology to practitioners in computer engineering. There were substantial language barriers to overcome, not only at the scientific level but also in terms of straightforward everyday communication.

19.4.2 Case Description

The case study is based on a substantive document developed from consultancy with a company. For the purpose of the case, the company is called SCANCO, a manufacturer of high precision electromechanical equipment, faced with a choice of options regarding its business future. While the example company has been made unrecognisable, many of the facts about the company (size, financial information) and the outline of its culture are drawn from the original, only name and product are changed. The company culture and situation is conveyed through a number of verbatim transcripts of interviews with senior management. The participants in the group activity are asked to read and annotate the document in preparation for the session which lasts between four and sixteen hours, depending on the audience and the organisers' objectives.

The overall goal of the exercise or session is the development of an information systems strategy for SCANCO which has 'islands of computer use' but no integrated business systems. In many industrial situations this is, in fact, the real life task facing managers and engineers taking part in the case study.

The objectives of the exercise are firstly to bring together groups of individuals with different skills and allow them to build a process for cooperation. This is useful later in that they more easily recognise the value of other disciplines' inputs and have a way of co-operating efficiently. Secondly, the exercise clarifies many integration issues; real-life complexity is conveyed and the participants complete the exercise, having tackled genuine people/organisation/technology integration problems. Lastly, the exercise is tough, achieving a sensible result in a short time increases team confidence — an important objective for the NATO ASI where serious challenges lay ahead.

In the Institute, the case study session followed a simple structure, based on the principle that we learn more by doing than by listening. After introductory scene-setting and explanation, a cyclical process is established. A schematic overview of the process is shown in Fig. 19.1, although it must be noted that the activities marked with an asterisk were not addressed, since they did not apply to the situation and also in order to save time. For each stage, a question is presented by the case facilitator, the teams separate into their own work-rooms to develop an answer, the answers are roughly presented to the other teams, teams review their answer in the light of all the answers and then the next question is presented. This process can cycle as quickly as 45 minutes; in the NATO ASI each cycle was approximately 2 hours (with some opportunity to add unscheduled time to this, such as lunch and evening). The longer period was necessary to cope with the desire for achieving high-quality understanding of integration in practice and to assist multi-cultural, multi-lingual cohesion.
The break up into teams of about seven participants is needed to provide everyone with a chance to take part. The choice of participants for each team was an important task, particularly in the setting of the ASI, undertaken by the designated observers. Based on c.v. information and observed personality, each team was selected to have a range of skills (eg. computing, manufacturing, human-computer interaction), a range of education and professional backgrounds (eg. industry, system implementation, service industry, researcher), a range of nationalities (though consideration of the need for multi-lingual interpreters was also necessary) and, lastly, for homogeneity of temperaments. In some learning environments, the inclusion of a range of temperaments may be used to facilitate understanding of the clash between some temperaments. In the NATO ASI, a number of demanding goals already existed and the teams were made up of individuals with some similar significant trait, for example, stronger communicators were teamed to reduce their potential impact on weaker communicators.

Moderators were trained and were present in each team room. Their role was to assist the communication and cooperation process where it was performing below par. Therefore no elaborate process review or feedback was given;

assistance was provided only in meeting tight time deadlines, ensuring everyone got heard, and clarifying mis-communication etc.

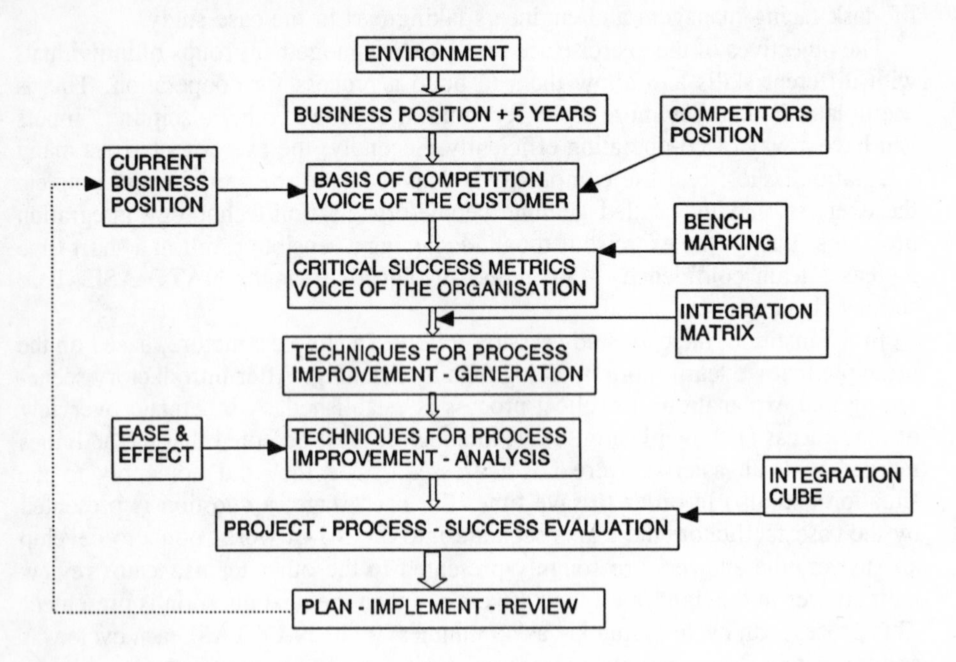

Fig. 19.1

19.4.3 Workflow

The introductory presentation explains all the goals of the exercise, introduces the company 'SCANCO' and briefly explains the environment in which it is operating. But first we must understand the customer — for it is only by knowing for what customers will pay that a company can hope to thrive. This forms the basis of the first question — "Why will SCANCO's customers continue to buy from them?". This question acts as a good ice-breaker as well, because everyone is a consumer and a customer and team members' skill differences are minimized in answering this question. The requirements placed on SCANCO are identified as an ability to be flexible, to respond to an ever-changing customer, to work more closely with customers, etc. This explains the need for a significant change in the way the company operates.

Even at this stage, it is possible to see some difference in output between teams. This difference reflects the simple reality that the SCANCO management team can and will make different choices in practice — many of which can be successful. As each question is answered each teams view of SCANCO slowly diverges until the final question — deliver a plan for action — can result in widely different outputs.

19.4.4 Observations

In common with other groups using the exercise, the teams spent most of the answering time on the first question in developing some common terms and a discussion/decision-making process, Also typical was the desire to answer the next (unasked) question: for example, the second question asks "What does the company have to be good at?". Many teams answer the third question instead — "How might they do it?", confusion between what is done and how it is done appear in all exercises and in real life, and was repeated in the NATO ASI.

Most teams correctly identify the need for a forward plan for the company which integrated the various people, organisation and technology issues. However, most teams develop only simplistic solutions — often calling for 'broad' strategies such as 'involve the user', 'more education and training' or 'get top management commitment'.

In the NATO ASI, it was hoped that the anthropocentric theme would attract participants who would have the desire and capability to develop a more focused solution, This proved to be the case. The result of 50 plus 'team-hours' work is far too extensive to discuss in detail but it is interesting that noticeably different tactics emerged to meet the integration strategic challenge.

19.4.5 Multiplicity of Solutions

One team developed a strong people/organisation integration strategy, with over 12 projects involving inter-department communication (such as co-locating design and production). The only computer technology project was a communication network! In this solution, improved inter-department communication will change the company so significantly that expensive technology aids should be delayed until the 'new' company emerges.

A second team took the theme of information integration — by firstly gaining information and insight into current processes (investigative projects) and then by using the computer to act as the information highway to bring departments closer together. Another team followed a similar information highway theme by planning multiple projects for linking departments (eg. sales-design, production - purchasing - suppliers).

Yet another team took the *learning by doing* approach by identifying a small number of key projects. The projects were different in nature — some people-led, some IT-led, some process-led — and the use of pilots would enable the company to learn what approach worked best in which conditions.

The last team took a logistics and coordination approach. They identified key projects where multiple departments could choose to work to the same plan — thus facilitating integration rather than prescribing it.

By the end of the process which, in the case of the NATO Advanced Study Institute lasted about ten hours, all the working groups had been transformed into reasonably functional teams which became stronger as they had to address further 'real' tasks arising throughout the rest of the Institute. Indeed, towards the end of the Institute, when it became necessary to allocate the remaining members of one group to two other groups there was very strong resistance from one of the groups and a partial loss of openness and effectiveness was the result.

A clearly heightened awareness of the need for involving all the people affected by the implementation of new systems has been an outcome of all the instances where the authors have conducted the SCANCO case study. This was never one of the objectives mentioned explicitly when starting the case study work with a new set of groups; it was a realisation at which the groups arrived naturally. Very often in their own discussions, they would lack information and guidance and would therefore experience sensations which people are faced with in similar real life situations: a dominance of technological issues and the lack of a goal to which all members could clearly aspire.

Although the SCANCO based case study offers many opportunities for developing people's awareness and for harnessing their inputs to a system design process, it requires a strong and experienced leader and manager. The members of the teams must be prepared to work hard. However, they will normally be highly motivated as a result of being involved in the first two stages of the case study. In industrial contexts it is essential that senior management back the exercise and show preparedness to adopt some of the results.

19.5 Conclusion

The case study approach described has proved its value in many different situations. Its use in creating functioning teams in the context of the NATO Advanced Study Institute proved to be very successful, evidenced by the establishment of a common language, a common approach to problem solving and a common theory/understanding of the Anthropocentric nature of real-life manufacturing problems. While these are useful abilities, the greatest value is in the recognition that only by bringing individuals with different functional skills, different experience and different viewpoints together that we can hope to meet the challenge of bringing People and Organisation and Technology together.

20. A Human Centred Approach to Requirements Specification

Linda Macaulay

Department of Computation, U.M.I.S.T. (University of Manchester Institute of Science and Technology), P.O. Box 88, Manchester M60 1QD, UK

Abstract. There is increasing recognition that the development of successful computer systems relies not only on the excellence of the technology but also on the people involved in the development process. In addition, the success of a system often depends on the level of acceptance and use by the people for whom it was intended.

In this paper, the author considers the requirements stage of the development process in some detail and argues that a human centred approach to requirements specification should have three major features. Firstly, the scope of the requirements investigation should be such that human and organisational factors are considered alongside technical software and hardware factors. Secondly the process of requirements specification should facilitate human communication between users, developers and other stakeholders. Finally the techniques used for knowledge development within the requirements stage should be such that they support the acquisition of abstract knowledge and concrete experience of the users' present work, the technological options and the future system.

A particular human centred approach called Cooperative Requirements Capture is briefly explained and evaluated against the three features: scope, human communication and techniques for knowledge development. The paper concludes with examples of use of Cooperative Requirements Capture in a number of commercial settings.

Keywords. cooperative requirements capture, requirements specification, human-centred methodologies in system design

20.1 Introduction

This paper is concerned with that part of a development project where the requirements for *what* needs to be developed are identified. Establishing requirements adequately can have a critical impact on the remainder of the development process and on the ultimate success of the system produced. The first three sections of this paper identify some of problems that can occur if insufficient attention is paid to the human aspects within requirements — all of these point to the need for a human centred approach to requirements specification. The author argues that a human centred approach to requirements specification should have three major features. Firstly, the *scope* of the requirements investigation should be such that human and organisational factors are considered alongside technical software and hardware factors. Secondly the process of requirements specification should facilitate *human communication* between users, developers and other stakeholders. Finally the techniques used for *knowledge development* within the requirements stage should be such that they support the acquisition of abstract knowledge and concrete experience of the users' present work, the technological options and the future system. In the fourth section, a particular human centred approach called Cooperative Requirements Capture is briefly explained and evaluated against the three features: scope, human communication and techniques for knowledge development. The paper concludes with examples of use of Cooperative Requirements Capture in a number of commercial settings.

20.2 Requirements Specification and the Scope of the Design Process

A requirements specification represents a specification of change. In particular changes to the user's job, changes to the operation and organisation of particular workgroups or departments and changes to organisations. Often requirements specifiers assume that changes to the user's environment is the responsibility of the user and consider that they are responsible only for the specification of the (functional) software.

It has been shown in the important study of Management Information Systems (MIS) carried out by Bjorn- Anderson, Eason and Robey [3] that the scope of the design process has a critical impact on the manager and the organisation. In particular, where systems were specified solely in terms of the software required and where the specifiers and designers held a narrow technical view of the world, a large number of accidental impacts occurred, especially in terms of unplanned changes to task complexity, to the workload of managers and to their power and influence. A particular case quoted in the study shows that one organisation had planned to use MIS to aid decentralisation but the result of introducing MIS was further centralisation. This again was in an organisation where the specifiers and designers held a purely technical view of the world, even though the intended scope of the design was that it should extend beyond the functional software and into the organisation.

At a finer level of detail, Bailey [1,2] has shown that the occurrence of errors in interactive systems can be traced to the fact that the data does not accurately represent 'real world' conditions or that the data does not meet the content or format requirements of the system. The first of these factors is directly related to an inadequate understanding of users and their environment, particularly in terms of use of language and task dependent terminology; an understanding of how to present information in ways which are 'natural' to the user and an understanding of the training and documentation needs of the user. Bailey's studies indicate that there are seven major causal factors related to errors in computer systems with the following relative importance: personal factors 35%, system design 20%, written instructions 10%, training 10%, human-computer interface 10%, environment 5%, organisational accuracy requirement 10%. Most of these causal factors are not necessarily related to the design of the software but to broader issues external to the actual code produced.

This discussion points to one of the major causes of problems, the 'scope' of design process and the software or technical orientation of techniques employed. The next section points to a second source of problem that of poor communication between system developers and users.

20.3 Requirements Specification and Human Communication

A requirements specification is primarily a vehicle for communication between the system specifiers, system users and system implementors. The system specifier communicates his or her views about the system through a 'specification' to the system users and implementors [11]. First, however, the system specifier must elicit the requirements from the user. This is usually achieved through the use of interviewing techniques, where the user plays a relatively 'passive' role. The communication problem occurs when the specifier has insufficient information about the proposed system to ask the right questions, and the user has little knowledge of the requirement capture process to provide the right answers. Socio-technical approaches, however, suggest a more active role for the user through participation in the specification and design of systems [4,6,13]. This view is supported by Palmer [14] who considers that the only true alternative to interviewing techniques is to have expertise in software development residing with both user and design teams. Exact communication linkages may then be established and maintained throughout the entire development process.

Eason [6] offers a number of options for the construction of the design team (who also have responsibility for requirements capture) where the roles of the 'technical experts' and the 'customers' are clearly identified. The technical experts contribute their skills to the creation of a system whilst the customers are concerned with the world they will have to inhabit after the change caused by the new system. The customers also have a wide range of specific knowledge about the way the organisation functions and the tasks it undertakes. The technical experts will want the system to help them advance their own design skills. Eason recommends therefore that the structure of the design team recognises the fact that both specialists and customers have expertise to contribute and vested interests in the solutions adopted.

The three options suggested by Eason are:

a) *Technical Centred Design* where customers commission and accept the system and are informed and consulted throughout the design process
b) *Joint Customer-Specialist Design* where user representatives are involved in all stages of the design process

c) *User-Centred Design* where the technical experts provide a technical service to the users and all users contribute to the design

In his discussion on the alternative design team structures, Eason suggests a number of criteria that could be used to evaluate the effectiveness of each structure. The first two criteria are concerned with the presence of technical skills needed and with the human and organisation specific knowledge needed if the proposed system is concerned with organisational change. Three and four refer to the expert contributions that can be made by potential users, particularly the extent to which users have the opportunity to contribute specific task knowledge or to assess the organisational effects of the proposed system. Five and six are concerned with the vested interests of the different stakeholders, for example, are stakeholders able to negotiate their interests and are users able to develop a feeling of ownership? The last two criteria deal with the practicality and acceptability of the design team structure as far as the commissioning organisation is concerned.

Eason's own evaluation of the alternative team structures suggests that each approach has strengths and weaknesses. The Technical Centred Design Team scores favourably on having the technical skills where needed, is a practical use of resources and acceptable to the commissioning organisation but fails on every other criteria. The Joint Customer Specialist Design Team, on the other hand, passes on all criteria except five and six whereby stakeholders cannot negotiate interests and users cannot develop a feeling of ownership. The third option, the User Centred Design Team, scores favourably on most counts. It most noticeably fails, however, on the last two criteria — it is not perceived as a practical use of resources and is generally not acceptable to the commissioning organisation.

None of the structures proposed is ideal. The Technical Centred design team finds favour with the commissioning organisation but largely ignores the need for participation of users and other stakeholders. The Joint Customer-Specialist design team is widely accepted but is likely to result in some stakeholder needs being ignored. The User-Centred design team, on the other hand, takes everyone's needs into account but is too inefficient in the use of resources.

The human communication problem thus concerns selection of personnel for participation in the requirements process such that technical experts', users' and customers' interests can be adequately represented. However, classifying personnel under these three headings is inadequate in terms of identifying all the interests which need to be represented. A fuller classification is suggested below.

A stakeholder is defined here using Mitroff's [12] terms, as all those who have a stake in the change being considered, those who stand to gain from it, and those who stand to lose. The author's own experience suggests that the stakeholders in any computer system will include:

(a) Those who are responsible for its *design and development*, for example, the project manager, software designers, communications experts, technical authors.

(b) Those with a *financial interest*, responsible for its sale (for example, the business analyst or in some situations the marketeer), or responsible for its purchase (i.e.the buyer).

(c) Those responsible for its *introduction and maintenance* within an organisation, for example, training and user support staff, installation and maintenance engineers and users' managers.

(d) Those who have an *interest in its use*, for example, users managers and all classes of users i.e. primary (frequent hands-on users), secondary (occasional users or those who use the system through an intermediary) or tertiary (those affected by the introduction of the system).

Some of the stakeholders identified above, particularly in categories (a) and (c) have a direct responsibility for the design and development of the various system components and hence have a major interest in being involved in the requirements capture process. Those in category (b) have a financial responsibility for the success of the computer system and therefore may also need to be involved. The stakeholders in category (d) will be the recipients of the resulting computer system, they also have a major contribution to make in terms of specific task knowledge and the ability to assess the likely effects of the new system. Thus one could argue that stakeholders from each of these categories should participate in the requirements capture process. Such a 'requirements team' would certainly possess a wide range of knowledge and skills and also have widely varying motives for being involved. See [9] for a fuller discussion of the potential problems of involving representative stakeholders in a requirements exercise. Thus the human communication problem concerns not only selection of personnel but also the means by which the people communicate with each other.

One important means of communication is through the use of techniques for developing mutual understanding and knowledge about users present and future needs. The next section discusses the role of techniques for knowledge development within requirements specification.

20.4 Requirements Specification and Knowledge Development

Often the system development process is described in terms of work products, for example, SSADM [88] is described in terms of numbers of stages, each stage has a number of steps, each step has associated inputs, processes and outputs. In line with many methods, the emphasis is placed on process and outputs or workproducts. This approach is attractive in situations where the development process is being audited, since workproducts can be seen and scrutinised as part of a quality assurance process. Unfortunately, the production of these work products is often given more importance than developing a 'real' understanding of the user needs. The results of the development process are, according to Kensung & Madsen [7], "a system and a complete technical and organisational implementation process". They argue that the intermediate results are documents and knowledge obtained by the participants. Regardless of the development model, be it waterfall, spiral, incremental or parallel, these results form the basis of important decisions. The author wishes to emphasise the fact that not only are documents produced as part of the process but that knowledge development is also part of the process. It is the development of knowledge which is often neglected within process oriented development methods.

Knowledge is developed by the people who are involved and different types of knowledge are needed at different stages in the development cycle. During requirements specification, a 'vision' of the future system needs to be acquired. Knowledge of users' current practices is needed. Projections of change using knowledge of the organisation and of external factors, knowledge of skills and motivations of the targets users are also needed, indeed there are many areas of knowledge required.

Kensung and Mansen, [7], suggest that six areas of knowledge and understanding are needed before system development begins. These areas are based on the thesis that:

"The main domains of discourse in design are:

- *users' present work*
- *technological options*
- *new system*

Knowledge of these domains must be developed and integrated in order for the design process to be a success".

In addition they suggest that "two levels of knowledge" of each of these domains of discourse is required. These are:

1. Abstract Knowledge: to get an overview of the domain of discourse
2. Concrete Experience: in order to understand that abstract knowledge

This leads to the six areas of knowledge shown in Fig. 20.1.

Each of these areas of knowledge needs to be developed as part of the requirements specification process. At the beginning of the process, some knowledge is already possessed, for example, the users have concrete experience of their present work (area 4) and the developers have concrete experience of technological options (area 6). Techniques are needed to facilitate sharing of this knowledge, users with developers as in area 4 or developers with users as in area 6. Other areas of knowledge, such as area 1 & 2, both users and developers need to acquire together, sharing a common vision of the future system and agreeing on relevant abstract structures of the users present work.

The type of technique used will influence the area of knowledge which can be developed and the nature of the communication between users and developers. Figure 20.2 shows a range of techniques and classifies them according to the six areas of knowledge described in Fig. 20.1.

The choice of techniques within any given development project will affect the capability of the requirements team (users, developers and other stakeholders) to develop a shared understanding of the users' present work, the technological options and the future system. Ideally a range of techniques should be employed on any given project so that all six areas of knowledge are developed.

It is interesting to note that many ■traditional■ requirements and design methods tend to favour the development of abstract knowledge. Concrete experience relies much more on human communication between users and developers.

Areas of Knowledge	*Abstract Knowledge*	*Concrete Experience*
Users' Present Work	1 Relevant Structures on users' present work Users & Developers need	4 Concrete experience with users' present work Users have, Developers need
New System	2 Visions and Design proposals Users & Developers need	5 Concrete experience with new system Users need
Techno-logical Options	3 Overview of Technological options Developers need	6 Concrete experience with technological options Developers have, users need

Fig 20.1 Six areas of knowledge, adapted from Kensing and Munk-Madsen, 1993

The next section describes a cooperative approach to requirements specification which provides a framework for including a variety of techniques, while maintaining a human centred focus.

20.5 Cooperative Requirements Capture

Cooperative Requirements Capture is based on a method called User Skills Task Match (USTM). The objective of this method is to encourage a strong user orientation throughout the feasibility and requirements stages. The underlying philosophy of USTM is socio-technical, i.e. there is as much emphasis on the user, social and organisational issues as on the technical issues. The method is designed to have a strong practical orientation — it has evolved through action-research, i.e. the current version of USTM is a result of actual successes and failures experienced through use with teams of stakeholders, who were attempting to establish the requirements for real products.

Tools and Techniques for Knowledge Development	*Abstract*			*Concrete*		
	1	2	3	4	5	6
Observations				√		
Interviewing Users	√			√		
Developers doing users' work				√		
Videorecording				√		
Mock-ups				√	√	
Think-aloud experiments				√	√	
Drawing rich pictures	√			√		
Ethnographic studies	√			√		
Object-oriented analysis	√	√				
Event lists	√	√				
Entity-relationship diagrams	√	√				
Future workshops	√	√				
Conceptual modelling	√					
Dataflow diagrams	√	√				
Card Games				√	√	
Formal Language Specifications	√					
Prototyping		√			√	√
Visits to other installations			√			√
Literature Study			√			
Study of standard software			√			√

Fig 20.2. Tools and Techniques for Knowledge Development (Adapted from Kensing and Munk-Madsen, 1993)

USTM has been designed to be acceptable to users, developers, and other stakeholders involved at the feasibility and requirements stages. It encourages team building through a series workshops (face to face meetings) and through providing a common language with which to discuss the users' present work and future needs. The workshops are run by a facilitator, who guides the team through the method and who facilitates communication between team members.

USTM is a collection of pro-formas, techniques and guidelines. The Human Factors knowledge required by the team in order to consider the user, social and organisational issues is presented through use of checklists. The team is encouraged to plan and carry out further user analysis and acceptability assessments beyond the workshop sessions.

In Cooperative Requirements Capture, the user and the user environment provide the focus of attention for the stakeholders. They 'explore' the user environment together, they are encouraged to describe what users do now and to envision how things might change in the future. They develop a shared understanding of the potential for change and a shared terminology for discussing the problem domain. Figure 20.3 gives an overview of the USTM method, which is the user centred method used as a basis for cooperative requirements capture.

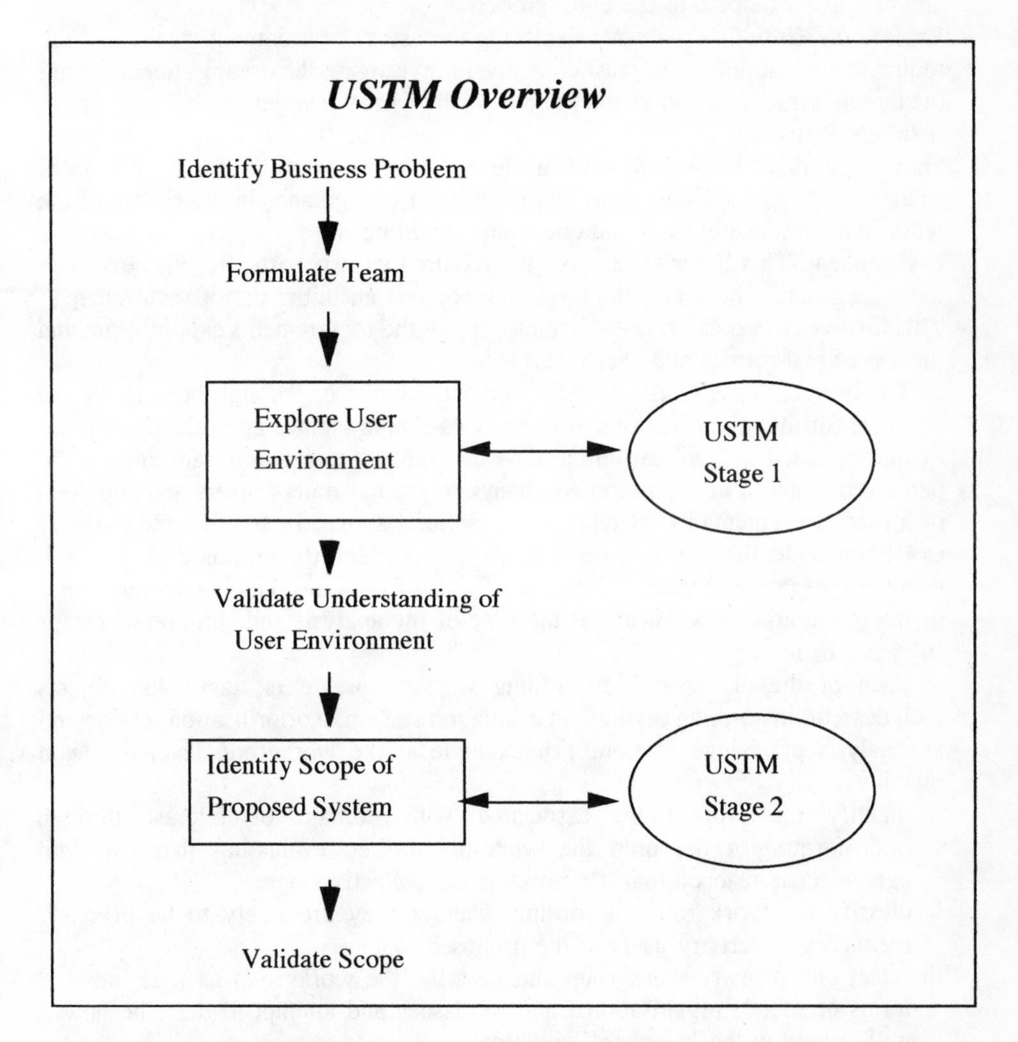

Fig. 20.3. Overview of USTM, a method for cooperative requirements capture

The method is introduced when a business need for change is first identified. *Identify Business Problem* is the first stage in the method in which the business need must be articulated. In the case of generic products a (draft) market segmentation statement would be produced which highlights the product concept, the projected costs and benefits, the target organisations and users, the buyer and market size. This statement provides a starting point for the workshop.
Formulate Team: This will normally involve the project manager or project initiator and the facilitator in identification of stakeholders and hence of the requirements capture team, ideally between six and nine stakeholder representatives will participate in the CRC process.
Explore the User Environment: Exploring the users' environment means that the requirements capture team must collectively investigate the organisational setting the target users are in and identify and describe what the target users do. The term 'explore' is used because the team is encouraged to 'find out' afresh, to share knowledge about users and to set aside preconceptions about what users need. They also assess the likely costs and benefits of change and, in the course of the workshop, produce of an initial document recording the shared view of the users environment. This 'User Document' is structured into six parts: the business case; the workgroups; the users; the tasks; the objects; an initial list of requirements. This involves a two day face-to-face meeting of the requirements capture team and the use of pro-formas and checklists.

The business case consists of a statement, by one of the stakeholders, of the rationale for the initiation of the project. This should include an initial description of the proposed system, an initial view on who the target users are and on the perceived benefits of the proposed change to the customers, users and suppliers or a market segmentation statement as described above. In addition the business case should identify the time perspective within which the proposed change will occur, for example, 2 years, 5 years or 10 years from now. Thus in the remainder of the discussion 'now' means at the time of the analysis and 'proposed' means 'n' years from now.

Each of the discussions concerning workgroups, users, tasks and objects includes a brainstorming session; an evaluation session; a prioritisation session and an analysis of change session. For example at the workgroup level the team members:

i identify the workgroups associated with domain of interest through brainstorming a list onto the white-board then evaluating that list until agreement is reached that it represents the collective view
ii classify the workgroups according whether they are likely to be primary, secondary or tertiary users of the proposed system
iii select one primary workgroup and describe the workgroup as it is 'now' it terms of social, organisational and job issues and attempt to describe how it will change in the 'proposed' situation.

At the user level, a similar procedure as for workgroups is followed. A list of generic users is agreed upon; these are classified according to their relationship with the proposed system and selected users described according to three sets of issues. The first set is concerned with how the organisation views the generic user, now and proposed. The second set on the personal attributes of the generic user now and proposed and the third on a typical 'day in the life of' the generic user now and proposed.

At the object level, the team is asked to brainstorm a list of objects which exist in the users' environment. These objects will normally be associated in some way with users and workgroups, they could be real world objects, knowledge about real world objects, procedures remembered by users and so on. Once a list has been produced, it is then evaluated. This entails clarifying the meaning of object names, looking for similar objects with different names or two different objects with similar names. In addition it may be possible to aggregate some objects with others. Once an agreed list is produced, the objects are then classified according to whether they are likely to be of interest to the proposed system. Selected objects are then described in further detail in terms of their 'now' characteristics and 'proposed' characteristics.

A task is defined as an action carried out by a generic user on an object. A list of tasks is produced, a task hierarchy (i.e. a task and its subtasks) is produced and the relationship between the tasks in the hierarchy and the proposed system identified. Tasks are classified and selected tasks are described using checklists of organisational issues, timing issues and human issues now and proposed.

The final level is concerned with consolidating the earlier analyses. In particular, combinations of user, object and task are examined to assess needs or requirements associated with the proposed system. The team is encouraged to make requirements statements of the form 'There is a need for...' , for example 'There is a need for version control' as opposed to 'The xyz system of version control will be implemented'. The purpose of this is that the team should be trying to identify future needs rather than deciding on the solution. In addition, the consolidation session includes a review of each of workgroups, users, objects and tasks in which the team is asked to make an honest assessment of the accuracy of their collective knowledge of the user environment. They are then encouraged to identify follow-up investigations that are needed in order to ensure that the future stages of requirements capture and analysis are based on a sound understanding of the users. The User Document is initially a collection of the pro-formas completed at the workshop.

Validate Understanding of User Environment: This normally involves one or two members of the requirements capture team under the guidance of the facilitator. It involves validation of the information recorded in the 'User Document' with expansion and updating where necessary. The techniques used for validation will depend on the specific problem — for a generic product further market research may be needed, for a bespoke product specific user interviews maybe necessary. In any case, the extent of the information gathering task will depend on the extent of the knowledge and expertise of the stakeholders who took part in the workshop. Here, techniques for developing concrete experience (areas 4,5,6 of Fig. 20.1) will be needed.

Identify the Scope of the Proposed System: This also involves a two day face-to-face meeting of the requirements capture team and the use of pro-formas and checklists. At this stage, the scope of the system is discussed. The scope of the proposed system is determined at a number of levels: Firstly the stakeholders decide which work roles are to be affected and then for each work role they decide what the role of the system should be in supporting that role. In particular, the role of the system is decided in terms of the extent of task sharing and degree of control and monitoring of tasks. The likely acceptability of this proposed change is considered. In addition, for each work role identified, an initial task model is produced. This helps to clarify and consolidate the understanding of the team with respect to specific roles. Secondly the team is asked to consider which objects from the user environment, that is those contained in the 'User Document', are likely to be of interest to the system. The team considers which objects will the system need to hold information about, which will it need to interact with, which will remain entirely in the user domain.

The scope of the proposed system is determined by the extent of support for the work roles and by the list of objects the system will need to support. In addition, the scope of the system is reviewed from the point of view of each of the major stakeholders to identify whether their needs will be met. The list of requirements also is reviewed from the viewpoint of each stakeholder. Once the scope of the system is decided and the list of requirements reviewed, the team is asked to identify and agree on usability targets for the proposed system. The outcome from this stage is an 'Initial Requirements Document' containing an agreed set of requirements for the first (or next) release of the system, the document is in six parts:

Part 1 : The Human Requirements
Part 2 : The High Level Functional Requirements
Part 3 : The Detailed Functional Requirements
Part 4 : The Requirements Metrics
Part 5 : Organisation and User Assistance Requirements
Part 6 : The Technological Requirements and Constraints

Each part is aimed at a specific set of readers and covers a distinct set of issues. A fuller description can be found in [8]. At this stage there is a need for abstract representations such as those described in areas 1,2 & 3 of Fig. 20.2.

20.6 Discussion

The process of developing the abstract representations to the level of detail needed for design is not explicitly covered by the Cooperative Requirements Capture method. However, the outcome of the method provides a sound basis for further analysis. The vision of the future system has been agreed and articulated in terms of the target users, the tasks and objects to be supported and the role of the technology in supporting the required change. The method has been applied successfully by a large number of product teams within ICL (International Computers Ltd, UK) who have now incorporated the method into their internal

'Marketing to Design' programme. The types of product include personnel systems, front-ends to operating systems, multi-media documentation, inventory control systems, network control systems and many others. A case study of a particular application of the method within the Electricity Distribution Industry can be found in [10].

The practical experiences of establishing requirements for new products all point to the importance of taking a human-centred approach. Many of those who are sceptical initially find that investigating user and stakeholders needs at an early stage leads to a more in-depth understanding of their proposed product and consequently enables them to proceed with their own task (design, marketing, documentation etc) more effectively.

Acknowledgements

The User Skills Task Match methodology was originally funded by the Alvey Programme of Research and Development, MMI/143, SERC grant GR/C/7295.2. Ken Eason and Susan Harker of HUSAT were consultants to the early stages of development of USTM. The author wishes to acknowledge the collaborators within the CRC (IED/1130) project. Cooperative Requirements Capture (CRC) is a collaborative project between UMIST, International Computers Ltd., Brameur Ltd. and Human Technology with financial support from the Department of Trade and Industry and the Science and Engineering Research Council.

References

1. Bailey R.W. (1982), Human Performance Engineering, A Guide for System Designers, Prentice Hall.
2. Bailey R.W. (1983), Human Error in Computer Systems, Prentice Hall.
3. Bjorn-Anderson N., Eason K. and Robey D. (1986) Managing Computer Impact: An International Study of Management and Organisations, Ablex Publishing Corporation.
4. Damodaran L., Simpson A., Wilson P., (1980), "Designing Systems for People", NCC Publications. 5, Downs, E, Clare, C., Coe, I., (1988) 'SSADM, Application and Context', Prentice Hall.
6. Eason, K.(1987) "Information Technology and Organisational Change", Taylor and Francis.
7. Kensung, F. and Munk-Madsen, A., (1993) "PD: Structure in the Toolbox", Communications of the ACM, June 1993, vol 36, No 4.
8. Macaulay, L.A., Fowler, CJH., Kirby, M., Hutt ATF., (1990) "USTM: a new approach to requirements specification", Interacting With Computers, vol2 no.1, 92 -117
9. Macaulay, L.A., (1993) "Requirements as a Cooperative Activity", Procs of the First IEEE Symposium on Requirements Engineering, RE'93, San Diego, IEEE Publications
10. Macaulay, L.A.,(1993) "Cooperative Requirements Capture: Control Room 2000",chapter in "Social and Technological Issues in Requirements Engineering", eds M.Jirotka, J. Goguen and M. Bickerton.

11. Mitra S. (1987), Techniques and Tools for Requirements Specification, Software Tools 87: Online Publications, Pinner, UK.
12. Mitroff, I.I. (1980), "Management myth information systems revisited: a strategic approach to asking nasty questions about system design" In Bjorn-Andersen, N. (ed.) "The Human Side of Enterprise" (Amsterdam, North Holland)
13. Mumford, E.,(1986) 'Designing Systems for Business Success, the ETHICS method', Manchester Business School Publication.
14. Palmer J.D., (1988) Uncertainty in Software Requirements, Large Scale Systems Journal, North Holland.

Synopsis and Discussion on the Helical Approach to Systems Design and Build

Andrew W. S. Ainger

Human Centred Systems Limited, Quantum House, Hemel Hempstead, Hertfordshire HP2 4SJ, England

Abstract. The 'Design and Build' section of the NATO Advanced Study Institute showed the benefit of multi-disciplinary collaboration in solving an under-specified problem using the Helical Approach. The results of a day's work by two multi-disciplinary teams were both interesting and novel — the approaches differed as the groups were free to set their own agendas; they also reflected the diverse interests and enthusiasms of the groups. Observing the groups in action, it became clear that facilitators were important in developing cohesion and direction in the groups even though as individuals they did not have any special expertise in the problem domain covered.

Keywords. System design, system build, helical systems design, teamwork

21.1 Introduction

There are many methods by which information systems can be designed. These range from the more traditional waterfall approach through the spiral design and onto the modern and innovative helical design method.

At the NATO ASI Conference, it was realised that as the awareness and understanding of organisational, technological and people issues improves, so will the information systems design methods. It was felt that at such an august gathering, the skills and collective experience of the group (some 60 people) gathered from all over the world could be exploited in a constructive way.

In an attempt to benefit from the collective experience, the group was split into 5 syndicates. The work of three of the syndicates is described by Hinde and Siemieniuch elsewhere. For the process reported here two of the syndicates were asked to solve an information systems design problem using the Helical Design Method. The solutions generated were not analysed in any detail, however, what was studied was the structured method by which the results were obtained.

This brief paper outlines and discusses the two quite different approaches the two syndicates used in adopting the Helical Design Method.

21.2 Background

Initially both teams were given a joint presentation on the Helical Design Approach. Both teams were then asked to solve the same problem using the Helical Method. Surprisingly both teams, by completely different routes, identified similar problems and suggested similar solutions.

For reasons of clarity, an outline of 'The Problem' (i.e. an overview of the company) is given first, this leads into "The Proposal (i.e. how the company saw the situation) and finally to a summary of the Syndicate work.

The problem

Company: The Quill Company Limited
Location: Located 50kms from the centre of Europe
Products: A wide range of writing products.

21.2.1 Company Information

The company has been in existence for a number of years and has a range of several hundred standard products (50% of the output of the factory). The other 50% of the products manufactured are customised products. These customised products are themselves split into small variances (i.e. logo changes, etc.) and more fundamental changes to product designs.

The company produces a range of writing implements such as pens, pencils, propelling pencils, fountain pens, ballpoint pens, etc.

The company has around 500 standard products which are made (on average) in 12 individual workcentres. The factory machines are formed into manufacturing cells. On average there are 4 workcentres per cell and the average product passes through 3 cells. The company purchases raw material from around 2 dozen single source suppliers, with which it has good business relationships. The average age of the workforce, (which totals 250), is 43.

The company already has an MRP I system which it is running on a rather antiquated centralised computer. The data it contains is roughly correct (75%) but everyone knows it needs to be up-dated. The computer is old and a refurbishment programme is about to be carried out early next year.

The factory occupies a site of 40 acres on which there are 3 buildings: (1) Goods-In, (2) Manufacturing and (3) Despatch. The offices are located above the shop floor (on the second floor of the building). These offices include Sales, Research and Design, Development, Finance, Personnel, Production Engineering, Stores, Maintenance, Quality, together with the Managing Director's office.

There have been plans to re-organise the office area but this has yet to be done. The manufacturing plant have 3 cells using high technology equipment, the remaining 6 cells run the older, slower, more traditional machines. The new equipment in cells 1, 2 and 3 can run around 90% of the products extremely fast and efficiently. The older equipment in cells 4 - 9 between them can run all the products in the factory, but at a much slower rate. The factory runs a 2.5 shift system with 60 people per shift.

21.2.2 Proposal

The company is eager and willing to try anything that it feels will benefit its competitive position. The company has been steadily losing money over the past 18 months and it is realised by all concerned that this trend has to be reversed within the next six months if the business is to survive. There is a vague realisation that although many sales orders have been taken, for some reason the 'profit' has not been as expected. There has been some discussion between the Sales people and Production Planning, however, this discussion normally ends as an unsolved argument.

21.3 Syndicate 1

Team 1's approach followed very closely the Helical Design Method. The team outlined the problem through a role playing exercise where each member of the team adopted a functional role within the company concerned. This exercise enabled the problems within the company to become more detailed and firm in everybody's mind. Very quickly the team had a shared common mental image of the problem space. At this stage there was a great tendency to move very quickly onto the solution scenario. However, this was resisted in order to complete the CATWOE Statement and to fix, in written form, the mental image formed by the role play.

It was the CATWOE Statement that gave the biggest problem. Difficulty was experienced in defining the roles and differentiating between the Customers and Actors in the CATWOE Statement. Although there was no purpose or objective expressed inherently in the Statement, it was found that, in the very first sentence, the objective or purpose of the system was expressed. Great discussion ensued as to whether the objective or purpose should be included in the CATWOE. A new acronym was proposed, COWPATE, where the "P" represented Purpose.

Subsequent to the COWPATE Statement, the solution scenario was enacted. This was found not be as much fun as the problem role playing. It appeared that the conflicts of the problem role playing was enjoyed far more than the co-operative and communicative solution scenario. However, the solution scenario appeared to work extremely well and smoothly.

The next item in the Helical Design Method is the 'one-liner objectives'. This followed on quite naturally in Team 1 from the solution scenario. The objectives were very quickly itemised and recorded. It was found that only a few people in the syndicate had experience of Data Flow Diagrams. However, after only a very few minutes of discussion, all the team members were quite happy discussing what was eventually called the systems 'communications flow diagram'. It appeared that the communications flow diagram stemmed directly and quite naturally from the solution scenario and the one-liner objectives. It was not as detailed as the Data Flow Diagram but appeared to be a necessary step for the team members. It was then a straight forward step to move to the pure Data Flow Diagram.

The paper screens were a natural extension of the flow diagrams. Rapid progress was made in this area; levels of detail were not extended due to time pressures. However, significant lessons had been learnt and it was felt that the Helical Life Cycle Approach speeded up significantly the design progress.

21.4 Syndicate 2

This team also enacted out a role playing problem exercise. However, when the CATWOE Statement was attempted once again great difficultly was experienced in defining the differences between Customers and Actors. There also appeared to be much more concern, not only in the objectives, which appeared to be missing from the CATWOE Statement, but also in the Soft issues. It was later discussed that the Soft issues related more to the quality and type of the final system design but should nevertheless be incorporated in some form into the CATWOE Statement. This syndicate chose a new acronym of CATWOES, where "S" represented the "Soft" issues of the social aspects.

After the generation of the CATWOES Statement the 'lift-shaft' was used in the Helical Approach and a simultaneous scenario/objectives discussion ensued. During this discussion various scenarios were acted out and conclusions/objectives were extracted and refined. In this team, much emphasis was placed on the quality of the solution. Most of the discussion centred around discrepancies and misunderstandings not in the problem but in the suggested solution. Agreement could not be reached as to the degree and use of the Soft issues. It was felt that there was an underlying philosophical agreement between various members of the team. Although all team members purported to support the anthropocentric approach this was not apparent in the solution scenario of certain syndicate members. When further investigations were conducted it was discovered that the team members who were from a more military background, although agreeing in principal with the human centred approach, found it extremely difficult to act out a scenario employing human centred principles.

21.5 Summary

To conclude it could be stated that the Helical Life Cycle Approach worked extremely well. However, certain recommendations can be made for future consideration. Firstly, the changing of the CATWOE Statement to include both purpose and Soft issues, i.e. CATWOE becomes COWPATES! This enables the CATWOE Statement to encompass both Purpose and the Softer/Social issues. Secondly, the Data Flow Diagrams need to be first expressed in a more general form. The Communications Flow Diagrams appeared to be very popular/easy to understand and extremely useful. Lastly, the parallel nature of the Helical Approach should be made more apparent. Although the helix is specifically drawn in the y axis and not in the x (i.e. time), some team members assumed (erroneously) that the elements on the helix must be done sequentially. The though that there could be a 'lift-shaft' inside the helix enabling the appropriate element of the helix to be adopted as and when necessary was not apparent.

Overall the detailed improvements to the Helical Project Life Cycle Method have been significant and it is believed will enable far more people to understand and gain benefit from the concept. These benefits and improvements could not have been achieved without:

(a) the umbrella of the NATO Advanced Study Institute
(b) the drive and organisational skills of Brunel University and Cranfield Institute
(c) the facilities provided by Loughborough University and, most importantly
(d) the individual contributions made by many people from 2 dozen countries.

22. Design and Build

C J Hinde & C E Siemieniuch

HUSAT Research Institute, Department of Computer Studies, University of Technology, Ashby Road, Loughborough, Leicestershire LE11 3TU, England

Abstract. This section of the NATO Advanced Study Institute showed the benefit of multi-disciplinary collaboration in solving a large under-specified problem. The results of a day's work by three multi-disciplinary teams were both interesting and novel — the approaches differed as each group was free to set its own agenda; the problems they tackled also reflected the diverse interests and enthusiasms of the various groups. Observing the groups in action, it became clear that the facilitators were crucial in developing cohesion and direction in the groups even though as individuals they did not have any special expertise in the problem domain covered.

Keywords. System design, system build, multidiscplinary approach, constraint based design, search spaces, engineering design, collaboration, human centred systems

22.1 Introduction

The design and build activity in the NATO Advanced Study Institute followed on from the specification and requirements activity. Although it may appear that this involved using the specification derived in the preceding activity in a somewhat sequential fashion, it was strongly felt that to do so would be to reinforce the waterfall model of design which was not the object of the exercise. The members of the Institute were split into five syndicates. The present paper describes the work of three of these syndicates while the work of the other two groups is described in the paper by Ainger elsewhere.

There were three main objectives to the design and build activity. The first was to focus attention on the issues that were germane to designing and building a large system — the constraints on the problem meant that although firstly humans would necessarily be involved there should be some elements of technology, probably in the form of computers. The second objective was to introduce the participants to multi-disciplinary working and also to show the benefits of addressing requirements specification, design and build and implementation as part of a gestalt activity. The third was to use the workshop to obtain new insights into computer aided design and manufacture which the authors had been involved in for some considerable time.

The section as a whole split naturally into four unequal parts. The first was to introduce the problem i.e. computer integrated manufacture in its entirety using a research project in this area as the background focus. The second involved splitting the attendees into their pre-selected groups so that they could work together to obtain some insights into the problem as posed — this included focusing the activity into manageable sub goals and then addressing those goals. The third required each group to construct a presentation of their results and rationale to be given in a plenary session and the final part consisted of each group making their presentation to all the other groups followed by a short discussion period after each presentation. During the second part of the activity, the authors moved from group to group as observers but also contributing as appropriate; interestingly the group cohesion became quite strong towards the end of the day's activity and so it became less and less relevant to make contributions to the group discussions. Finally these observations were communicated to the groups. To describe these activities, this paper has been divided into three main sections; the first describes the problem area as presented by the authors to the attendees, covering aspects such as the differences and limitations of a purely technical or human approach to problem solving in system design, followed by a brief discussion on the advantages of collaboration between these approaches. This is followed by a brief outline of the problem statement presented to the groups which were then asked to consider in their group workings. The final section presents a precis of two of the groups presentations in order to provide the reader with some case study examples of the benefits of an interdisciplinary approach to problem solving in the domain studied.

22.2 The Problem Domain

The problem description took place on the Saturday morning to three groups, starting at 0900 and continuing to 1300. The basic details of the problem were based on work carried out by the authors on a Large Scale Demonstrator project under the UK Alvey Initiative in the 1980s.[1-8]. The aim of the project entitled 'Design to Product' (DtoP) was to design an innovative, integrated AI-based system covering the design to manufacture process for a complex, mechanical, precision-engineered component. It was a collaborative project led by G.E.C. Electrical Projects and Lucas C.A.V. The collaborators were, in alphabetical order:

Department of Artificial Intelligence, Edinburgh University.
Department of Computer Studies, Loughborough University.
Department of Manufacturing Engineering, Loughborough University.
Department of Mechanical Engineering, Leeds University.
G.E.C. Avionics.
G.E.C. Electrical Projects.

G.E.C. FAST division.
HUSAT Research Institute, Loughborough University.
Lucas Diesel Systems, Gillingham.

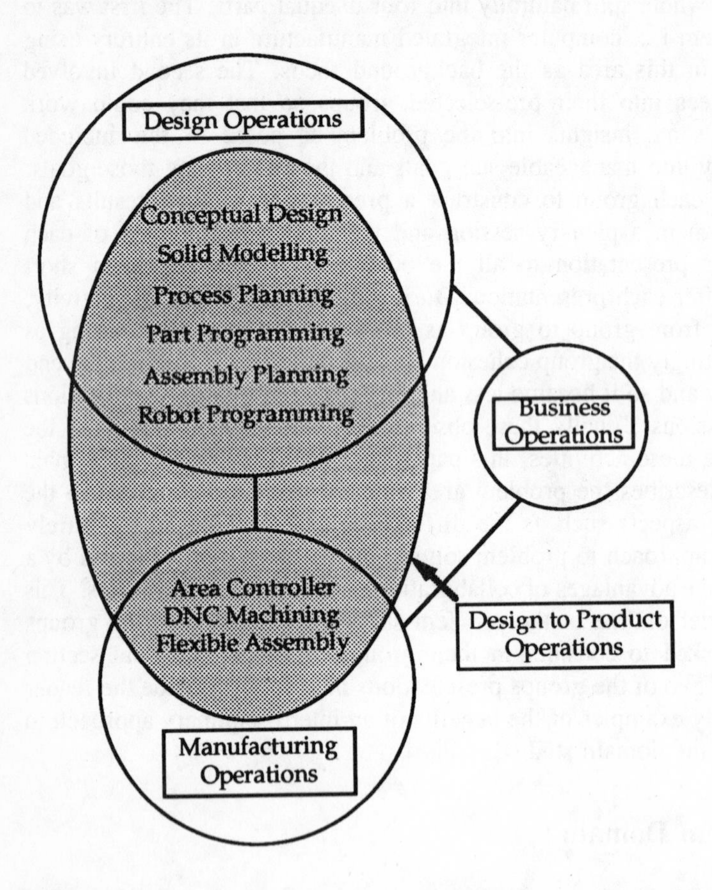

Fig. 22.1 Illustrating the major aspects of Design to Product, the central idea was that of integration. The shaded part indicates the areas of product design and manufacture that the project addressed, the areas outside indicate that not all aspects of design were to be automated.

The project was in two phases, lasting 2.5 years each; the first phase was to design the components of the Design to Product system, the second to integrate them together. There are many aspects of the projects which are of interest and which are documented elsewhere [1-11]. Fig. 22.1 illustrates some of the aspects of the field of product design and manufacture that Design to Product addressed. The central feature of the research was that of integration of various parts which were designed to address various aspects of computer integrated design and manufacture; Fig. 22.2 illustrates the software harness used to integrate the various parts constructed by the research teams. However, what was not

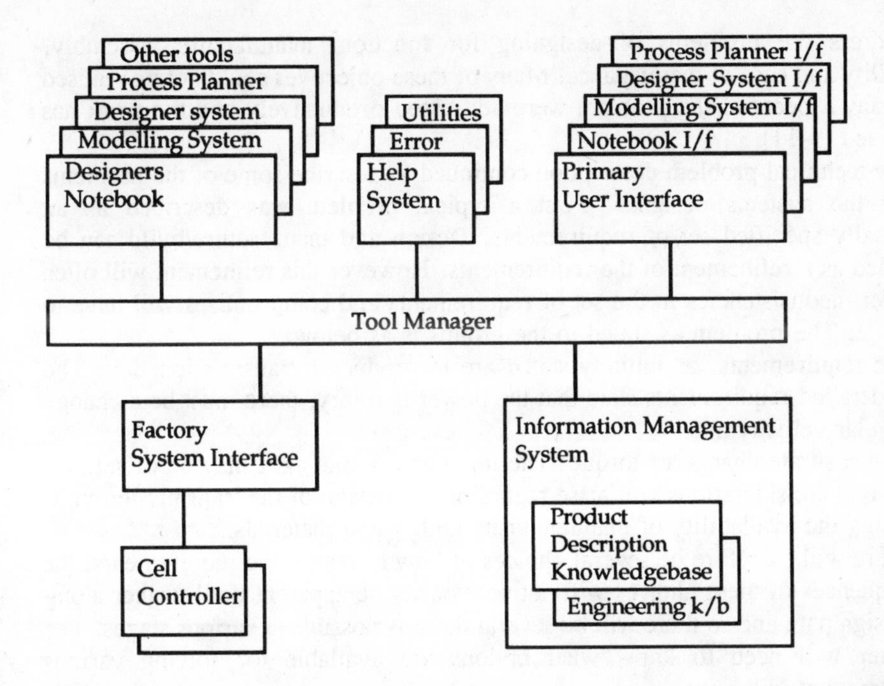

Fig. 22.2. Illustrating the harness used to integrate the various sub-systems together

adequately documented was the lessons learnt from such a large scale project with respect to collaboration amongst different disciplines and across many different sites. The authors would like to acknowledge the experience gained in this project. The project was initially highly underspecified and very large, we sought to recreate some of these aspects for this institute.

The introduction to the problem was in three major parts: the first was to introduce some of the technical aspects of computer integrated manufacture and to take a technical centred view of the problem (i.e. largely ignoring the human factors); the second to take a human centred view of the problem (i.e. largely ignoring technical aspects); the final part was to show the benefits of collaboration to illustrate how a "better" solution could be obtained by addressing all aspects of the problem from all available viewpoints.

22.2.1 The Technical Aspects

The context of the Design to Product demonstrator at its inception was to address the problems of integrated design and manufacture. At the time, most computer aided design systems embodied a sequential model of design to manufacture where the engineering drawings were passed to the production engineering department so a manufacturing plan could be produced to manufacture the product. The objective was to produce an integrated system to address the problems of designing for function, manufacture, assembly, reliability and ease of maintenance. Many of these objectives could not be realised but many aspects of the problem were addressed productively and the work has continued [9-11].

The technical problem description continued to describe some of the problems facing the systems designer. First a typical problem was described as an informally specified set of requirements. Design and manufacture/build can be regarded as a refinement of the requirements. However this refinement will often uncover inconsistencies in the set of requirements and compromises will have to be made. The problem as stated to the groups is as below:

The requirements, as initially stated are to produce a transmission unit. The more detailed requirements state that the power is rotary, there must be a change of angular velocity and
a commensurate change of torque. The input and output axes may be offset.

Several considerations will arise regarding the design of the transmission unit, including the availability of manufacturing ability and materials.

There will therefore be several choices of how to realise the requirements, the consequences of these choices will not necessarily be apparent until further along the design path and so there will be several designs possible at various stages. The designer will need to know what options are available for solving various problems that will arise.

The problems facing the design engineer and the manufacturing engineer related to:

- the analysis of tolerances to various parts of the product
- the assignment of manufacturing processes which could deliver adequately closely toleranced process plans which were both efficient and reliable.

This section concluded with an illustration of the number of possible assignments of processes and tolerances which would result in an adequate product. This number is computationally intractable to explore. However adequate tolerance and process assignments have been made manually for some time.

The 'almost conventional' approach to reducing search spaces is to apply artificial intelligence. However the natural solution to this problem, which eliminates the knowledge elicitation bottleneck, is to use the extensive experience of the company's engineers to help solve this problem. We conclude that technology requires people to solve problems that are in many respects technically intractable. Although it is stated by some that people cannot operate efficiently without the help of technology, it is clear that technology cannot function in a human world without significant contributions from 'real intelligence' supplied by humans. Although very many 'purely' technical problems remain they are both alleviated by and added to by the need to communicate these problems adequately to their human counterparts, and also to allow the humans to contribute to and control the design and manufacture activity. How do we form a collaborative system which enhances the positive aspects of both humans and technology?

22.2.2 The Human Centred Approach

Work carried out early on in the project confirmed the philosophy that the whole DtoP system should be seen as a user support tool, with end-users very much 'in charge'. This contrasted with the original view within the project that IT sub-systems could exist almost as autonomous entities controlling the factory, with users operating more in a supervisory role, ready to intervene only when things went wrong. It became clear from a range of task and other analysis work carried out that autonomous, expert-system tools, able to undertake the real, multi-variable, qualitative and quantitative problem-solving tasks currently faced by humans in the target working environment, would require knowledge bases and user interface management systems way beyond the resources available within the project, and probably beyond the resources of all but the biggest organisations. This realisation directed the development of all the user interfaces within the DtoP system. It also became obvious that, if users were to perform successfully in this sort of role, their overall tasks had to be clearly defined in order to ensure an appropriate allocation of sub-tasks between end-users and the software support tools. A user centred design methodology was applied [10] but it became very clear that a purely human factors approach would not be sufficient to achieve realistic and usable user interface design for the various modules of the system. Basic issues such as the lack of a Reference Architecture, out of phase development of many of the software tools, unrobustness of the software developed, incompleteness of existing HCI guidelines, all contributed to the difficulties in specifying, designing and evaluating prototype interfaces for the system. But many other important lessons were learnt [8] some of which are detailed below:

- The necessity of a top-down user centred approach to designing user interfaces, based on the functions the users must carry out and the knowledge required to carry out these functions.
- It is essential to have a clear and coherent definition of the users' tasks and requirements for interaction with complex CIM systems.
- It is also essential to have a common understanding and model of the engineering design to manufacture process and the downstream requirements for knowledge and data that must be provided by this process. For example in process planning, it is very important to have feedback loops for data, both up to the design stage and down to manufacturing, if true integration and interaction between these stages is to occur.
- The relevance of scenarios and walkthroughs in specifying and evaluating user interfaces was underlined. The usefulness of these techniques, both to capture parallelism and sequence in human task performance and to understand the real life context in which the tools would be used, cannot be underestimated.
- The importance of fully understanding the implications of navigation problems through complex, layered interfaces, especially when users are exploring the boundaries of the tool. Another example here would be the problem of navigating through a complex, layered interface as the problem solution

develops and through extensive databases when the initial query is vague, possible incorrect, and contains errors. Many design queries are of this nature.
- The requirement to maintain consistency of look and feel of user interfaces across a number of very different tools, given that they will be used at varying frequencies by users of many different skill levels and very different cognitive styles. Consistency across system tools also serves to minimise error and decrease the learning effort required when users move between tools, it is also important to maintain this consistency whenever new tools are added.

22.2.3 Collaboration in the Problem Solving Process

In order to demonstrate the benefits of a cross disciplinary approach i.e. a combination of the Technical and Human Centred approaches, the authors focused on one particular user interface design problem — the presentation of process planning information to the user within the artificially intelligent process planning system being developed in the project.

Any process plan generated by the system will have a set of constraints associated with it e.g. sequencing constraints or grouping by machines or tooling; the sequencing constraints arise from the requirement that some operations must precede others, the grouping constraints arise from the requirement that operations to be performed on the same machine should be performed with no interruption from another process but may occur in any sequence within that group. Any single human readable form of the plan for a particular component generated by the system and presented to the user will be a valid way of manufacturing the component, but not the only way and not necessarily the best way i.e. there are alternative plans all of which will have a set of constraints associated with them. The problem here was to present the plan to the user in such a way that all associated constraints could be visible to the user, but also allow the user to modify the constraints set easily and efficiently. The main difficulties were twofold: firstly there was a basic information presentation problem i.e. the use of text or graphics, depth versus breadth of information, clarity and consistency of displays etc.; secondly understanding the relationships between the various constraints sets and the consequences of modifying them.

One of the primary problems in developing the user interface in the initial stages of the project had been the lack of understanding and interaction between the software developers and the user interface designers. On the one hand this meant that the 'human factors' expert tended to design screens based on accepted human factors principles which could not be applied to the system, as they did not reflect the underlying functionality of the planner and were also not capable of easy implementation given the available resources and technology at that time. On the other hand there was the impression that the software being developed was too ambitious for the technology and therefore response times were unsatisfactory. This problem was solved by both interface and software developers taking their time to understand the others viewpoint and the rationale behind their arguments. Once a common model of the problem and solution domains had been established development work progressed more rapidly and both the system and the interface benefited from the cross disciplinary input.

It was agreed within the project that direct manipulation principles would be applied and also that a combination of text and icon based representation of the process plan content would be desirable. In an attempt to solve the problem referred to above the 'human factors' expert drew up a series of sketches which were agreed in principle with the user representatives. These were then discussed with the software developers who were able to expand on one particular idea to the extent that it became the basis for the user interface. The point being emphasised here was that by working together and combining expertise from two different domains, a simple idea was transformed into a usable and efficient interface which was highly rated by the users during evaluation. Without that close cooperation, the end result would have been far less innovative.

22.3 Problem Statement

The problem given to the groups was based on the problem faced by the members of the Design to Product team at the outset although the groups would be given far less time to explore the ideas. The specification of what the groups were to address and how they were to address it was deliberately vague so this was a presentation of a real problem and not a tutorial scenario. One of the desired outcomes from this session was the results of a brain storming session, possibly some insights that would be of general benefit.

The groups were asked to explore the organisation of a CIM system, in particular to address Design and Process Planning. One of the problems encountered by the DtoP researchers was to identify what exactly was meant by design and process planning. At the outset of Design to Product there seemed to be as many viewpoints about these aspects as there were people willing to venture an opinion. One common viewpoint was that simultaneous engineering was important, and yet the expert designers and process planners actually employed techniques and methods that drew them towards sequential engineering and away from the idea of simultaneous engineering. One manifestation of this was the inconsistency of some of the knowledge obtained from interviewing.

The groups were then given short descriptions of various techniques that they might find useful, although they were not guided towards one particular technique or method of organising their knowledge or thoughts.

Establishing who the major stakeholders are in achieving a particular goal is important as this will indicate the people to interview in depth; in this exercise the set of people available to contribute was severely limited and specified at the outset. The problem in this exercise is to establish to goals of the system and the tasks involved in achieving those goals. In fact the problem is at a higher level than this — the higher level problem is to decide how to analyse the relevant tasks and goals.

Outline descriptions of hierarchical task analysis and goal decomposition techniques were outlined to the groups as was a shortened version of Booch's object oriented analysis notation [12].

22.4 Precis of Group Interactions

The attendees had been divided into 3 groups, membership of which had been arranged earlier in the workshop. Once the problem domain had been presented as described above, the groups were free to decide among themselves what issues they felt were important and how they would structure both their working time and the final presentations. Each group had a facilitator, whose role was to act both as a catalyst and a coordinator of ideas generated within the group. As an example of the work of these groups, a precis of the final presentations of two of the groups is presented below. The presentations are as given during the Institute — the authors of this paper have not altered their content in any way.

22.4.1 Group 1: Human-Centred Case-Based Process Planning (HCCBPP) An Interdisciplinary Team Work case Study

Introduction
As part of their involvement with this NATO Advanced Study Institute, the participants were asked to consider the many problems encountered by C. Hinde and C. Siemieniuch in their attempt to improve the state of computer integrated manufacturing. In particular, they have focused on the central issues of computer assisted design and process planning. The participants' task was, then, to choose some aspect of these problems and see what light they could shed upon it. After Hinde and Siemieniuch presented their research, all participants had the evening to think about what aspect of the problem interested them and what they might be able to offer in pursuit of its solution. We were then to split into teams and, together, were to produce some result to present to the group as a whole.

Our team was comprised of a multi-disciplinary, multi-national collection of people that included manufacturing specialists, industrial representatives, human factors specialists, and computer scientists from various countries of Europe, the Middle East, and North America. Upon returning the next morning, we each presented the fruit of our evening's labour to the team as a whole. Much to our amazement, we were pleased to find that there was a great deal overlap of thinking between the represented disciplines. We then coalesced this overlap and produced the results that follow. First the problem is delineated, our solution overviewed and detailed, and finally our conclusion is presented.

Statement of Problem
Process Planning is the determination of a plan for the manufacturing of a given design that details the order, type, etc. of processes to produce that design in the most cost efficient manner. Unfortunately, Process Planning often suffers from duplication of work and frequently sub optimal results. This is due, in part, to the

great number of variables involved and the dynamic character of the manufacturing environment.

Although current computer based approaches to this problem, termed Computer-Assisted Process Planning, have improved the procedure of Process Planning, they have exhibited problems in terms of accuracy and the handling of complex designs.

Overview of Solution

We propose a marriage of Computer-Assisted Process Planning, Case-Based Reasoning, and Human-Centred Design as the foundation for a new approach to the problem of cost efficient process planning. We term our hybrid approach Human-Centred Case-Based Process Planning. In this approach, we attempt to improve the state of Computer-Assisted Process Planning by using a Case-Based Reasoning approach that itself is made more realisable by the incorporation of Human Centred Design tenets.

Components of the Problem Solution

There are three main components, Computer-Assisted Process Planning, Case-Based Reasoning and Human Centred Design.

Computer-Assisted Process Planning (CAPP)

CAPP systems currently attack the problem of efficient process planning from two fronts: retrieval (or various) systems and generative systems.

Retrieval-type CAPP systems attempt to retrieve past plans for designs similar to some given current one by means of group technology codes. A process of classification and coding allows components to be grouped into families and the design and/or manufacturing attributes of each group to be defined by means of an alphanumeric code. These past plans are indexed in this manner by designers and process planners using a varying number of fairly vague attributes. In order to prevent undue replication of planning, an attempt is made to define the current design using these attributes as well and this definition is used by the system to retrieve a number of plans whose indices match it in some degree. The retrieved plan most closely resembling the current design is then chosen by the planner and it is then modified to conform to all aspects of the current design and manufacturing environment. These systems have proved somewhat useful but suffer from a vague feature coding language which is difficult to use and a lack of incorporation of any of the dynamic qualities of the manufacturing environment (i.e. current status of machines). Further, no assistance is given in the modification of the plan for the current design goal.

Generative-type CAPP systems attempt to produce a process plan from a specification of all values of the variables involved and do so without human intervention. This is an attempt to remove the human from the process entirely in the hope of increasing the speed and accuracy of the process. These systems have been found to be incapable of all but the most basic of designs due to the exponential character of the algorithms involved.

Case-Based Reasoning (CBR)

In his presentation, C.Hinde stated "Everything has something like it designed before." Although this was stated in the context of design and process planning, it could be thought of as a founding principle of CBR. Stated in a slightly more pointed fashion, why should work be redone from scratch if there is some previous work that can be used as a starting point for the achievement of a given goal that can be modified to achieve this goal? It seems highly likely that the modification of this work will be considerably less costly than producing the work from scratch. If we can find the appropriate previous work in due time, therefore, it seems likely that we will spend less time overall and, further, will take into consideration the lessons learned by that previous work, implicitly.

CBR is an area of artificial intelligence (AI) research that is concerned, in a fundamental sense, with this reuse of previous plans. This is to be contrasted with research that is concerned with producing plans from scratch. The parallells between these research areas and the dual pronged research in process planning previously described are obvious.

It should be noted the CBR research is not domain dependent; there exists a wide range of possible application of which process planning is just one example. In this case, a ideal CBR system would, when presented with a design for realisation, find a plan (case) in its database of plans (casebase) that most closely matched the features of the current design goal and modify it to satisfy this current design goal.

The difficulties encountered with CBR are the difficulties experiences with AI research in general — how can the processes of human reasoning be automated? In the case in point, for instance, how can the system extract the important features of the design goal? How can it choose amongst competing candidates plans? How can it modify plans to suit the current design goal? In other words, how can such a system be completely automated?

Human Centred Design (HCD)

A basic tenet of HCD states that a system should balance its tasks between the human user and the computer giving each those tasks at which they are best. HCD finds fully automated systems too inflexible (or simply unimplementable) for truly difficult problems, particularly those problems that are poorly understood. This seems to characterise the hard problems of CBR in particular and we, therefore, attempt to soften these problems by adherence to this HCD tenet.

The hybrid approach

Task Partitioning

We see task partitioning as a first step in defining our hybrid approach. That is, if we are to use CBR modified by HCD to improve the state of CAPP we must adhere to the basic tenet of HCD and decide which tasks are best performed by the human and which tasks are best performed by the computer. The method by which we accomplished this was straight-forward. We first listed all the subtasks that were necessary to accomplish the main task. This list came from an analysis of the steps that needed to be performed to accomplish the main task. We then ordered these tasks along a continuum with tasks at one end of the continuum being considered easy to automate and tasks at the other being considered in need of human intelligence. We then used this partial ordering to produce our first pass at such a partitioning. The final result of this is given in the table below:

Human's Best Use	**Computer's Best Use**
Design Concept	Storage of Previous Plans
Feature and Process Extraction	Feature and Process Extraction Support
Candidate Plan Selection	Candidate Plan Retrieval
Modification of Candidate Plan	Plan Modification Support
	Indexing and Storage of New Plan

System Flow

Given the creative talents of humans, we have decided to leave the conception of the design in their hands (a human-centred system's approach to the problem of design is an obvious extension to the current proposal). The computer is expected to have current knowledge about the status of machines on the shop floor and to bring that knowledge to bear in its user supporting role. We envision a system using our approach as following this basic flow:

1. User presents design to system
2. User and system co-operatively decide defining features of design (size, shape, threading, etc.) and important processing attributes and constraints (what machines are down, which machining process is needed to produce a given design feature, etc.).
3. System retrieves a number of candidate plans from its store of plans
4. User further tightens or loosens features/attributes/constraints untildesired number of candidates plans are found. This is an iterative process.
5. User chooses plan from candidate plans presented.
6. User and System co-operatively decide on appropriate modifications to the chosen plan to meet current design goals and manufacturing constraints.
7. System indexes and stores new plan for future retrieval.

Further, at each step of the process, the system should be able to justify any choices it has made.

A system such as this seems somewhat more feasible than a fully automated CBR system or generative CAPP system and the support offered by it to the planner should make it much more useful than a simple retrieval CAPP system. The HCD tenet of partitioning tasks between the human and computer has, in this case, produced tangible positive results.

Conclusion

We found that each discipline's perspective on the problem at hand complemented the others. In particular, the problems currently being experienced in industry by computer-assisted planners had been generalised by researchers in the artificial intelligence community under the name of case based reasoning. Further, the hard problems associated with case-based reasoning seemed to soften when viewed from the human factors perspective of human centred design.

It seems unlikely that any one individual would be privy to the wide range of perspectives represented in a team such as ours and, therefore, unlikely that any one individual would put forth a solution such as did our team. We offer our experiences as a modicum of empirical evidence in support of multi-disciplinary team effort and human-centred design principles in pursuit of solutions to difficult problems.

22.4.2 Group 2: From DUCTCESS to SUCCESS

The group has ventured into the creation of words to handle:

I becoming T – from 'integration' to the 'team' of workers rather than simply moving towards a future of:

I becoming H – from the 'integration' to the 'human approach'. We are thus acknowledging the difference between working alone/in a team.

Working Procedure

The working procedure adopted by this group can be summarised as follows:

- *Identify* "CIM related issues".
- *Classify* them into
  "ORGANISATIONAL INTELLIGENCE oriented"
  "CIM or Technology oriented"
- *Understand* "HUMAN/MACHINE/COMPUTER capabilities".
- *Identify* the need for a new professional profile:
  "DUCTCESS ENGINEER"
  answering the demands of
  "DUCTCESS DESIGN"
  i.e. the "simultaneous design of PRODUCT/PROCESS, a new definition.
- *Propose*
  meta-skills development ("become a T")
  of humans skilled and prepared for Team work
  instead of
  new skills development ("become an H")

Allocation of function

What are the strengths and weaknesses of Humans, Machines & Computers?

Humans	Machines	Computers
+interpret complex data +flexible +pattern matching +learning from experiences +purpose driven +overview (synthesis) +handling irregular products +problem solving +self reflection +expecting errors +widespread skills +able to handle uncertainty +motivation -variation in skills -need rest to recover +own decision making +can work with incomplete specification	+big forces +velocity +mass +power +accuracy +efficient -flexible +repeatability -expecting errors	+administration +computation +consistency checking +data crunching -self reflection +deterministic functions

Issues involved in introducing CIM

- These can be summarised as follows:
  - Shop floor workers supervise machinery instead of controlling
  - Testing staff takes care of production tests instead of product tests
  - Process planning engineers provide NC tools instead of written documents
  - Product designers (and their CAD system) take over process planners' tasks in case of CNC

This in turn can cause problems and contradictions between:

- Traditional controlling tasks and new supervisory tasks of shop floor staff
- Traditional testing expertise and new (process oriented) testing requirements
- Traditional process planning tasks/skills and new process planning needs
- Traditional division of work and new integration of product and process design

The solution requires the availability of "ALLROUND" (Multidisciplinary, meta-skilled) engineers in the Integrated product/process design office and on the Computer controlled shop floor (supervision). Also the availability of QA staff. All staff should have a computerised background and be dedicated to teamwork.

Effects of CIM Perspectives

- Products get more and more "Variational" & "Parametrised"
- Processes get more and more "Parametrisable"

- Process planning task is no more "Design process to product" but "Design processes to product families"
- Product design task is no more "Design product" but "Design product family"

CIM is most exploitable where CAD/DA support is advanced and where CIM is a motivating development of CAD/DA tools and systems.

Skill integration in CIM.
Figure 22.3 below shows the integration of skills across various communicating collaborating team members compared to the incorporation of a large skill set in one individual.

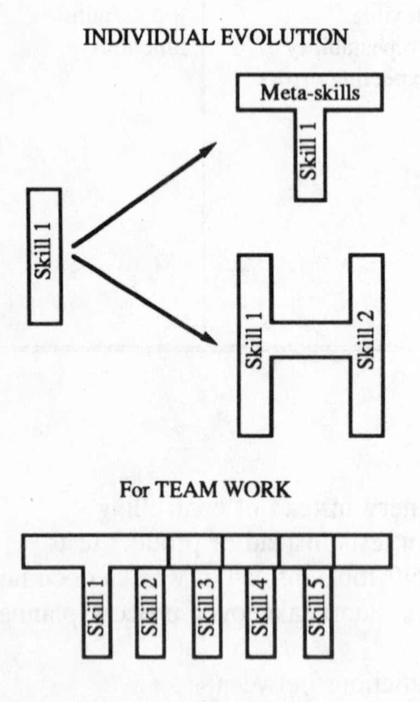

Fig. 22.3. Showing the integration of skills across various communicating collaborating team members compared to the incorporation of a large skill set in one individual

Attributes of Meta-Skills

- Conditioned by organisational culture
- Conditions organisational culture
- Horizontal Communication
- Authority and responsibility is a meta-skill
- Utilisation of Information
- Data relationships and tools
- Synthesis of information and concepts
- Creativity — actively think differently
- Open Minded - passively think differently

- Time management
- Development of team management skills

22.5 Conclusions

The groups were given a "real" problem, one which there is no known correct solution and as in "real life" the problem was highly underspecified. Conventionally this might have resulted in rather poor performance in the group working but the evidence presented suggests that the groups worked well and produced excellent results in a short time. The relative success of the group working indicates the composition and leadership of the groups played an important part in the success. Further research involving a set of groups, some homogeneous control groups and some heterogeneous would be valuable in further validating the evidence presented in this paper.

References

1. Burrow, L.D., 1989, The Design to Product Alvey Demonstrator. I.C.L. Technical Journal, Vol.6 No. 3.
2. Burrow, L.D., & Hinde, C.J., 1990, Integrated Information Systems for Design and Manufacture, Business Benefits of Expert Systems, sponsored by the S.G.E.S., Sept. 1990.
3. Hinde, C.J., 1990, Loughborough University Manufacturing Planner, Business Benefits of Expert Systems, sponsored by the S.G.E.S., Sept. 1990.
4. Millington, K., 1990, Edinburgh Designer System. Business Benefits of Expert Systems, sponsored by the S.G.E.S., Sept. 1990.
5. Popplestone, R.J., Smithers, T.M., Corney J., Koutsou,A., Millington, K. & Sahar G., 1986, Engineering Design Support Systems, in 1st International Conference on Applications of Artificial Intelligence, Southampton.
6. Smithers, T.M., 1985, The Alvey Large Scale Demonstrator Project "Design To Product", Proceedings of the Technology Assessment and Management Conference of the Gottlieb Duttweiler Institute Ruschlikon, Zurich, Switzerland.
7. Sinclair, M.A., Siemieniuch, C.E. & John, P.A. 1989. A user centred approach to define high-level requirements for next generation CAD systems for mechanical engineering. IEEE Trans. Engineering Mgt. & Systems, 36(4), pp. 262-270.
8. Siemieniuch, C.E. & Maclean, R.O. 1990. User centred approach to building an interface for an expert process planning system. Ergonomics of hybrid automated systems II. Proceedings of the 2nd Intl. Conf. Human aspects of advanced manufacturing and hybrid automation,Hawaii, Elsevier. pp. 471-478.
9. Hinde, C.J. & Bray, A.D., 1992, Concurrent Engineering Using Collaborating Truth Maintenance Systems. in Ed. Max Bramer, Research and Development in Expert Systems, C.U.P.
10. Siemieniuch, C.E. & Sinclair, M.A. 1992. Problems of designing task-based user interfaces for large scale CIM systems. Computer Integrated Manufacturing systems, 5(2), pp. 91-96.
11. Siemieniuch, C.E. 1992. Design to Product: a prototype system to enable design for manufacturability, in Human factors in design for manufacturability, ed.

Helander, M. & Nagamichi, M. Taylor and Francis, London. pp. 35-54, ISBN 074840 009 5.

12. Booch, G., 1986, Object-Oriented Development, IEEE Trans. on Software Eng., Vol. SE12 No 2 Feb. 1986, pp. 211-221.

23. User Interface Quality and Evaluating Ease of Use

B. Serpil Acar

Department of Computer Studies, Loughborough University of Technology, Loughborough LE11 3TU, UK.

Abstract. The evaluation of user interface quality may be important to everyone for different reasons. It is not easy to judge usability in general, and learnability in particular, objectively, however; both can have a dramatic effect on user performances. In this paper, problems in evaluation have been considered. Some solutions are suggested and a mathematical technique to measure learning times is included.

Keywords. usability, user friendly, learning models, interface quality, quality metrics, easy to use, easy to learn, quantitative techniques, user interface.

23.1 Introduction

The major purpose of using computers is to receive assistance in solving problems accurately and speedily. Here the term 'problem' is used in its very general form. For example, the problem might require calculations or data analysis (in the case of scientific or engineering packages). The problem could be to achieve an effective presentation (in the case of word processors, draughting systems) or it could be storing and organising the data as part of an administration duty (as in the case of databases, spreadsheets).

In the 1980s, the software houses thrived. Each software system solved the 'problem' in its own way, to compete with others. Each one of them promoted its speciality and methods. The story is quite different now, in the 1990s. One can easily observe that the functionality of similar packages are substantially merged. This means that more than one way of solving the problem accurately is possible, and provided that they are executed on the appropriate hardware, they are all very fast.

Furthermore, the decreasing computer prices and improvements in other areas such as portability, reliability, efficiency, and ease of use, have helped the creation of a whole new set of users. This set no longer consists of only scientists and secretaries but also someone from almost every level of professions, management to shopfloor in the factory, consultant surgeon to assistant nurse in the hospital, professors to research assistants in the universities. Having extended the user set quite dramatically has put some extra pressures on the vendors to improve the quality of their product and especially the ease of use. Some set up human-computer interface laboratories to improve it, some supported research in this area, some conducted small scale in-house research (and some did nothing) but all claimed that their product is 'easy to learn' and 'easy to operate'; in summary 'easy to use'.

It is quite natural to look for an additional advantage if more than one system can do the job but there is more to a good user-interface than that. Human-computer interface is only a natural extension of the general human-tool interface that we all experience in everyday life. People prefer the tool that they are most comfortable with even if there is a purpose-designed tool available which is awkward to use. A cook might prefer his/her favourite knife to cut almost anything despite the fact that there are separate knives available to be used in the kitchen. The judgement is not simultaneous, but a 2-stage elimination process. At the first stage the tools which do not meet the functionality requirements are eliminated. At the second stage the user-interfaces are judged. There can be a trade-off in favour of a good user-interface only if an acceptable functionality can be demonstrated.

Suppose seven competing systems A, B, C, D, E, F, G have been ordered according to their usability, i.e. C, A, B, D, E, G, F. Then a threshold, an acceptable level of functionality, has been chosen as shown in Fig. 23.1. In this fictitious case, the systems C, F and G will not even be considered since they failed the functionality test. Despite having passed the first test with flying colours, B is not the winner of the whole test as it scores low at the usability front. The winner in this case is system E.

One must remember that a good user interface is a necessary condition, not a sufficient one. In other words the cook's knife must cut well.

23.2 Usability

Much has been said about usability and there are very encouraging developments in this interdisciplinary field, involving psychologists, ergonomics, mathematicians, computer scientists, technical writers and designers. An account of recent attractions to this field in the world can be found in Shneiderman [9]. Shackel [8] gives a quick history of the definition of ease of use and provides Bennett's [3] final formulation:

'The capability to be used by humans easily and effectively'

Chapanis [5] provided a similar definition and confesses that the definition seems to be circular because of the inexact words 'easily' and 'effectively'. Quality modellers, for example Oh and Lee [6], propose evaluation frameworks for measuring qualitative and quantitative quality metrics and include ease of use as an important metric which cannot be measured quantitatively. This is because usability is often presented as a function of learnability and operability and it is believed that it is not possible to measure learnability objectively and

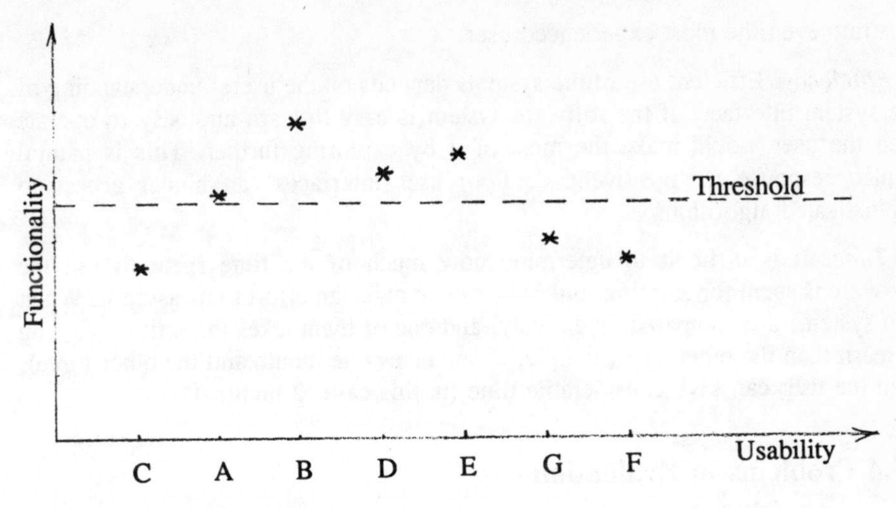

Fig. 23.1. Two stage elimination process considering functionality and usability

quantitatively. In this paper this view has been challenged by showing how it may be possible to measure ease of learning. The aim is to move learnability from qualitative metrics to quantitative metrics.

23.3 Quality and Evaluation

Evaluating the quality of a product has always been important. The meaning of quality however, may vary. For the producer (including manufacturer and marketing officer) quality is proportional to economic results

'Good quality product brings better profit'

For the purchaser — a person of a group of persons who actually pays the money to the producer, often at managerial positions — quality is the relation between costs and benefits.

'A good quality product is worth paying the cost'

On the other hand quality for the users is measured by the response to their requirements and satisfaction of needs. Usability is one of the requirements of today's users.

'A good quality product can do the job user wants in the way user wants'.

Evaluating usability is important for each of these groups for different reasons as seen above. Usability in general and learnability in particular influence the performance in three ways:

a. *The 'Put-off' factor*. Although the consequences of a poor quality interface are not very difficult to see, it is still necessary to measure the user interface quality. If the user is put off by the system, it is difficult to change this human perception. This affects the user's willingness to use the system. A poor user interface will frustrate even the most experienced user.

b. *Efficiency*. Efficient use of the systems depends on the users' understanding of the system interface. If the software system is easy to learn and easy to operate then the user would make the most of it by exploring further. This is natural human response to 'positiveness'. Poor user interfaces can hinder access to sophisticated algorithms.

c. *Time*. It is difficult to determine how much of the time spent to use the software is spent for learning, unless someone make an effort to measure it. When two systems are compared objectively, and one of them takes three times as long to learn than the other (for example, if one takes one month and the other three), then the user can save considerable time (in this case, 2 months).

23.4 Problems in Evaluation

23.4.1 Definition

The first problem of evaluating user interfaces is the lack of a concrete definition of ease of use. Chapanis [5] propose a modified definition from a definition by Shackel [8]

> 'The usability of a computer (system) is measured by how easily and how effectively the computer can be used by a specific set of users, given particular kinds of support to carry out a fixed set of tasks, in a defined set of environments.'

This definition would be very helpful only if the evaluator would like to conduct the experiments with questionnaires, interviews etc. to find out the opinion of a user or a group of users on ease of use of user interfaces. Some of the suggested 'observable' and measurable ways of defining ease of use for example

> 'ease of learning, the time required to learn how to do a set of tasks'

or

> 'overall evaluation, some mathematical combination of two or more of the measures'

themselves are still problems that evaluators are seeking the solutions for.

23.4.2 Techniques

The lack of objective techniques to measure ease of use is another major problem in evaluation. This problem is closely linked with the first one (definition). At the moment mostly used techniques are surveys and interviews. Surveys are not very time consuming and can give a general opinion of large number of people, notably, much fewer number of people than the experimenter approaches. Interviews with individuals or groups of people are time consuming, but usually give in-depth information.

Surveys and interviews can be conducted to include learnability and operability and may be useful to compare user interfaces if one of the user interfaces is obviously superior to the other. But they are subjective and can not provide exact times to learn. Furthermore, it is possible to affect the users' answers by constructing the questions or even choosing the order of the possible multiple choice answers carefully.

4.3 Using the Glossy Brochure Terminology

This problem is a consequence of problems above, namely lack of definition and techniques. Because there is no specific test available the vendors can use anything they like to promote their products. They create their own terminology sometimes including senseless sentences and for example use phrases like 'reduced learning curves'. They may reach the customer who assumes they mean the system is easy to learn. The problem is, people start using the same terminology and it becomes a public phrase. There is no such thing as 'reduced curve'. Unfortunately, evaluators of some interfaces now try to find out whether they can fit a 'reduced curve' to their data.

23.4.4 Learnability and Operability

Usability is often considered as a function of learnability and operability. When an interface is declared as easy to use it is not very clear that whether it is easy to learn or easy to operate or both.

Some systems are very easy to learn but too difficult to operate. Conversely some systems are difficult to learn but once the users grasp what to do, they find it easy to operate.

As evaluators are we going to classify these systems as 'easy to use' or not.

Suggested solutions to the problems raised in this section, can be found in the following section.

23.5 Solutions

23.5.1 Definition

The shortened definition of usability in Shackle [8]:

'the capability to be used by humans easily and effectively where
easily = to a specified level of subjective assessment
effectively = to a specified level of (human) performance'

is taken as basis here. Furthermore, usability has been factorised to its components, levels of ease has been defined and following definition has been reached.

'usability is the capability to be learned by novice people and operated by experienced users by achieving a pre-defined ratio of experts performance level in time and accuracy'

Although the term 'pre-defined' in this definition may sound like a non-exact term, it has been deliberately left open as this level may change according to the nature of the job and consequence of acceptable level of performance in time and accuracy. For example it may be acceptable to type half as fast or make three times more mistakes than an expert typist whereas such is not acceptable in operating an emergency power cut mechanism.

23.5.2 Techniques and Terminology

The principles of the mathematical techniques were previously mentioned at other conferences (Acar [1], Acar [2]), and the procedures are briefly explained in Case and Acar [4]; however they have been included here in this paper in deatil for the purpose of completeness. These techniques also provide a set of appropriate terms hence bring a solution to the 'terminology' problem:

Learning is defined as change of behaviour as a result of practice. It has always been desirable to measure it. Learning involves the combination of prior knowledge in a similar area and intelligence, and has not been measured in a pure form. One approach is to find a relationship which enables performance to be defined as a function of practice. This approach leads to the fitting of learning curves, related to the likelihood of a correct response.

The goal of a learner is ideally to perform as well as a very experienced user. One reaches the goal if he or she completes a given task accurately by spending as much time as an expert. In this paper, performance, level of learning, is based on measurements of multiple of 'the expert time spent' by the subjects for completion of the task during the experiments.

Preparations

The objective of the experiments is to measure the performance of new users working on systems. It is therefore very important to satisfy the following requirements:

- Learners should be selected amongst subjects who know what to do but are inexperienced in how to do it.
- All aspects of the interfaces to be compared should be covered in various real and hypothetical test pieces.
- Presentation of the test process should be prepared in a way to highlight the differences in systems.

Experiments

The experiments consist of measuring performance of the learners in terms of expert time. Therefore, it is necessary:

- First to measure the performance of the experts, i.e. number of achievements of an expert in a fixed time interval and to record them,
- Then to measure the performance of each learner (in the same time interval) repeatedly until convergence is observed within a certain confidence band, and to record them.

The stopwatch is started each time with the system's prompt and stopped when the subject has completed his or her response.

Learning Models

Replacement and accumulation models are two well known learning models used to generate learning curves. In the replacement model, some erroneous habits are replaces by new habits — ideally correct — as the total number of entities remains constant. On the other hand, in the accumulation model, new responses - ideally correct — are added to existing habits. The total number of entities increases after every experimentation.

In probabilistic terms these learning models are explained in Restle and Greeno [7] as follows: Think of a subject in a learning experiment as having an urn containing white and red marbles representing correct responses and errors respectively (Fig. 23.2). At each trial, certain (say k) number of marbles are drawn and

1. in replacement model, these marbles are taken away and the same number of marbles (k) are added from the tutor's urn to the student's urn, (ideally) all white (correct).
2. in accumulation model, the marbles are put back in the student's urn. Furthermore, the same number of (ideally) white (correct) marbles are added from the tutor's urn to the student's urn.

If the proportion of white marbles in the tutor's urn is a (ideally a=1); the initial level of performance is b; and the proportion of marbles drawn from the student's urn is θ; replacement and accumulation model curves are given by the following equations, derivation of which can be found in Restle and Greeno [7] in probabilistic form.

$$y_r = a - (a - b)(1 - \theta)^{x-1} \qquad (1)$$

$$y_c = \frac{b + \theta a (x - 1)}{1 + \theta (x - 1)} \qquad (2)$$

where x denotes practice (trial)

a denotes the asymptotic level
b denotes the initial level
θ denotes the learning parameter
y_r, y_c denotes performance

These models can be interpreted as follows:
Replacement Model. Learning by changing (correcting) one's habits, ideally never making the same mistake again and ultimately becoming an expert.

Accumulation Model. Learning with the possibility of making the same mistake again, but ideally with a progressively smaller probability and ultimately becoming an expert.

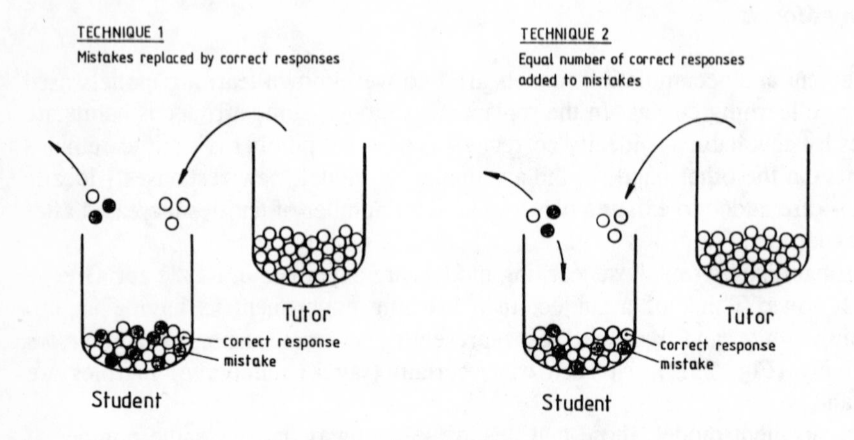

Fig. 23.2 - Urn Representation of Theory of Learning Curves

Generation of Learning Curves

The data obtained in Section 23.5 can be used to generate learning curves, explained in Section 23.5, to see the progress of the learner on one system. However, the measurements taken during the experiments on learners contain the information about 'how easy to use' the systems as well as 'how easy to learn' them. To isolate the learning factor, the data should be normalised by dividing the average of learner data by the expert data at each trial. Therefore, plotting the new set of data means using:
X axis : practice; trial numbers (positive integers 1,2...)
Y axis : performance; proportion of achievements in terms of expert times (real numbers between 0 and 1)

Learning curves can then be approximated by using equations (1) and (2) with the new set of data.

Introduction of learning level α is necessary to identify the number of trial where the desired level of learning is achieved.

Example

The following data is merely contrived to illustrate the method when any learning curve is used. Suppose the following data is the record of performance of a learner in the first five units of trial

y = 40, 52, 60, 65, 67

and suppose expert's number of achievements in the same time interval is 100. The first data set could be rescaled as

y = 0.4, 0.52, 0.6, 0.65, 0.67

Figure 23.3(a) shows this data with a supposedly fitted learning curve $f_{l.}$

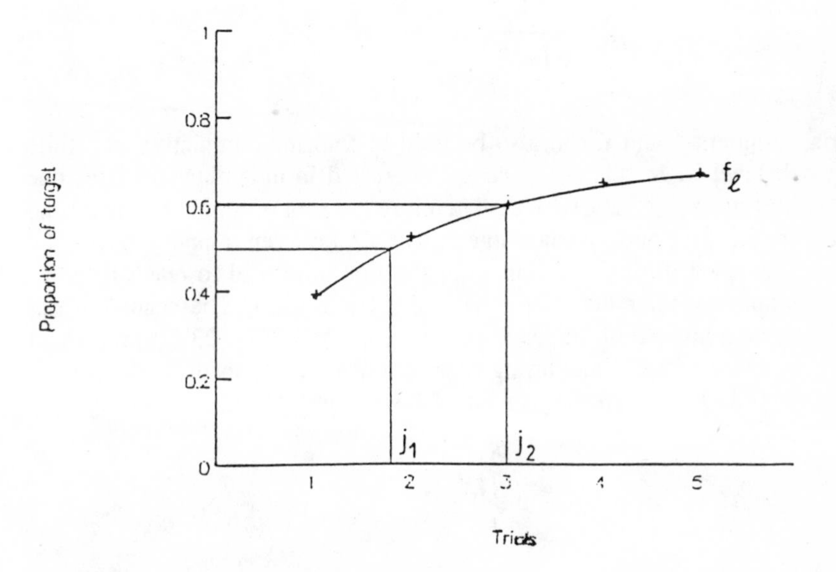

Fig. 23.3(a) - Fictitious data and learning curve f_l

To be able to make inferences from learning curves, let us specify the level of achievement α as a proportion of the target. In this example, if we accept 50% of the expert performance as 'good' and 60% of it as 'very good' performance, the corresponding number of trials j_1 and j_2 of the levels of achievement $\alpha_1 = 0.5$ and $\alpha_2 = 0.6$ can be found from the fitted learning curve equations as shown in Fig. 23.3(a). Note that j does not have to be an integer since the learning curves are continuous.

Calculation of Learning Times

The trial number j_o corresponding the level of achievement $\alpha_o = 1$ represents the trial number where the learner performs as well as an expert. Although it is possible to measure it in theory, it requires long term engagement and usually impractical. Instead, one can determine a 'sufficient' level of achievement α and calculate the learning times until the learner reaches this level.

From equations (1) and (2) we can find the number $\in R$ of trials j_r and j_c, for the replacement and accumulation model respectively, for a given α as follows:

$$j_r = \frac{\log(\frac{\alpha - a}{b - a})}{\log(1-\theta)} + 1 \qquad (3)$$

$$j_c = \frac{\alpha - b}{\theta\,(a - x)} + 1 \qquad (4)$$

The trial numbers j_r and j_c can also be used to find the cumulative unit time spent to reach level α. In this case, we are interested in unit time spent for one complete unit of work, i.e. $1/y_r$ or $1/y_c$. Therefore the sum of number of unit time spent between the first and j_{th} trials integral of f_l^{-1} between 1 and j, gives the cumulative time spent during the trials after the first until trial to reach level α.

As an example consider the simple data of section 5.2.5. The shaded areas, $A_1,\ldots,A_5$ under the inverse of the learning curve, f_l^{-1}, as in Fig. 23.3(b) represent time spent, in terms of unit time during each unit trial. Time spent by the subject to reach $\alpha_1 = 0.5$, shaded area A_{j1} in Fig. 23.3(c) can be found by adding

$$\int_1^{j_1} f_l^{-1}$$

to the time spent during the first unit trial.

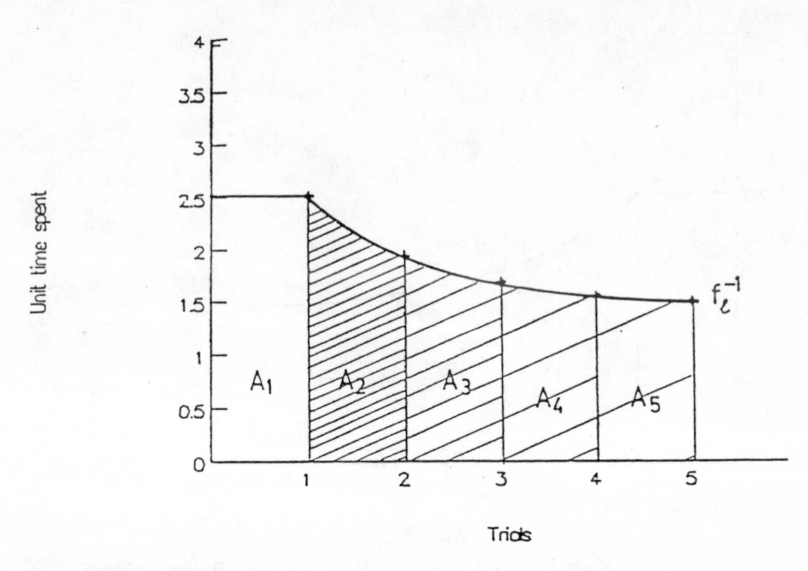

Fig. 23.3(b) - Time spent in terms of unit time during the trials

For the replacement curve; the time spent between first and jth trial is

$$I_{j_r} = \int_1^j \frac{1}{a - (a-b)(1-\theta)^{x-1}} dx$$

$$= \frac{x-1}{a} - \frac{1}{a \log(1-\theta)} \log(a-(a-b)(1-\theta)^{x-1})]_1^j$$

$$= \frac{1}{a} \{(j-1) - \frac{1`}{\log(1-\theta)} \log(\frac{a-(a-b)(1-\theta)^{j-1}}{b})\} \quad \textbf{(5)}$$

and for the accumulation curve it is:

$$I_{j_c} = \int_1^j \frac{1+\theta(x-1)}{b+\theta a(x-1)} dx$$

$$= \frac{1}{a} (x + \frac{a-b}{\theta a} \log(b+\theta a(x-1)))]_1^j$$

$$= \frac{1}{a} \{(j-1) + \frac{a-b}{\theta a} \log(\frac{b+\theta a(j-1)}{b})\} \quad \textbf{(6)}$$

The values of equation (5) and (6) are meaningful (positive) if the value of b, the initial value for proportion of target/unit time, is less than α (j is greater than 1). Otherwise, the number of trials to reach level would be taken as 1, which

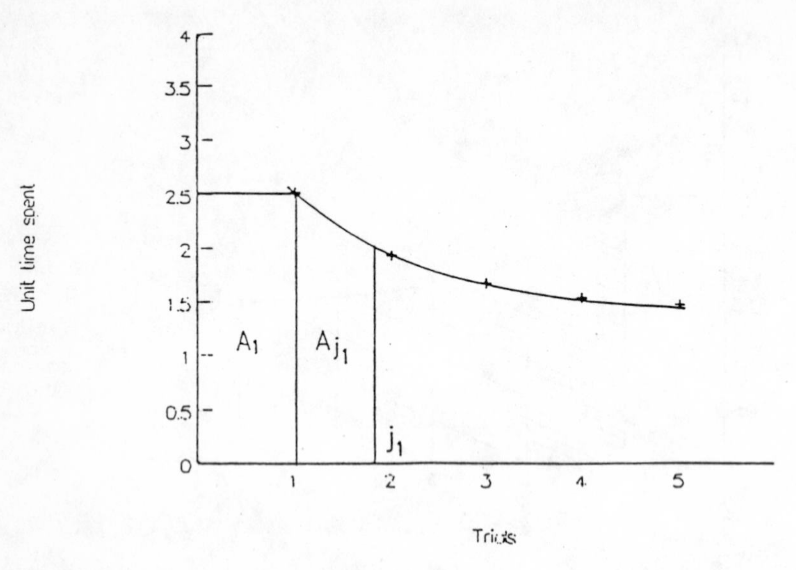

Fig. 23.3(c) - Time spent to reach $\alpha_1 = 0.5$

makes the value of (5) and (6) zero. In each case the total time spent is found by adding the time spent in the first trial to example (5) or (6). That is:

$$I = I_1 + I_{(1,j)}$$

$$\text{where } I_1 = \frac{1}{b}$$

and substituting (1) and (2) in (5) and (6) gives:

$$I_{(1,j)} = \begin{cases} 0 & ;\ b>\alpha \\ \dfrac{1}{a}\dfrac{1}{\log(1-\theta)}\log\left(\dfrac{b(\alpha-a)}{\alpha(b-a)}\right) & ;\ b<\alpha \text{ repl. mod.} \\ \dfrac{1}{\theta a}\dfrac{\alpha-b}{a-\alpha}+\dfrac{b-a}{a}\log\left(\dfrac{b(\alpha-a)}{\alpha(b-a)}\right) & ;\ b<\alpha \text{ accum. mod.} \end{cases} \quad (7)$$

23.5.3 Learnability and Operability

Learnability and operability are usually considered as two independent factors of usability. Some systems maybe easy to learn but difficult to operate or difficult to learn but easy to operate.

As an example of the former case, consider an everyday life event. We, adults can learn how to open a child-proof medicine bottle or a milk carton in a very short time interval and can demonstrate it, even teach others how to open it. Surprisingly, most of us have difficulty to open it when we need it. This could be because we need that extra concentration and care to be able to perform some tasks. Sometimes, a large number of actions have to be performed to complete a task. This would also help deterioration in concentration and hence performance as in some editing facilities of word processors.

The world is full of examples of the latter case, systems which are difficult to learn but easy to operate, for example some of the CAD systems, word processors, activities like driving can be counted in this group.

Difficulty of learning in these example originates from learning new skills, such as thinking in the way the particular computer software wants us to think; or co-ordinating hands, eyes, feet movements and quick thinking. It is true that, sometimes, for a certain apprenticeship period people find even the most 'difficult to learn' systems, easy to operate. This shows; they acquired new skills and they do not need to think as long as before. Actions are taken automatically.

23.6 Conclusion

Evaluation of operability has been performed by several professional usability laboratories to compare and improve the software products. This emphasises the importance of testing the ease of learning.

It is not easy to determine whether a system is easy to learn or not by using the techniques explained here. These techniques have been successfuly used to compare some CAD systems objectively. It is hard to design and conduct the experiments and analyse the results. But the results are equally valuable. Chapanis [5] say

"Good evaluations are hard to find"

I would like to sum up by reversing his statement

"Hard evaluations are good to find"

References

1. Acar B S : "Testing the Ease of Learning of Industrial Systems", ECMI Volume 7, Ed: M Helio, pp127-130. B G Teubner Stuttgart and Kluwer Academic Publishers, Netherlands, 1991. (ISBN 0-7923-1317-8)
2. Acar B S : "Evaluating the Quality of User Interfaces" AQuIS'91 , Ed:P Ancilotti and M Fusani pp 75-89. Editrice Publishers, Italy,1991

3. Bennett J L : "Managing to Meet Usability Requirements" Visial Display Terminals: Usability Issues and Health Concerns pp 161-184, 1984
4. Case, K., and Acar, B.S., "Learning studies in the use of Computer Aided Design systems for discrete-parts manufacture", (1989) Behaviour and Information Technology, Vol.8, No. 5, 1989, pp.353-368.
5. Chapanis A : "Evaluating Usability" , Human Factors for Informatics Usability Eds: B Shackel, S Richardson, Cambridge University Press, pp 359-395,1991
6. Oh and Lee : "Evaluation Framework for Quality Metrics AQuIS'91 Ed:P Ancilotti and M Fusani pp 75-89. Editrice Publishers, Italy,1991
7. Restle F and Greeno J G : "Introduction to Mathematical Phychology", Addison Wesley,1970
8. Shackel B : "Usability- Context, Framework, Definition, Design and Evaluation"Human Factors for Informatics Usability Eds: B Shackel, S Richardson,Cambridge University Press, pp 21-37, 1991
9. Shneiderman : "Designing the User Interface". Addison-Wesley, 1992

24. Group Work Output

Stephen Evans

The CIM Institute, Cranfield University, Cranfield, Bedford MK43 0AL, UK

Introduction

The following papers are the direct result of the main group work undertaken during the Advanced Study Institute. The general alm of the group work was to explore the issues of people, organisation and technology in production systems. This was felt to be too vague to guide participants efforts and a specific process was developed to create focus. The primary aims of the session were:

- to bring scholars from different disciplines together
- to learn some of each others language, style, methods, knowledge and views, by focusing on industry as the customer
- to establish the practical difficulties of P/O/T integration
- to propose solutions and to generate ideas for research

By being practical, it was hoped that the pressures felt by industry would provide a framework or common view plus a common target, so helping the process of interdisciplinary cooperation. Real problems are rarely simple and focus on them encourages participants to share — especially in a non-competitive situation such as the NATO ASI. Similarly too tight a goal might stifle creativity and be seen as an imposition, so a large degree of freedom was built into the output expectations.

The mechanism used to achieve this was to combine working sessions with provoking presentations on the theme of the P/O/T project life cycle — strategy, specification, design, build, implementation and evaluation. The life cycle was not prescriptive. Each group combined working sessions in a separate room with attendance at presentations following the theme. The groups were the same as for the SCANCO exercise — a deliberate attempt to remove the higher stress levels of early group forming in preparation for this more challenging task.

Prior to starting the work itself, a notional output was described — a workbook to advise industry-based practitioners undertaking development of integrated P/O/T systems. The workbook would cover all phases of the project life cycle. Each group was given an opportunity to reflect on its own strengths and interests and decide their own target output before starting. One chose to tackle the problem described, others chose to focus on different parts of the life cycle, another chose to tackle it from a different viewpoint altogether by studying People and Organisations, yet another chose to add a new task of defining 'human-centredness'.

The papers are therefore very different — each looks at different parts of the same P/O/T integration problem, they take different viewpoints, they are developed by different groups with differing combinations of disciplines and they vary from highly reflective to highly practical (usually in the same paper!) Please read them recognising these differences are part of our search for ways forward.

The output and the process can be thought of as a kaleidoscope — each individual piece may not be a breakthrough but the combinations and patterns may help generate insight for those able to find it. The process allowed different views to come together for a short time and maybe the patterns generated in such a hurriedly-built kaleidoscope are not yet mature; but some useful observations can be made:

- The process of inter-disciplinary cooperation is vital if we academics are to tackle real life problems with the best weapons available. Absurdly narrow problems or single-dimension solutions to complex situations will continue to be the norm if we do not.
- There are many valuable insights easily available from other disciplines. You do not have to have a deep understanding or a lengthy learning period to pick up much useful advice.
- It is easier to hold a multi-disciplinary conversation around a specific problem. Only mature cooperators can hold the generalised conversations we often have with peers within our own discipline.
- Cooperation is personality driven. Research is an individual activity; research cooperation works best when you known you can work together. (In this sense the NATO ASI, as with other similar events, is a form of dating agency!).
- Inter-disciplinary cooperation is an exciting process because it can refresh your views and ideas as well as act as the catalyst for new insights. This may well be the most important observation; by being exciting, it may attract individuals who are willing to overcome the difficulties of inter-disciplinary cooperation - then we may have a community who can make real progress in the problem of People /Information/Technology.

Group A
Human-centred Design, Implementation and Operation of Man-Machine Systems

edited by L.Bálint[1] and M.Iken[2]

[1] Hungarian Academy of Sciences, Budapest, Hungary
[2] Brunel University, Uxbridge, Middlesex, United Kingdom

Human-centred design, implementation and operation of man-machine systems (MMS), is one of the key topics among the issues related to anthropocentric production systems [Key problem].

Human-centred system (HCS) theory and practice need a (new) multi-disciplinary framework [HCS theoretical background].

A comparison of (production) systems without humans, involving humans and integrating humans may lead to basic recognitions concerning HCS. Similarly, clarification and definition of human and machine properties (strong and weak points) may lead to selection criteria for optimum man-machine work division [Basic approach].

Collection of different, even extreme, aspects/views/opinions from sources of different cultural background, then, extracting common ideas/views and finally, integrating the collected/extracted separate findings into a well supported general scheme is a helpful way of achieving new ideas regarding HCS [Multi-cultural approach].

HCS-oriented investigations should concentrate:

(1) on introducing a taxonomy of HCS-related topics/problems,
(2) on the analysis of existing computer-integrated systems,
(3) on classification and characterisation of different generations of man-machine systems,
(4) on outlining and illustration of the proposed/projected next generation(s) in HCS
(5) on examining how to get to the proposed/projected next generation in practice [Basic investigations on HCS].

Within the basic question of what properties may the future HCI generation have, there appear some important (secondary) open questions regarding the role of humans, computer-integrated manufacturing (CIM), organisational intelligence, team-working, cultural background, decision-making and function-allocation in the HCS [Open questions on future HCS].

The significance of human presence, supervision and control in man-machine systems is evident but it is difficult to determine what kinds of humans are most adequate in the different system categories and system functions/subfunctions [Role of humans].

In principle, there are five fundamental categories of human characters (mentality, behaviour, capabilities etc.), complementing each other. God makes miracles, wizards make magic, artists perform art (by knowing "what"), technicians master procedures (they know "how") and scientists create models (by telling "why") [Human characters].

The most important advantageous specific human properties and capabilities are: strength in interpreting complex situations, flexibility and adaptivity, aptitude of pattern matching, talent for learning from experiences, purpose-driven behaviour and activities, ability of overviewing and synthesis, capability of handling irregular situations, proficiency in problem solving, talent to self-reflection, familiarity with error-handling, widespread skills and competence, adequacy to handling uncertainty, motivation-orientedness, ability of own decision-making and mastery in working with incomplete specification [Advantageous human attributes].

Humans are weak (relative to machines) with respect to the following properties: danger of stress/frustration, hazard of erroneous perceptions/decisions/actions, risk of fatigue/faults/mistakes, varying skills/capabilities/performance and finally, necessity of rest to recover [Weaknesses of humans].

Machines (computers or computerised machinery) are created (designed and realised) intentionally by taking into account human-made specifications. They function deterministically and their behaviour and operation can be, in principle, well described. They are able to transfer energy, power and force within extreme limits, to move even with extreme velocities, to handle objects even of extreme mass, to perform operations with high efficiency/accuracy/repeatability, without rest and recreation. But their flexibility is limited, they require complete specification and control and sometimes they fail [Machine properties].

Computers, as special machines, are strong in administrative operations, in computational capabilities, in consistency checking, in data crunching and in deterministic functions, but they don't have self-reflection, are unable to handle unforeseen errors and have a limited adaptivity [Computer properties].

Well-working man-machine systems require (1) staff members of appropriate capabilities, motivation, innovativeness, wide-range skills and expertise, readiness to learn and willingness to create friendly atmosphere, (2) physical infrastructure built up from efficient, reliable, accurate (and flexible) equipments for design, manufacturing and testing as well as an integrated, networked information technology sub-system, (3) an organisation being innovation-oriented, having a well established and well working information-policy, stressing a substantial focus on technological R&D and supporting a well working team structure and finally, (4) input/output relations comprising materials-oriented, information-oriented and money-oriented processes [MMS prerequisites].

Man-machine systems have four generations. MMS history can be divided into the periods of (1) no automation, (2) automation aided humans, (3) human aided automata and (4) future human/automata symbiosis. All four periods are characterisable with respect to products/services provided (variety, uniformity, complexity, precision and performance), human and machine activity types, level of machine intelligence and knowledge, properties of man-machine interaction and MMS advantages/drawbacks [MMS generations].

Future man-machine systems are best characterised:

(1) by the balance between customisation and mass production, re-usability and creativity as well as minimum production effort and maximum production output

(2) by the harmonious co-operation between man and machine

(3) by dependency of humans on their machine partners [MMS perspective].

Among human skills directly exploitable by man-machine system operation there are two groups well distinguishable: individual skills and collective skills. Individual skills are either physiological/physical or mental/behavioural while collective skills are cooperative/communicative [Human skills].

The historical evolution of human skills occurred in three, partly overlapping steps, i.e. in the gradual enhancement of:

(1) the physiological/physical skills

(2) the mental/behavioural skills

(3) the cooperative/communicative skills

This very process of evolution has been copied by the evolution of the artificial means supporting the enhancement of the related skills in human activities: the "artificial hands" (early tools) were first introduced tens of thousands years ago, the first "artificial muscle" (first steam machine) appeared in the late eighteenth century, the "artificial brain" (the electronic computer) started it's revolutionary development after World War, the second and, there came the "artificial nervous system" of the society (computer networking), about twenty years later. The continuous evolution of all the mentioned human skills and their artificial counterparts allows gradually increasing efficiency, reliability and cost-effectiveness in the operation of human-centred man-machine systems [Human skill evolution].

Traditional human skills can be successfully integrated into the activities of an organisation only if a set of meta-skills is also brought in by the staff members. Meta-skills are secondary skills not belonging directly to a specific field of human activities, but enabling people to overcome the problems arising when a plain group tries to became a team. Most important meta-skills are: horizontal communication within an organisation, elevated authority and responsibility, utilisation of information, recognition of data relationships, understanding the significance of tools, synthesis of information and concepts, creativity (thinking differently in an active manner), open-mindedness (thinking differently in a passive manner), time management and development of team management skills [Meta-skills].

The introduction of CIM, as one of the key issues in industrial production-oriented computer-integrated systems, means that:

(1) shopfloor workers supervise machinery, instead of directly manipulating, operating or controlling the machines

(2) testing staff takes care of production (process) tests instead of product tests

(3) process planning engineers provide NC (numerical control) tools instead of written/plotted documents

(4) product designers with their CAD (computer-aided design) systems take on process planners' tasks in case of CNC (computer numerical control) technologies

(5) logistics and full production-oriented administrative activities are computer-controlled and computerised

(6) the full line of computer-supported production-oriented activities is integrated into a computer-controlled system [Introducing CIM].

By applying CIM, a highly efficient, reliable and in many cases extremely cost-effective production system can be set up: products get more and more "variational" and "parametrised", processes get more and more "parametrisable", process planning gets more and more product family-oriented instead of the earlier simple product-orientedness and the earlier distinguished role of product design decreases while difficult design efforts are more and more associated to designing product families [Features of CIM].

CIM is feasible where, beside NC and CNC manufacturing, CAD or DA (design automation) is also well advanced. The introduction of CIM itself is motivating the rapid development of these computer-supported design methods, as well [Feasibility of CIM].

CIM increasingly requires human-centredness, supposing, among others, cautious staff selection, personnel education/training and team-working while, at the same time, postulates thorough consideration of friendly workplace atmosphere, healthy shopfloor circumstances and special care-taking of staff members [CIM and human-centredness].

Professional persons belong to at least two different activity spheres and in order to develop proper HCS it is of outstanding importance to take into account the totally different requirements people are exposed to in these spheres. The two most important spheres are the "social (private)" sphere and the "business (professional)" sphere. At least four distinct levels can be recognised in either spheres, with common top and bottom levels of "society" and "individual", respectively. Intermediate levels in the social sphere are neighbourhoods and families/clubs while, in the business sphere, organisations and teams [Human activity spheres].

There are a number of issues determining how the related structural items function, operate and behave. Among the most important such issues there appear lifecycles, motivation, missions/tasks, authority/responsibility, capabilities/skills, knowledge, information, relation/linking/interaction between spheres/levels and costs/benefits (of partial and entire operations). Special care is to be taken of the team level because this is most important regarding the processes related to human-centredness [Human activity issues].

Different cultures and different geographical areas differ in their characteristics related to the introduction of human-centredness. As far as conformity, enhancement of individuals' contribution, social responsibility and homogeneity are concerned, Western Europe, Eastern Europe, the USA and Japan are representing diverse features. While in Western Europe social responsibility is combined with homogeneity, Eastern Europe manifests high conformity and homogeneity, the US appears to be strong in conformity, enhancement of individuals' contribution and social responsibility and Japan exhibits outstanding values in all four properties. Nevertheless, Western European countries are also differing from each other (higher conformity in Germany whereas higher enhancement of individuals' contribution in France, etc.). These kinds of information may serve as a good basis for determining specific region-dependent (culture-oriented) aspects of organising HCS [HCS and cultural background].

Team-working requires some conditions to be met. Beside technical skills, the role of meta-skills is increasing in successful team-working. However, their significance is mostly underestimated. Meta-skills are, on one hand, conditioned by the organisational culture, but, on the other hand, they do inseminate the organisational culture, as well. Another aspect is that successful HCS operation supposes not only a multi-language, but also a multi-cultural composition of the teams. Additionally, the intellectual property of results produced by team-work should be clarified explicitly [Conditions of successful team-working].

The process of decision-making is of high importance in HCS success. Humans will identify with the system if they are involved into the decision-making, but without identifying, they don't participate effectively. The role of negotiation skills and styles, the ability to recognise common interests and the belief that win/win-compromises are achievable is substantial. Therefore, the task of building team relationships is extremely important. The development of mediation skills is another crucial factor. Both models of decision-making (consensus-building process and representative decision-making) are to be utilised. Authority and responsibility are to be in harmony [Decision-making and HCS].

Humans in a man-machine system should be able to perform efficiently and reliably their routine tasks, should be able to achieve recovery from system errors, should learn continuously (improve themselves) and should innovate (enhance) system operation. These requirements suppose appropriate human properties, abilities, skills and performance [Humans in HCS].

The tasks of the staff members are decreasing by the introduction of CIM but these tasks get, at the same time, much more demanding:

(1) the new supervisory tasks totally differ from the traditional controlling tasks
(2) there is a tremendous difference between the traditional testing expertise and the new (process-oriented) testing/QA requirements
(3) the new tasks and skills being supposed by the new process planning needs are totally differing from the traditional tasks and skills
(4) there is a significant contradiction between the traditional division of work and the new integration of product and process design/planning

The solution of the emerging problems require careful system planning and implementation, attentive selection/education/training of the personnel, cautious and selective involvement of advanced computer practice and conscientious introduction of team-working in the fully integrated system [Introducing CIM].

In MMS organisations, one important step towards HCS is the introduction of team-working. When creating teams, some important points are to be considered.

No real change is possible until the management and even the top-management are ready to change their attitudes and behaviour. The management has to accept rules for do's and dont's in order to give the teams the appropriate amount of freedom, by setting up clear tasks, goals and targets but without interfering the process of the on-going team-work [Management and team-working].

When a "big" team is to be established, it is important to begin with a relatively small group (up to 10 persons). After this group has become a team it is possible to step-by-step introduce new members. By this incremental process it is possible to build up big teams but trying to create very large teams in a single step is dangerous and often failing [Forming large teams].

Continuity of the team is extremely important. The team is to be set up as early as possible during the related project. The team should work together full-time. A separate workplace for the team will guarantee undisturbed team activities [Team-working conditions].

A number of factors are to be taken into account in order to achieve well established and well working teams. Most important of such factors are: diversity (multi-culturalism and anti-conformism), task dependent team structure, enhancement of individual contributions, focus on informal/flexible structure, common culture of co-operation, equal opportunities, principle of repre sentation democracy, principle of consensus building, due processes in decision-making, avoidance of urging to conform instead of encouraging sometimes inconvenient but nevertheless good and important questions to come up [Team-working prerequisites].

Beside the need of complementary skills from the different team members, communication between the team members requires overlapping between the meta-skills of the participants. In contrast to traditional assumptions, this requirement doesn't suppose that each team member is to be an expert in at least two different skill areas, but participants should have just one skill, provided that different meta-skills overlap each other [Skill requirements in team-working].

Team members (or prospective team members) need not to get into intensive education for gaining expertise in totally new skill areas in order to enhance in-team cooperation. Individual evolution should aim at achieving new meta-skills only. As far as engineering-like activities are concerned, this evolution results in a new model of team-like engineering and thus, in contrast to the traditional product- and process-engineer prototype, a new engineer ideal is emerging. This new ideal, being strong in meta-skills, may be called "ductcess-engineer", indicating on one hand that product- and process-orientedness are getting integrated and suggesting on the other hand, that ductcess-orientedness is the key of success-orientedness [Individual evolution and team-working].

Group B
Strategy, Specification, and Design

Edited by Jim Witzerman

School of Industrial Engineering, Purdue University, West Lafayette, IN 47907-1287, USA.

This group examined the process stages of strategy definition, specification development, and initial system design. These early stages are critical to the eventual success of a project. A well-constructed strategy facilitates the justification and evaluation of system changes, while specification error is a principal reason that delivered software systems fail. The group discussed software systems development, but the following issues and procedures closely parallel those required to plan changes in organizations and manufacturing systems.

Within each of the stages of strategy, specification, and design, the group addressed the following issues:
What are the goals of the stage? What are the primary inputs and products of the stage? What is the process that takes place within the stage? Who is involved in the process? What are their interests and concerns? What information is generated in the stage? How is the information collected, managed, and presented? When does the stage begin and end?

Strategy
Strategy has two major elements: the standing policies of the enterprise, and the identification and definition of a problem that warrants a change to the existing system.

Goals
Strategic assessment, corporate objectives, and perceived needs are combined to develop a strategy for a new or modified system. The strategic assessment examines the economic and competitive state of the company and predicts trends. It also considers structures and relationships within the organization. The corporate objectives are policies that define how the company normally addresses technological, financial, and social issues. The need is a determination that a process should be changed to improve overall company operations.

The output of the strategy stage is a statement that defines the problem area, its symptoms, and the desired goals for a new system. These system goals should be defined in terms of adding value to the company's product or operations. They should not limit potential solutions. [Problem definition and goals]

Process
In some cases, a few individuals in a company may attempt to dictate a solution to the problem before it is adequately defined. This method has a very high risk

of failure, due to considerations not anticipated by the proponents of the solution. An interdisciplinary working team of knowledgeable personnel (the project management team) may avoid this pitfall by bringing differing perspectives to discussions. [Beware of the easy answer]

This team evaluates and discusses the state of the company and the nature of the problem to identify key success factors and dependencies at the corporate level. They must understand how a system change would constructively contribute to the company's objectives. The team then establishes business, technological, and social goals for the system, based on existing policies. They also define how to evaluate the attainment of these goals by the system.

Time frames must be established for system development, considering the desired date for full operational capability and the expected lifetime of the system. Risks and contingencies must be assessed in the event the development process fails to produce an adequate, timely, or cost-effective system.

It is also necessary to consider a strategy to assess the social impacts of the design tools that may be used in software development. Design tools and environments inherently affect the role of people in the developed system. An assessment is conducted during the design stage, which allows the project management team to prevent systematic social problems with the new system.

People

The problem statement should be developed by the project management team in consultation with potential users and other stakeholders. The team should represent a cross-section of departments that will be affected by a change to the existing system. Designers and other specialists should be consulted only in exceptional circumstances during this stage.

User input must begin early in the process and continue throughout system development. For this analysis, the term user applies to any individual who provides input to the system, as well as anyone who uses information or physical outputs of the system. Therefore, operators, supervisors, and managers associated with the problem area must be identified and included in the process to provide an accurate perspective of the existing system and the impacts of changes. User input is not a one-time event in developing a system. [Involve the users up front]

Other stakeholders include customers, suppliers, and employees who are not the direct users of the system. The team developing the strategy must consider the desired and expected impacts of the new system on these individuals and organizations.

The company may need to review its contracting policies for customized software. A traditional waterfall project cycle, with a fixed specification as part of the contract, often fails to produce a suitable product for both users or customers. Contract modification costs cause an inherent unwillingness to make changes. A more flexible arrangement with the software developer may be appropriate. [Flexibility in contracting]

Information

Information used to develop the strategy includes standing (but not static) policies that define the business, technological, and social objectives of the company. The social policy should define the respective roles of people and machines in the company, realizing the maximum potential from each. Reports of market share, financial state of the company, and workforce attitudes must also be considered. All of this information must be current, accurate, relevant, and objective.

Support tools at this stage of development include market analysis and simulation. These are used to assess the sensitivity of corporate operations to change and help determine the potential benefit of system changes.

The problem statement is a document that defines the reasons for a system change and the goals of the new system. It should be disseminated to all people who have an interest in the system, including direct users, indirect users, managers, and other stakeholders. This encourages feedback early in the development process. [Disseminate the problem statement]

Timing

Strategic assessment is a continuous process used to evaluate the state of the company and determine its future needs. This analysis should include the anticipated impacts and risks of any ongoing projects. When a problem is recognized and defined through this assessment, the specification process may be initiated. During the later stages of development, the strategy may be reviewed and amended as required by changing circumstances. Effective response to such changes requires consistent assessment methods and relatively stable corporate objectives and policies. The strategy phase for a specific project ends when the system is implemented and satisfies the parameters of the problem.

Specification

Goals

The project strategy is combined with the specific needs and comments of the stakeholders to produce a coherent and organized set of system requirements. A specific technical or organizational solution should not be selected during this phase.

The system requirements must satisfy the collected needs of the users. Relationships must be identified, including complementary or mutually exclusive sets of requirements. Priorities must define the relative importance of particular requirements. Technical, financial, and schedule issues should be considered.

A means to evaluate how a system meets or fails to meet the requirements must be established. The specification developers must also prepare a tentative implementation strategy. The new system may be used in parallel with an existing system; it may be implemented in one or more phases; or it may immediately and completely replace an existing system. This information is of vital interest to both the designers of the software and those planning training and support for the new system. [Implementation proposal]

Process

Multifunctional work groups that represent various affected interests should develop the system specification. The group's particular process and schedule should be matched to organizational dynamics and needs.

The helical life cycle model presented at the conference is a useful tool for the development of a specification for a proposed system. The CATWOE (Customer or beneficiary, Actors in the system, Transformation, World image, Ownership of the system, Environmental constraints) statement (or a similar tool) should be used to refine and evaluate the goals of the proposed system. Social factors should be addressed in parallel with the CATWOE statement to ensure that the users of the new system have a sense of importance as a part of the organization.

The helical life cycle provides a structure for the development of requirements, while incorporating feedback and consistency checking though the process. In some cases, jumps through the model may be safely and effectively made, especially when the participants share a common view of the problem. The results of these jumps should be verified against the CATWOE statement to ensure the process is still proceeding properly. [Flexible and cyclic method]

The needs of users and other actors, in terms of functions and usability, must be collected and validated. Metrics must be established to measure how a system might meet them. Relationships among these needs should be determined, along with relative priorities and resource limitations, to develop the system requirements. Existing competitive or candidate systems may also be evaluated through market analysis, usability testing, or reverse engineering. [Compile and relate all needs]

People

The team developing the specification must collect and evaluate needs from a number of sources. Workers, managers, and possibly temporary workers must be involved in the development of requirements. The needs of actors who are not users of the system, but will be affected by it, must also be determined. The team must consider the impact of the new system on the existing organization, departments, and teams, as well as the image the company wishes to project to its potential customers and to the public at large. System developers may be consulted to help determine technological possibilities and constraints in this phase, but they must not be allowed to impose a technological solution at this stage.

It is counterproductive to simply automate current operations without careful analysis and justification. Often "the way things are done" become system requirements by default. The specification development team must determine the value of each task or requirement. [Justify retained methods]

Information

Both functional needs and usability requirements must be addressed in the specification process. For this purpose, usability includes both initial learning and long-term operating issues. User needs may be collected using a variety of tools, including: user satisfaction surveys; diagnostic surveys of the existing system; requirements surveys for the proposed system; role-playing exercises; interviews; and work group sessions.

Data collection tools that may be useful in this phase include audio-visual equipment to record interviews, job practice, and laboratory simulations; and equipment for direct database input from the point of observation.

The current system requirements should be maintained in a central repository. The idea is to prevent inconsistent versions of the requirements from causing problems. A networked database system may be an appropriate tool for this purpose. After new data is collected, the current requirements must be reassessed to prevent conflicts and amend priorities.

Timing

The specification phase may be started when a particular problem has been identified and a strategy is clearly stated. It is finished when the users and management are satisfied with the design. This is likely to be a cyclic relationship. User satisfaction is the most desirable evaluation standard for moving between stages of the development process. Project dates or technically based criteria are, at best, indirect measures of the effectiveness of a software development project. The next phase, design, may be initiated when the first set of valid, prioritized, and coherent requirements exists. Early design work may begin before the specification process is completed, but the designers must be flexible and allow for changes to the requirements.

Design

Goals

The purpose of this stage is to translate the set of valid requirements into a number of design options and select the most appropriate design to meet the users needs. The methodology and tools used must support the company's social policy, and should not constrain human-cantered design.

Process

Initial models need not be fully functional, but should allow user evaluation of the interface. System models should be iteratively developed and evaluated to meet usability and functional needs, while satisfying other requirements, such as development schedule and system cost. The evaluation metrics that were defined in the specification stage must be objectively applied to select among design options. [Cyclic model testing]

People

User/designer cooperation is essential. This takes the form of cyclic validation and verification of models and/or prototypes. However, either too much or too little interaction can cause problems for both the designers and the potential users. As the software is developed, the developer must encourage the users to evaluate models or prototypes and suggest ways to make the final product more suitable for the environment in which it will be used. Features that seem intuitive to a software developer may be confusing to a user, while features that are obvious to the user might not occur to the developer. [Continue active user participation]

The system designer must have a clear and complete perspective of the user environment. External customer interactions with the user and the system must be considered. For example, a sales support system that requires a postal code or telephone number to be the first data item input (before the client's name) makes it difficult for a sales representative to establish a personal rapport with a potential customer. [Designer's view of the task]

Information

Design and build tools tend to constrain the design process, so the project management team must ensure that the tools, techniques, and methodology are evaluated. This is accomplished by examining successes or failures of systems developed using particular tools. Some criteria for such an evaluation are: usability of the tool, tailorability, adaptability, user locus of control, and skill enhancement provided in the system. [Evaluation of design tools]

Timing

The design phase may begin with the first coherent set of validated requirements. It may be conducted concurrently with parts of the specification phase, requiring flexibility in the design process. Design ends when users are satisfied with a prototype or implemented system.

Bibliography

Clegg, C., People and Computers: How to Evaluate Your Company's New Technology, Chichester, Ellis Horweed, Ltd., 1988.

Mumford, E. and D. Henshall, A Participative Approach to Computer Systems Design, London, Associated Business Press, 1979.

Mumford, E., Systems Design for People, Computers and the Manager, Book 3: Economic Evaluation of Computer Based Systems. Manchester, National Computing Centre, Ltd., 1971.

Group C

Edited by Robert Gassman

The CIM Institute, Cranfield Institute of Technology, Cranfield, Bedford, MK43 0AL, England

Specification

People

Have a 'suggestion system' that enables people to identify problems or symptoms within the organisation. Provide a framework which will enable suggestions of people to be recognised and implemented. Reward people that are the most active in this process and that go 'beyond the call of duty'. [Empowerment of people]

Continually verify, validate and improve the ability, efficiency and social interaction capabilities of the organisation. [People as the feedback control of the organisation]

The top management must have a strong commitment to initiate and support the specification of the system [Emphasis on the importance of the top management in the change process]

The specifications should be done by the team assigned to the project. The size of the team should be from 4 to 8 members. The team should consist of technical experts, a leader and the users of the system. Possibly a guest developer or consultant may be a member of the team as a facilitator. The team must work on the project full-time. The team must have their own work area, that is separate but nearby the production area. Identify the profile of the team responsible for the next stage in the design process [Project team structure and process]

Define a 'code of practice' of the organisation that includes the mission, goals and generic rules. The 'code of practice' must be dynamic, implying that it is to be continuously reviewed and reassessed according to changes in the environment. [Promotion of organic, people based organisation]

Carry out social studies to gain an impression of the characteristics of the people in the organisation. These studies would be used to contribute to the development of teams and the relationships between people. [Social compatibility]

Consult external users and other sources (technical journals, symposiums and exhibitions) to obtain views of people in similar industries to help obtain ideas regarding the requirements of the system. This will help to create a rich exchange of views and ideas, and to benefit from the experiences of other. External users may be consulted, for example, by conducting a marketing survey about the features of a product along with their preferences. Internal users should compare the requirements of the system against their current skills and identify the need of further skills. The users should determine what benefits they want from the system and include these in the requirements. [Managing the contributions of people]

Technology

Define a common platform (Hardware and Software) that enables the handling of information. For example the specification team must use the same operating system and word processor for producing documentation. Wherever possible electronic media should be used to exchange information. For example use e-mail instead of conventional mail. Just identify the features of the technology that may be used. Do not select any equipment because it may constrain the development of the proposed system. [Compatibility and simplification]

Information

Identify a person responsible for editing and for controlling the different versions of every document produced. Keep records as accurately as possible and store information in an accessible, common database. Always keep a second copy of all information. Present the information clearly and professionally and define a common format for all the documentation. To aid clarity use graphical descriptions, annotated with a formal language. For instance, use data flows and communication diagrams. [Information control]

'Live' with the users wherever possible in order to collect information for the specification. Conduct structured interviews and distribute questionnaires for gathering specification information. [Managing the contributions of people]

Process

Define a schedule for the specification stage with checkpoints for reviewing the completed work with the users and stakeholders of that system. [Project management]

Define the most important functions that must be performed by the system, using predefined metrics. For example, the number of products, the quantity of each product, the number of working shifts and the number of items per delivery. [System performance validation]

Compare the fixed costs (machines, energy, lighting and buildings) and variable costs (training and system development), against the benefit each function provides. The benefits may be viewed in terms of time (operation or delivery), quality (integrity of product and perceived quality by the user) and environmental impact (pollution and energy used). [Cost-benefit evaluation]

Goals

Ensure that the system will fit into the needs of the business. For example, if a new product is coming out in six months time, the system must have been integrated and accepted by the company beforehand. [System compatibility with business]

The specifications must identify that there is a need for diversity and flexibility in the proposed system. The specification should enable the building of a functional model of the system. Do not try to get a 'perfect' specification first time. The generation of the specification is an iterative process which must be reviewed throughout the course of the development of the system. [Evolving the specification]

Implementation

The implementation stage should ideally begin as soon as possible, during the design and build stage. [timing]

People

Conflicts of interest must not be overcome in isolation. A 'systems' approach involving all stakeholders and conflicting parties should participate in any mediation. Stakeholders should describe (or agree on) certain rules which may be used to facilitate mediation and satisfaction of all parties. [Tackling internal conflicts]

The communication between users, developers and organisation must be co-ordinated to facilitate the sharing of current information. The stakeholders should consider all the needs of different departments, by organising into interdisciplinary meetings. They should agree that the system is correct only when it meets the agreed specifications. They should not be allowed to work independently. [Interdisciplinary problem solving]

The developers should observe the users, record and evaluate problems and assess the usability of the system. They should also educate and inform the users, and advise and steer organisation change. There should exist a 'hand in hand' approach to problem solving: close co-operation between users and developers. This means that the developers should not impose a solution upon the users but rather identify each problem and solve to the satisfaction of all parties. Evaluation is carried out until the stakeholders perceive that the system meets the agreed specification. They may not force the users to adapt to perceived errors in the system. The users should operate the system thoroughly in order to identify any problems, and should actively participate in the implementation of the system. Technical assistance should be available during the course of implementation. A degree of technical knowledge should be transferred to the users in order to develop ownership and transparency of the system. ['Hand in hand' development]

The culture of the company should absorb the new system. 'Absorb' in this context means that the system should adapt to the company to adhere to the traditions and culture of the company. Likewise, the company should try to adapt to the system to ensure that the system maintains its usefulness. The organisation should behave like a crucial integrating factor of the process of implementation. Factors that may enable the organisation to obstruct the system should be identified as early as possible and overcome. [System-organisation compatibility]

Technology

Allow the users to arrange and organise physically the technology (tools) to satisfy the physical environmental needs. This creates a personalised environment which helps to promote a feeling of ownership. The technology should be changed if it is not suitable, and software should be adapted to the needs of the users.

Information

The information on the system may be collected using any of the following techniques: interviews, tracer studies, discussions, time and motion studies, video, measuring the number of errors of a system and its users (for example poor software design) and the 'crisp packet approach' (this may be used to help assess the likelihood of bottlenecks in the information system). [REF: *Human Centred Approach For The Design And Implementation Of Computer Systems*, Kozar, K.L. (1989), N.Y.] [Information gathering]

There should be a common store of information with an agreed format. Do not set fire to important documents. [Information storage]

Process

A system may be implemented using one of the following approaches: full implementation throughout the company, implementation in stages or steps, or for a trial period isolated from the rest of the company. To minimise the risk and to facilitate the management of the change process, it is advisable to adopt the latter, more experimental approach. This way one may test for system correctness. The system should be implemented ensuring that there is minimum disruption and in a form that represents the state of the system which will exist when it is fully implemented. All stakeholders should be consulted to discuss the measured impact approach. [Implementation format approach]

Goals

The goals for implementing the system should include tangible (quality, money, time and delivery performance) as well as intangible benefits (greater responsiveness, morale, improved atmosphere, etc.). The implementation of the system should encourage a co-ordinated workforce, ensure the satisfaction of the stakeholders and involve continuous communication between stakeholders with continuous feedback. Do not try to get a perfect implementation at the first attempt. Be realistic and do not consume too much time tackling insignificant details. [Goal selection]
The table summarises some aspects that must be considered in the different development stages of a HCS:

	People	Technology	Information	Process
Specification	Determine needs of: 1. Customers/ Market 2. Users 3. Organization 4. Developers	Needs created from 'process' specification	Collection: ● Interview ● Live with ● Observations ● Questionnaires Presentation: ● Transparency ● Computer ● Video ● Statistics Storage ● Folders	Methodology ● Identify relevant objects ● Primary, Secondary, Tertiary users ● Object Classification (ref. Booking Office Example)
Design	● What people need to know to operate the system under different conditions ● Training: Who?, What? How? ● Reflective Training Programme	Supports the process: the tools for people to use.	● What? Form? Source? Correctness? Accuracy? Collection (Frequency), Responsibility ● Awareness of the input role	● Helical Approach ● CATWOE (P, I, O) ● CARDBOARD (S/W)
Build	● Organise in a Stable Team ● Users estimate performance of the system ● Should have champion	Supports the process	● Based on specifications Incorporates feedback of users ● Collected from users	● Design and build simultaneously ● Have a prototype test quickly ● Evaluate prototype with the users
Implementation and Evaluation	● Users informed and trained Refine user help functions ● Have a support team to help users	Supports the process.	● Suitability of training ● Useability of system.	● Staged implementation ● Periodic review against metrics

Group D
Strategies for Successful CIM System Design and Implementation

Edited by Angela Martin

Dept. of Mechanical, Manufacturing and Software Engineering, Napier University, Edinburgh, EH10 5DT, Scotland.

Introduction

It is recognised that complex automated production systems must be well designed if the benefits they offer are to be fully realised. There has been considerable interest in new approaches to the process of system specification and design, particularly as recent evidence suggests that many implementations have yielded less than optimal results. More rigorous consideration of human factors and the use of multi-disciplinary teams are seen as ways of improving the situation, especially when used in conjunction with sophisticated data capture and system design techniques. The following article outlines some recommendations for effective systems development as derived by a multi-disciplinary team comprising engineers, computer scientists and human factors experts.

In order to discuss the development of human-centred computer systems (HCS) we must start by defining the type of systems of interest. The work of this group has focused on automated production systems: we shall take this to mean computer integrated manufacturing (CIM) systems which may comprise several elements such as computer aided design (CAD), computer aided process planning (CAPP), and computer aided manufacture (CAM). Such systems are now seen as being of *strategic* importance to the organisation rather than simply providing functionality in some operational area.

We start with the basic premise that fully automated CIM systems do not work well, at least in their present form. One possible diagnosis is that there is a mismatch of the human and machine elements of the system, the system being considered to comprise the manufacturing equipment (e.g. CNC machines), the computer (hardware and software), and the human. (Note : others have defined the system in more complex terms. Ramanathan views it as comprising four elements : technoware, humanware, inforware, orgaware.) This may result in systems which do not have good usability, usability being defined by Battison as *"the sum of the characteristics that make a product easily understood, easily used and effective"*. Poor usability leads to higher system development and operating costs, as well as decreased operator satisfaction.

In a human centred manufacturing system the human is considered to be the most important system element as s/he is the creator of the design concept. The role of the production machinery and computer equipment is to function as a set of tools which the human operator may utilise to assist him/her in the process of transforming this design concept into a physical reality. At a basic level, the HCS approach helps to ensure that these tools suit the operator and may therefore be used effectively, but it may have greater significance as a motivating factor which releases the human element of the system to higher levels of creative performance. Thus it may be argued that the best type of CIM systems are actually those that have been developed as *anthropocentric* production systems (APS).

Strategy

Definition

A strategy may be defined as a way forward rather than a detailed plan. Generation of a strategy is normally preceded by an analysis of the current state and articulation of the vision and goals which define the future state. Strategies are characterised by long time scales, uncertainty, risk , as well as importance to the overall enterprise.

Although the concept of corporate strategy is a familiar one, it is important to recognise the need to develop strategies for sub-systems of the wider organisation, e.g. the manufacturing strategy, the information systems strategy.

Obstacles to Technical Strategy Creation

It would appear that the reticence of technical staff to get involved in strategy development (and/or the reluctance of their managers to allow them to participate) is part of the problem in ensuring that technical decision-making is effective and set in its proper organisational context. Some of the blame for unsatisfactory computer system implementation can also be attributed to senior managers who do not have a realistic view of the complexities and limitations of computer systems. In particular, there is a commonly held and mistaken idea that computers have the inherent ability to solve an organisation's problems without much human intervention and planning. This leads to the view that a simple purchase is all that is required, therefore computer systems strategy development is unnecessary and wasteful of management time.

HCS Strategy

Consideration of HCS development rightly belongs within the strategic considerations of the organisation. Human factors are considered at corporate level as a matter of course for all other areas, usually under the heading of employee relations, but should not be neglected within specific areas such as computer system development.

Opponents may argue that an HCS strategy is simply philanthropic and that modern industry, particularly when struggling in the depths of recession, has not got the time or the money to consider it. It may be worth asking whether this is a dangerous position to take, particularly if we believe that people are the only organisational resource to appreciate with time, and that the quality of working life must be at least considered alongside, if not before, profit.

A stronger, or at least more popular argument for HCS may be that experience has shown that the anticipated benefits (specifically in terms of productivity) have not been fully realised and that a different approach is needed to release the potential of automated production systems. Failure to adopt a different approach may result in the organisation "putting all its eggs into the one basket" of technology, only to see them broken as the neglect of human factors leaves a vulnerable technocentric system.

Thus an HCS strategy may comprise statements which affirm human supremacy in the workplace, and recognise that the computers should be implemented in such a way as to enhance human skill and improve both operational procedures and the working environment. It is unlikely that such a far-reaching strategy could be developed at one stroke and is therefore best seen as an iterative process, with flexibility and continuous improvement as key features.

Representatives of as many as possible of the affected staff should be involved in strategy development and its realisation. This is facilitated by flat rather than multi-layered organisations. In fact, strategy development could utilise a star configuration, where several groups sent representatives into the core strategy determining group. This should result in a strategy which is user-oriented and users which are strategy-aware.

Particularly as the strategy is centred on humans, it is important that the communication of the strategy and all associated information to the people involved is well thought out. There should be transparency within a structured horizontal and vertical information network, and this should provide speed and precision of input and feedback. Computers, with their increasing array of communication tools, could provide useful assistance in this area, e.g. through the use of electronic mail. Such a system would provide an increase in sources of information and allow for simultaneous collection of that information. Computer systems used for this process will need to have sufficient memory capacity to handle the transactions, distributed facilities and appropriate user interfaces to support ease of updating.

Technology in the Human Centred Organisation

Technological determinism is a philosophy where the way ahead is mapped out by the developments in technology, and this technology is adopted unquestioningly. This is not seen to be the best way to implement systems as it does not give due regard to the specific circumstances of the individual organisation and how these needs may effectively be matched to the technology available. Stubborn rejection of what technology offers is a recipe for commercial disaster, but rather the middle ground may be seen as offering a solution which offers the benefits of technology as long as appropriate systems are selected and sensibly implemented. When both technical and human aspects are considered as in, for example, the "dual design" method, then a balanced system should result.

Specification of Requirements

General

The goal of the system requirements specification stage is to build a sound foundation for the development of a system which is efficient, effective, facilitates a higher level of productivity and exhibits greater system usability.

Before embarking upon this there is a need to know the organisation, - its culture, how it works, policies, business objectives, current corporate strategy. There should be understanding of the financial situation of the organisation and the implications for system development. (It should also be remembered that there may be difficulties with calculating return on investment for some complex computer systems.) On a more detailed level, information should be gathered on other software and software development methods used within the environment.

Users are often disappointed in the delivered systems and one reason for this is inaccurate specification of user requirements. It is perhaps unkind to imply that deficiencies in system specification are always the users' fault as it is often the case that the people for whom the system is intended are left out of critical stages of development and are not adequately guided in stating their requirements by the computer professionals even when they are asked to participate. Both these points need to be addressed in order to improve the situation: this would involve not just a new methodology, but a change in attitude by all concerned. (Note : Some helpful advice is given in British and ISO standards such as BS 6719 "British Standard Guide to Specifying User Requirements for a Computer Based System" and BS 5515 "British Standard Code of Practice for Documentation of Computer-Based Systems".)

People

Knowledge and skill are both required in order to specify appropriate systems and in many cases, particularly in small or medium sized enterprises, there may not be sufficient in-house expertise. Of course, this may be hired in the form of consultants although it is important to recognise that this may bring its own problems. What the consultant has to offer by way of computer system and applications expertise s/he lacks in terms of knowledge of that particular organisation, its culture, its procedures and its people. Overcoming this obstacle takes time, requires attention to communication procedures and costs money. It is rarely seen as easy.

Once the organisation's objectives and constraints have been defined the system developers have the responsibility of working with them. So, if a human-centred approach is deemed appropriate, the organisation will state this and may impose this stipulation contractually. As part of this they may request a human factors expert on the consultancy team.

The whole process must be effectively steered, preferably by a team of people representing all the affected areas within the organisation; this team should include senior management. The future users of the system should also be represented; this may be complex as users may be categorised as primary, secondary or tertiary and have other distinguishing characteristics. The team would normally be led by the system developers who would be expected to come up with the main ideas. Provision must be made for effective team communication. Perhaps the services of an ethnographer could be useful in helping analyse the environment and implement effective communication strategies.

Methodology
The aim is to develop user requirements specification methodologies which are efficient, reliable, cost-effective *and flexible* enough to be adaptable for different situations. Such methodologies should include the means to create truly human-centred systems, while bearing in mind the economic and industrial realities.

The current emphasis is on multi-disciplinary team working, close collaboration with user groups, and utilisation of hardware and software tools to support the process. These features are seen in the new methods are being developed, such as "Co-operative Requirements Capture".

Any methodology must look in detail at effective ways of gathering information, e.g. selective use of interviews, more extensive use of well designed questionnaires, electronic mail, observation (including video recording), and protocol analysis, where the operator behaviour is recorded along with operator comment. Innovative techniques include computer supported collaborative working (CSCW), where team work is conducted via a networked computer system. A means of clearly presenting this information to both development staff and users is required. Perhaps multi-media could be useful here.

Timing
Pressure to minimise the importance of the specification of requirements stage will often be felt and must be resisted, as it is vital to be clear about the objectives at the start of the project. However the financial realities should be borne in mind and every effort made to structure the process well and control the time spent.

Design and Build

Collaboration
The notion of team working and participation of users at various levels which was developed in the requirements specification stage must be continued within the design and build phase. The main players are the system developers, although these must frequently co-opt others from the organisation as required. If it has not already done so, the team may also consider including a human factors person to specifically address areas such as ergonomics and usability.

Good project management is vital for effective team working and appropriate planning tools and techniques should be fully utilised to structure and control the design process and keep the task on target. This is particularly important where teams are working independently on different modules of a large project. It would also seem important to carefully plan team composition and size in order to facilitate clear and productive communication.

The methodology and technology must allow for easy input of ideas to the design process and efficient storage of these for access by other participants. A speedy and frequent feedback system is required in order to report progress to all concerned, allow the design to be further refined, and inform participants about how their ideas have been incorporated.

Design Process
Computer aided software engineering (CASE) tools will normally be used to generate the essential design documentation, and prototyping and simulation tools for system mock-ups. Rapid prototyping is an important aspect of the process and may be assisted by the use of hypermedia.

The aims of the process are to produce software which has the following characteristics :

- Easy to understand
- Easy to maintain
- Has reusable code
- Allows inheritance
- Allows information hiding
- Facilitates modularity

Object oriented design (OOD) methodology promotes better understanding, cleaner design and maintainable system and reusability. Participatory design (PD) and joint application design (JAD) represent a move towards more collaborative practices within the software design process. Object oriented CASE tools may then be used for development.

The result of following such a process should be greater human satisfaction with the design process and better system design due to greater human input.

Concurrent Engineering
It is worth mentioning that the principles of concurrent engineering (CE), which are utilised for product and manufacturing system design, are very similar to those discussed in connection with human centred systems design. At least some of the aims of these approaches seem to be shared, i.e. improvements of the quality of the delivered product and in system effectiveness, as are some of the methods, e.g. collaborative working, multi-disciplinary teams, computer-supported design. It would seem that HCS and CE should be considered together when contemplating design of CIM systems.

Implementation

The disruption to the operation should be minimised by phased introduction of the system instead of the "big bang" approach. The implementation team should remain flexible in order to accommodate achievement of organisational and operational objectives while integrating the system.

The benefits of involving the users from the specification of requirements stage should be seen here in the form of greater acceptance of the system, higher level of user satisfaction, and a sense of ownership. From the organisation's viewpoint it should have a fully functioning, "fit for purpose" system.

Conclusions

Despite great advances in technology people are still a key factor in effective CIM systems design and operation. While the importance of professional systems designers has not been much disputed, it is now realised that many other people are significant players in the development process, notably the current or future system users. When the needs of all categories of user are thoroughly investigated and incorporated into the system by its developers that system could be said to be a human centred system.

The appropriate starting point for the development of a human-centred computer system is consideration of strategy. Two strategic components must be considered here: the corporate strategy and how computers can help realise business objectives, and the methods and priorities adopted by the organisation in the development of its computer systems.

It would appear that object-oriented design and analysis methods offer the best approach to development of systems of this kind. This, in combination with techniques such as JAD and PD, should result in rigorous design which effectively caters for the needs of all the people involved - system developers, users and stakeholders.

Methodologies should be flexible and adaptable to a given situation. This may mean that it is better to have a set of guiding principles which reflect the key issues and allow system developers to use these like tools in a manner appropriate to an individual organisation.

A tool which has recently received much attention is multi-media and it is felt that this could contribute to more user-friendly computer systems and be helpful for information presentation in the systems development process itself.

Multi-disciplinary teams have much to offer in terms of helping to obtain a more accurate set of user requirements and designing more usable programs by utilising the expertise of each member at an early stage in the systems development process. One important consideration here is group size: complex design tasks are best carried out by small teams of well-briefed individuals whose expertise has been closely matched to the problem and to that of the other team members.

Perhaps development of methodologies and techniques for HCS is only relevant when developers, and perhaps more importantly, stakeholders are convinced that human-centred systems are beneficial. The criteria for determining benefit are usually based on financial and functional issues and may not include consideration of what is best for the people. Experience of advanced CIM systems and the study of the philosophical issues surrounding automation may help clarify the real priorities and point the way to optimum integration of people and computers.

Review of NATO Advanced Study Institute 'People and Computers'

Felix Schmid

Department of Manufacturing & Engineering Systems, Brunel University, Uxbridge UB8 3PH, UK

The NATO Advanced Study Institute 'People and Computers — Applying a Human-Centred Approach to Integrated Production Systems and Organisations' was a great deal of hard work for everybody involved. It was also a success and an excellent and memorable experience. 67 people participated in the event and most devoted two full weeks of their lives to listening, thinking and speaking about the need for a positive approach to the use of computers in production environments. As befits a NATO ASI it was not a one-way transmission of ideas and views but a discussion meeting of people from many different backgrounds. Not only did participants come from a number of very different countries but they also represented a range of different disciplines. In contrast to many other meetings with a very focused topic, this was of necessity a truly interdisciplinary forum.

The Institute began with a programme of lectures which were concerned with the issue of how to build computer supported systems where people were still encouraged to make a substantial and positive contribution to their operation. This was to some extent a departure from the original precept of 'the flexible manufacturing system in which the operator is not subservient to the machine' postulated by Howard Rosenbrock. It was a departure in that most speakers saw the capabilities of people and machines as so different that a discussion of who was subservient to whom did not make sense. The 'tool image' of the computer was asserted but put into the context of serving the business as a whole rather than an individual working in the organisation. However, the discussions highlighted that people were essential to the running of any organisation while the use of computers had to be justified either on a case by case basis or as a systemic solution to an organisation's information or control problems.

Interestingly, the speakers did not deal in-depth with the technology of computer integration and concentrated on the human aspects. The delegates too, in general, were far more interested in these issues. This was, in retrospect, one of the weaker features of the Institute since there are many unresolved problems in the technology field: the interface between user/operator and the machine, the confidentiality of stored data and the prevention of unauthorised access to this information and its misuse, the methods for generating software as well as the currently achievable levels of accuracy, reliability and dependability of software and hardware. All too often, it is still the availability of a new display technology or more computing power which prompts the development of new 'tools' (taken as equipment to assist in the solving of a task, not the narrow computing definition), rather than the need for a particular tool for a specific activity prompting the development of such a tool. The two examples described below were touched upon during the Institute.

The 'mouse' type interface which is being applied universally and often indiscriminately to almost any software can lead to cumbersome and therefore stress and fatigue inducing patterns of interaction. In many cases, keyboards of a standard layout or with reduced or enhanced functionality would be more appropriate. A combination of an analogue, 'mouse'-like interface, with a powerful keyboard type interface could allow operators more choice in the way they handle their tasks. A similar discussion arose over the issue of 'windows' type environments which purport to assist the user by providing a proper desktop. They therefore also present some of the same problems as conventional, wooden or metal, desktops: the risk of clutter and that of the temporary loss of an important note or document. In the 'windows' situation this could mean the obscuring of a safety critical operating interface by less important routine management tasks and reports. In many industrial situations, e.g., power station control, chemical plants and railway signalling installations it is important to prevent such risks.

Set against the criticism of not dealing with technical problems, it should be recognised that the emphasis on people was:

a. chosen by the participants

b. a deliberate attempt to counter the traditional bias towards technology

This critical comment should not detract from the very high quality of the discussions and the wide spectrum of topics covered, from issues of manufacturing strategy in an information intensive environment to the responsibilities of the individual.

Before entering the second block of the Institute, concerned with the key phases of systems development, that is, specification, design, build and test (or evaluation), the delegates were divided into groups based on their backgrounds, their interests and, to some extent, their personalities. Led by Steve Evans and his crew of moderators, the groups then spent a very intensive and tough day being forged into teams through the SCANCO experience. This was a complete success since four of the five teams started to function almost immediately. The fifth team was made up of a group of very capable and determined individuals — the 'professors'!

As a sort of relaxation after this short but gruelling experience the participants joined one of three industrial excursions: to the Boots pharmaceutical plant, a large coal-fired power station and the SPEEDO swimsuit factory. Learning, however, could not be prevented since the three production environments were very different, both in terms of the equipment used and the level of computer integration. From the extreme of the clothing company which relied on some spreadsheets and computer controlled cutting machinery to the power station which offered the operators a dual control interface, that is, manual with individual analogue input and output devices and digital, based on a highly reliable computer system, there was much scope for discussion. The operators of the power plant, for instance, were quite happy to run up the plant by hand or automatically, depending on the commercial circumstances (by hand was faster).

The second block started with a day of interactive learning on the needs and methods of requirements specification for people-machine systems. The manager of the session, Linda Macauley, provided brief lectures, each finishing with a particular task for the teams. The day was therefore livened up by presentations from the teams — there was not always deadly seriousness, but much experience and knowledge was disseminated during this process. On the Saturday morning of the Institute, Andrew Ainger and the tandem of Carys Siemieniuch and Chris Hinde presented their respective approaches to the design and build of software based systems. The group work associated with this session, however, was postponed until after the weekend to give people an opportunity to join excursions to a local steam railway and to these delights of the Derbyshire countryside, Chatsworth House and Buxton, the old spa town in the Peak District.

The design and build phase continued on Monday with very intensive group work, culminating in a most interesting set of presentations in the evening which allowed a comparison of the two approaches adopted by the leaders of this activity. While two teams, those using the CATWOE approach, had reached a pre-defined target, the other three teams presented ideas and innovative concepts — quite in line with the personalities of the two leaders.

The final element of the second block, concerning the evaluation phase of software systems projects was less of a success than the activities covering the prior two phases. This can partly be explained as the result of exhaustion of both the participants and course management but could also be a reflection of the relative lack of clear and well described methods of project evaluation. There are a great many factors and possible forms of measurement to be considered, while there is also a great deal of debate on whether an evaluation phase should exist at all. In fact, this had been one of the key discussions during the preparation of the Institute. Only due to the time constraints and the inevitably linear structure of the Institute had a special session on evaluation and implementation been decided upon. In any real project the task of evaluation must be a constant parallel or integrated activity.

The third block of the Institute was devoted entirely to group work. Originally there had been an intention to develop a handbook for the implementation of human centred computer integrated systems and to test this set of guidelines against some 'real life' cases. However, this proved to be beyond the scope of an ASI and the directors therefore decided to devote the last two and a half days of the Institute to an activity where each team created their own guidelines for the development of human centred systems with an obligation to present these on the last day. This was a success even though it did not result in a coherent 'textbook' type approach.

Perhaps one of the most important results of the Institute was the extension of a key element of Checkland's soft systems methodology, the CATWOE statement.

Normally this includes **C**ustomers, **A**ctors, **T**ransactions, **W**eltanschauung (or world image), **O**wnership and **E**nvironment. The teams added to this the two terms **P**urpose and **S**ocial aspects. While the former is to some extent part of the Weltanschauung it must be stated explicitly since it is one of the distinguishing characteristics in the people versus machines debate. The latter should be included in the Environment but is often not considered fully due to the establishment of too narrow a boundary for the environment in which the system is to operate. The transformation of CATWOE+PS into the new acronym COWPATES was perhaps somewhat facetious but gives a good idea of the friendly atmosphere in which the Institute was run.

It can be asserted that a team-work based approach to learning in an Advanced Study Institute is well worth the additional effort required. However, it can never be guaranteed to be a successful experience throughout since it depends to some extent on the participants and since it demands a great deal of involvement from all the people attending the Institute.

Finally, this is perhaps the right place to reiterate a great thank you to all who participated in the ASI People and Computers and to NATO for supporting this event.

List of Participants

Serpil B. Acar, Department of Computer Studies, Loughborough University of Technology, Loughborough, LE11 3TU, UK.

Andrew Ainger, Human Centred Systems Ltd, Hemel Hempstead, Herts, HP2 4SE, UK.

Frank Ainscow, Ravenswood, Winchester, Hants, SO22 6AA, UK.

Igor Akimov, Institute of Cybernetics, Academy of Sciences of the Republic of Belarus', Minsk, 220012, Belarus.

Mustafa Akkurt, Mechanical Engineering Faculty, Istanbul Technical University, 80191 Istanbul, Turkey.

Selma Akkurt, Mechanical Engineering Faculty, Istanbul Technical University, 80191 Istanbul, Turkey.

Patrick Algoud, Kade-Tech, F-69130 Ecully, France.

Michael Anderson, Computer Science and Engineering, University of Connecticut, Storrs, CT 06269-3155, USA.

Nikitas Assimakopoulos, Department of Information Science, University of Piraeus, GR-185 34 Piraeus, Greece.

Lajos Balint, Natural Science Department, Hungarian Academy of Sciences, H-1051 Budapest, Hungary.

Robbin Battison, Quality Services, IBM Nordic, S-181 09 Lidingo, Sweden.

Mikhail Bayakovsky, Department of Social Informatics, Institute of Youth, Moscow, 111442, Russia.

Robert Bear, Department of Manufacturing and Engineering Systems, Brunel University, Uxbridge, UB8 3PH, UK.

Diana Burkhardt, Applied Sciences, Luton University, Luton, Beds, LU1 3JU, UK.

Mike Cooley, Technology Innovation Associates, Slough, Berks, SL1 1NN, UK.

Simone Creux, Department of Production Technology and Management, Swiss Federal Institute of Technology, CH-8092 Zürich, Switzerland.

Vytautas Cyras, Department of Computer Science, Vilnius University, Vilnius 2600, Lithuania.

Christine Delon, École Centrale Lille, F-59651 Villeneuve d'Ascq, France.

Sacit Dundar, Erdemir EBIM Binasi, Kdz. Eregli, Turkey.

Johannes Ehrhardt, Philtec Communications, D-27581 Bad Gandersheim, Federal Republic of Germany.

Steve Evans, The CIM Institute, Cranfield University, Cranfield, Beds, MK43 OAL, UK.

Oleg Evseev, M.I.E.M., A.I.P.U., Moscow, 109028, Russia.

Jean-Noël Ézingeard, Department of Manufacturing and Engineering Systems, Brunel University, Uxbridge, UB8 3PH, UK.

Zoltan Fekete, Research Institute of Chemical Engineering, Hungarian Academy of Sciences, H-8200 Veszprem, Hungary.

Stefan Fritz, Department of Manufacturing and Engineering Systems, Brunel University, Uxbridge, UB8 3PH, UK.

Robert Gassmann, The CIM Institute, Cranfield University, Cranfield, Beds, MK43 OAL, UK.

Karamjit Gill, Department of Library and Information Studies, University of Brighton, Brighton, BN1 9PH, UK.

Maciej Gorkiewicz, Biocybernetics Department, Medical Academy of Krakow, PL 31-034 Krakow, Poland.

Robert J Grieve, Department of Manufacturing and Engineering Systems, Brunel University, Uxbridge, UB8 3PH, UK.

Stephen Hagan, Applied Computing, University of Ulster, Londonderry, BT48 7JL, Northern Ireland.

T Hayashi, c/o Technology Innovation Associates, Slough, Berks, SL1 1NN, UK.

Katja Heitmann, Hochschuldidaktisches Zentrum, HDZ-KDI, Rheinisch-Westfälische Technische Hochschule Aachen, 52068 Aachen, Germany.

Jan Hensgens, Research Institute of Knowledge Systems, 6200 AL Maastricht, The Netherlands.

Chris Hinde, Department of Computer Studies, Loughborough University of Technology, Loughborough, LE11 3TU, UK.

Markus Iken, Institut für Werkzeugmaschinenbau, Universität Stuttgart, D-70174 Stuttgart 1, Federal Republic of Germany.

Kimberly Jenkins, Department of Chemical and Petroleum Engineering, University of Pittsburgh, Pittsburgh, PA 15261, USA.

Goel Kahen, Kobler Unit, Centre for Cognitive Systems, Imperial College, London, SW7 2AZ, UK.

Jeremy Klein, Scientific Generics, Cambridge, CB4 2PF, UK.

Sergey Kirpich, Institute of Cybernetics, Academy of Sciences of the Republic of Belarus', Minsk, 220012, Belarus.

Milan Kvasnica, Institute of Physical Electronics SAV, Banska Bystrica, SK 97401, Slovakia.

Kate Laskowitz, Department of Organisational Leadership, Purdue University, West Lafayette, IN 47907-1420, USA.

Linda Macauley, Department of Computation, University of Manchester Institute of Science and Technology, Manchester, M60 1QD, UK.

Hamish Macleod, Department of Psychology, University of Edinburgh, Edinburgh, EH8 9JZ, UK.

Janek Mann, Philtec Communications, D-27581 Bad Gandersheim, Federal Republic of Germany.

Angela Martin, Dept. of Mechanical, Manufacturing and Software Engineering, Napier University, Edinburgh, EH10 5DT, UK.

Tim Martin, Bedford, MK41 8DU, UK.

Roy McKelvey, Department of Design, Carnegie Mellon University, Pittsburgh, PA 15213, USA.

Konrad Morgan, School of Information Science, Portsmouth University, Portsmouth, Hants, UK.

Ewa Nowak, Ergonomics Research Department, Institute of Industrial Design, PL 00-236 Warsaw, Poland.

Henrique O'Neill, The CIM Institute, Cranfield University, Cranfield, Beds, MK43 OAL, UK.

Paul Ormerod, Meta-Generics Ltd, Cambridge, CB4 4WS, UK.

Margit Pohl, Technical University of Vienna, A 1040 Wien, Austria.

James Powell, Department of Manufacturing and Engineering Systems, Brunel University, Uxbridge, UB8 3PH, UK.

Janet Rachel, CRICT, Brunel University, Uxbridge, UB8 3PH, UK.

Felix Schmid, Department of Manufacturing and Engineering Systems, Brunel University, Uxbridge, UB8 3PH, UK.

Thomas Schmid, Luegislandstrasse 16, CH-8051 Zürich, Switzerland.

Patrick Serrafero, Kade-Tech, F-69130 Ecully, France.

Marcin Sikorski, Ergonomics Department, Faculty of Management, Technical University of Gdansk, PL 80-952 Gdansk, Poland.

Nigel Slack, Business Management Systems Prog., Warwick Business School, University of Warwick, CV4 7AL, UK.

Carys Siemieniuch, HUSAT, Loughborough University of Technology, Loughborough, LE11 3TU, UK.

Chris Thomson, IBM UK Ltd, Greenock, PA16 0AH, UK.

Lorna Uden, School of Comuting, Staffordshire University, Stoke-on-Trent, ST4 2DE, UK.

James Witzerman, School of Industrial Engineering, Purdue University, West Lafayette, IN 47907-1287, USA.

Werner Wobbe, FAST Programme, European Community, B-1049 Brussels, Belgium.

Ramazan Yaman, Makina MUh. Fak., Balikesir Universitesi, 10100 Balikesir, Turkey.

Konstantin K. Zographov, Disarmament Directorate, General Staff of the Bulgarian Armed Forces, 1000 Sofia, Bulgaria.

NATO ASI Series F

Including Special Programmes on Sensory Systems for Robotic Control (ROB) and on Advanced Educational Technology (AET)

Vol. 1: Issues in Acoustic Signal - Image Processing and Recognition. Edited by C. H. Chen. VIII, 333 pages. 1983. *(out of print)*

Vol. 2: Image Sequence Processing and Dynamic Scene Analysis. Edited by T. S. Huang. IX, 749 pages. 1983.

Vol. 3: Electronic Systems Effectiveness and Life Cycle Costing. Edited by J. K. Skwirzynski. XVII, 732 pages. 1983. *(out of print)*

Vol. 4: Pictorial Data Analysis. Edited by R. M. Haralick. VIII, 468 pages. 1983.

Vol. 5: International Calibration Study of Traffic Conflict Techniques. Edited by E. Asmussen. VII, 229 pages. 1984.

Vol. 6: Information Technology and the Computer Network. Edited by K. G. Beauchamp. VIII, 271 pages. 1984.

Vol. 7: High-Speed Computation. Edited by J. S. Kowalik. IX, 441 pages. 1984.

Vol. 8: Program Transformation and Programming Environments. Report on a Workshop directed by F. L. Bauer and H. Remus. Edited by P. Pepper. XIV, 378 pages. 1984.

Vol. 9: Computer Aided Analysis and Optimization of Mechanical System Dynamics. Edited by E. J. Haug. XXII, 700 pages. 1984. *(out of print)*

Vol. 10: Simulation and Model-Based Methodologies: An Integrative View. Edited by T. I. Ören, B. P. Zeigler, M. S. Elzas. XIII, 651 pages. 1984.

Vol. 11: Robotics and Artificial Intelligence. Edited by M. Brady, L. A. Gerhardt, H. F. Davidson. XVII, 693 pages. 1984.

Vol. 12: Combinatorial Algorithms on Words. Edited by A. Apostolico, Z. Galil. VIII, 361 pages. 1985.

Vol. 13: Logics and Models of Concurrent Systems. Edited by K. R. Apt. VIII, 498 pages. 1985.

Vol. 14: Control Flow and Data Flow: Concepts of Distributed Programming. Edited by M. Broy. VIII, 525 pages. 1985. *Reprinted as Springer Study Edition 1986.*

Vol. 15: Computational Mathematical Programming. Edited by K. Schittkowski. VIII, 451 pages. 1985.

Vol. 16: New Systems and Architectures for Automatic Speech Recognition and Synthesis. Edited by R. De Mori, C.Y. Suen. XIII, 630 pages. 1985. *(out of print)*

Vol. 17: Fundamental Algorithms for Computer Graphics. Edited by R. A. Earnshaw. XVI, 1042 pages. 1985. *Reprinted as Springer Study Edition 1991.*

Vol. 18: Computer Architectures for Spatially Distributed Data. Edited by H. Freeman and G. G. Pieroni. VIII, 391 pages. 1985. *(out of print)*

Vol. 19: Pictorial Information Systems in Medicine. Edited by K. H. Höhne. XII, 525 pages. 1986.

Vol. 20: Disordered Systems and Biological Organization. Edited by E. Bienenstock, F. Fogelman Soulié, G. Weisbuch. XXI, 405 pages.1986

Vol. 21: Intelligent Decision Support in Process Environments. Edited by E. Hollnagel, G. Mancini, D. D. Woods. XV, 524 pages. 1986.

Vol. 22: Software System Design Methods. The Challenge of Advanced Computing Technology. Edited by J. K. Skwirzynski. XIII, 747 pages. 1986. *(out of print)*

Vol. 23: Designing Computer-Based Learning Materials. Edited by H. Weinstock and A. Bork. IX, 285 pages. 1986. *(out of print)*

Vol. 24: Database Machines. Modern Trends and Applications. Edited by A. K. Sood and A. H. Qureshi. VIII, 570 pages. 1986.

NATO ASI Series F

Including Special Programmes on Sensory Systems for Robotic Control (ROB) and on Advanced Educational Technology (AET)

Vol. 25: Pyramidal Systems for Computer Vision. Edited by V. Cantoni and S. Levialdi. VIII, 392 pages. 1986. *(ROB)*

Vol. 26: Modelling and Analysis in Arms Control. Edited by R. Avenhaus, R. K. Huber and J. D. Kettelle. VIII, 488 pages. 1986. *(out of print)*

Vol. 27: Computer Aided Optimal Design: Structural and Mechanical Systems. Edited by C. A. Mota Soares. XIII, 1029 pages. 1987.

Vol. 28: Distributed Operating Systems. Theory und Practice. Edited by Y. Paker, J.-P. Banatre and M. Bozyiğit. X, 379 pages. 1987.

Vol. 29: Languages for Sensor-Based Control in Robotics. Edited by U. Rembold and K. Hörmann. IX, 625 pages. 1987. *(ROB)*

Vol. 30: Pattern Recognition Theory and Applications. Edited by P. A. Devijver and J. Kittler. XI, 543 pages. 1987.

Vol. 31: Decision Support Systems: Theory and Application. Edited by C. W. Holsapple and A. B. Whinston. X, 500 pages. 1987.

Vol. 32: Information Systems: Failure Analysis. Edited by J. A. Wise and A. Debons. XV, 338 pages. 1987.

Vol. 33: Machine Intelligence and Knowledge Engineering for Robotic Applications. Edited by A. K. C. Wong and A. Pugh. XIV, 486 pages. 1987. *(ROB)*

Vol. 34: Modelling, Robustness and Sensitivity Reduction in Control Systems. Edited by R.F. Curtain. IX, 492 pages. 1987.

Vol. 35: Expert Judgment and Expert Systems. Edited by J. L. Mumpower, L. D. Phillips, O. Renn and V. R. R. Uppuluri. VIII, 361 pages. 1987.

Vol. 36: Logic of Programming and Calculi of Discrete Design. Edited by M. Broy. VII, 415 pages. 1987.

Vol. 37: Dynamics of Infinite Dimensional Systems. Edited by S.-N. Chow and J. K. Hale. IX. 514 pages. 1987.

Vol. 38: Flow Control of Congested Networks. Edited by A. R. Odoni, L. Bianco and G. Szegö. XII, 355 pages. 1987.

Vol. 39: Mathematics and Computer Science in Medical Imaging. Edited by M. A. Viergever and A. Todd-Pokropek. VIII, 546 pages. 1988.

Vol. 40: Theoretical Foundations of Computer Graphics and CAD. Edited by R. A. Earnshaw. XX, 1246 pages. 1988. *(out of print)*

Vol. 41: Neural Computers. Edited by R. Eckmiller and Ch. v. d. Malsburg. XIII, 566 pages. 1988. *Reprinted as Springer Study Edition 1989, 1990.*

Vol. 42: Real-Time Object Measurement and Classification. Edited by A. K. Jain. VIII, 407 pages. 1988. *(ROB)*

Vol. 43: Sensors and Sensory Systems for Advanced Robots. Edited by P. Dario. XI, 597 pages. 1988. *(ROB)*

Vol. 44: Signal Processing and Pattern Recognition in Nondestructive Evaluation of Materials. Edited by C. H. Chen. VIII, 344 pages. 1988. *(ROB)*

Vol. 45: Syntactic and Structural Pattern Recognition. Edited by G. Ferraté, T. Pavlidis, A. Sanfeliu and H. Bunke. XVI, 467 pages. 1988. *(ROB)*

Vol. 46: Recent Advances in Speech Understanding and Dialog Systems. Edited by H. Niemann, M. Lang and G. Sagerer. X, 521 pages. 1988.

NATO ASI Series F

Including Special Programmes on Sensory Systems for Robotic Control (ROB) and on Advanced Educational Technology (AET)

Vol. 47: Advanced Computing Concepts and Techniques in Control Engineering. Edited by M. J. Denham and A. J. Laub. XI, 518 pages. 1988. *(out of print)*

Vol. 48: Mathematical Models for Decision Support. Edited by G. Mitra. IX, 762 pages. 1988.

Vol. 49: Computer Integrated Manufacturing. Edited by I. B. Turksen. VIII, 568 pages. 1988.

Vol. 50: CAD Based Programming for Sensory Robots. Edited by B. Ravani. IX, 565 pages. 1988. *(ROB)*

Vol. 51: Algorithms and Model Formulations in Mathematical Programming. Edited by S. W. Wallace. IX, 190 pages. 1989.

Vol. 52: Sensor Devices and Systems for Robotics. Edited by A. Casals. IX, 362 pages. 1989. *(ROB)*

Vol. 53: Advanced Information Technologies for Industrial Material Flow Systems. Edited by S. Y. Nof and C. L. Moodie. IX, 710 pages. 1989.

Vol. 54: A Reappraisal of the Efficiency of Financial Markets. Edited by R. M. C. Guimarães, B. G. Kingsman and S. J. Taylor. X, 804 pages. 1989.

Vol. 55: Constructive Methods in Computing Science. Edited by M. Broy. VII, 478 pages. 1989.

Vol. 56: Multiple Criteria Decision Making and Risk Analysis Using Microcomputers. Edited by B. Karpak and S. Zionts. VII, 399 pages. 1989.

Vol. 57: Kinematics and Dynamic Issues in Sensor Based Control. Edited by G. E. Taylor. XI, 456 pages. 1990. *(ROB)*

Vol. 58: Highly Redundant Sensing in Robotic Systems. Edited by J. T. Tou and J. G. Balchen. X, 322 pages. 1990. *(ROB)*

Vol. 59: Superconducting Electronics. Edited by H. Weinstock and M. Nisenoff. X, 441 pages. 1989.

Vol. 60: 3D Imaging in Medicine. Algorithms, Systems, Applications. Edited by K. H. Höhne, H. Fuchs and S. M. Pizer. IX, 460 pages. 1990. *(out of print)*

Vol. 61: Knowledge, Data and Computer-Assisted Decisions. Edited by M. Schader and W. Gaul. VIII, 421 pages. 1990.

Vol. 62: Supercomputing. Edited by J. S. Kowalik. X, 425 pages. 1990.

Vol. 63: Traditional and Non-Traditional Robotic Sensors. Edited by T. C. Henderson. VIII, 468 pages. 1990. *(ROB)*

Vol. 64: Sensory Robotics for the Handling of Limp Materials. Edited by P. M. Taylor. IX, 343 pages. 1990. *(ROB)*

Vol. 65: Mapping and Spatial Modelling for Navigation. Edited by L. F. Pau. VIII, 357 pages. 1990. *(ROB)*

Vol. 66: Sensor-Based Robots: Algorithms and Architectures. Edited by C. S. G. Lee. X, 285 pages. 1991. *(ROB)*

Vol. 67: Designing Hypermedia for Learning. Edited by D. H. Jonassen and H. Mandl. XXV, 457 pages. 1990. *(AET)*

Vol. 68: Neurocomputing. Algorithms, Architectures and Applications. Edited by F. Fogelman Soulié and J. Hérault. XI, 455 pages. 1990.

Vol. 69: Real-Time Integration Methods for Mechanical System Simulation. Edited by E. J. Haug and R. C. Deyo. VIII, 352 pages. 1991.

Vol. 70: Numerical Linear Algebra, Digital Signal Processing and Parallel Algorithms. Edited by G. H. Golub and P. Van Dooren. XIII, 729 pages. 1991.

NATO ASI Series F

Including Special Programmes on Sensory Systems for Robotic Control (ROB) and on Advanced Educational Technology (AET)

Vol. 71: Expert Systems and Robotics. Edited by T. Jordanides and B.Torby. XII, 744 pages. 1991.

Vol. 72: High-Capacity Local and Metropolitan Area Networks. Architecture and Performance Issues. Edited by G. Pujolle. X, 536 pages. 1991.

Vol. 73: Automation and Systems Issues in Air Traffic Control. Edited by J. A. Wise, V. D. Hopkin and M. L. Smith. XIX, 594 pages. 1991.

Vol. 74: Picture Archiving and Communication Systems (PACS) in Medicine. Edited by H. K. Huang, O. Ratib, A. R. Bakker and G. Witte. XI, 438 pages. 1991.

Vol. 75: Speech Recognition and Understanding. Recent Advances, Trends and Applications. Edited by P. Laface and Renato De Mori. XI, 559 pages. 1991.

Vol. 76: Multimedia Interface Design in Education. Edited by A. D. N. Edwards and S. Holland. XIV, 216 pages. 1992. *(AET)*

Vol. 77: Computer Algorithms for Solving Linear Algebraic Equations. The State of the Art. Edited by E. Spedicato. VIII, 352 pages. 1991.

Vol. 78: Integrating Advanced Technology into Technology Education. Edited by M. Hacker, A. Gordon and M. de Vries. VIII, 185 pages. 1991. *(AET)*

Vol. 79: Logic, Algebra, and Computation. Edited by F. L. Bauer. VII, 485 pages. 1991.

Vol. 80: Intelligent Tutoring Systems for Foreign Language Learning. Edited by M. L. Swartz and M. Yazdani. IX, 347 pages. 1992. *(AET)*

Vol. 81: Cognitive Tools for Learning. Edited by P. A. M. Kommers, D. H. Jonassen, and J. T. Mayes. X, 278 pages. 1992. *(AET)*

Vol. 82: Combinatorial Optimization. New Frontiers in Theory and Practice. Edited by M. Akgül, H. W. Hamacher, and S. Tüfekçi. XI, 334 pages. 1992.

Vol. 83: Active Perception and Robot Vision. Edited by A. K. Sood and H. Wechsler. IX, 756 pages. 1992.

Vol. 84: Computer-Based Learning Environments and Problem Solving. Edited by E. De Corte, M. C. Linn, H. Mandl, and L. Verschaffel. XVI, 488 pages. 1992. *(AET)*

Vol. 85: Adaptive Learning Environments. Foundations and Frontiers. Edited by M. Jones and P. H. Winne. VIII, 408 pages. 1992. *(AET)*

Vol. 86: Intelligent Learning Environments and Knowledge Acquisition in Physics. Edited by A. Tiberghien and H. Mandl. VIII, 285 pages. 1992. *(AET)*

Vol. 87: Cognitive Modelling and Interactive Environments. With demo diskettes (Apple and IBM compatible). Edited by F. L. Engel, D. G. Bouwhuis, T. Bösser, and G. d'Ydewalle. IX, 311 pages. 1992. *(AET)*

Vol. 88: Programming and Mathematical Method. Edited by M. Broy. VIII, 428 pages. 1992.

Vol. 89: Mathematical Problem Solving and New Information Technologies. Edited by J. P. Ponte, J. F. Matos, J. M. Matos, and D. Fernandes. XV, 346 pages. 1992. *(AET)*

Vol. 90: Collaborative Learning Through Computer Conferencing. Edited by A. R. Kaye. X, 260 pages. 1992. *(AET)*

Vol. 91: New Directions for Intelligent Tutoring Systems. Edited by E. Costa. X, 296 pages. 1992. *(AET)*

Vol. 92: Hypermedia Courseware: Structures of Communication and Intelligent Help. Edited by A. Oliveira. X, 241 pages. 1992. *(AET)*

Vol. 93: Interactive Multimedia Learning Environments. Human Factors and Technical Considerations on Design Issues. Edited by M. Giardina. VIII, 254 pages. 1992. *(AET)*

NATO ASI Series F

Including Special Programmes on Sensory Systems for Robotic Control (ROB) and on Advanced Educational Technology (AET)

NATO ASI Series F

Including Special Programmes on Sensory Systems for Robotic Control (ROB) and on Advanced Educational Technology (AET)

Vol. 116: Control Technology in Elementary Education. Edited by B. Denis. IX, 311 pages. 1993 *(AET)*

Vol. 118: Program Design Calculi. Edited by M. Broy. VIII, 409 pages. 1993.

Vol. 119: Automating Instructional Design, Development, and Delivery. Edited by. R. D. Tennyson. VIII, 266 pages. 1994 *(AET)*

Vol. 120: Reliability and Safety Assessment of Dynamic Process Systems. Edited by T. Aldemir, N. O. Siu, A. Mosleh, P. C. Cacciabue and B. G. Göktepe. X, 242 pages. 1994.

Vol. 121: Learning from Computers: Mathematics Education and Technology. Edited by C. Keitel and K. Ruthven. XIII, 332 pages. 1993. *(AET)*

Vol. 122: Simulation-Based Experiential Learning. Edited by D. M. Towne, T. de Jong and H. Spada. XIV, 274 pages. 1993. *(AET)*

Vol. 123: User-Centred Requirements for Software Engineering Environments. Edited by D. J. Gilmore, R. L. Winder and F. Détienne. VII, 377 pages. 1994.

Vol. 124: Fundamentals in Handwriting Recognition. Edited by S. Impedovo. IX, 496 pages. 1994.

Vol. 125: Student Modelling: The Key to Individualized Knowledge-Based Instruction. Edited by J. E. Greer and G. I. McCalla. X, 383 pages. 1994. *(AET)*

Vol. 126: Shape in Picture. Mathematical Description of Shape in Grey-level Images. Edited by Y.-L. O, A. Toet, D. Foster, H. J. A. M. Heijmans and P. Meer. XI, 676 pages. 1994.

Vol. 127: Real Time Computing. Edited by W. A. Halang and A. D. Stoyenko. XXII, 762 pages. 1994.

Vol. 129: Human-Machine Communication for Educational Systems Design. Edited by M. D. Brouwer-Janse and T. L. Harrington. X, 342 pages. 1994.

Vol. 130: Advances in Object-Oriented Database Systems. Edited by A. Dogac, T. Özsu, A. Biliris and T. Sellis. XI, 515 pages. 1994.

Vol. 131: Constraint Programming. Edited by B. Mayoh, E. Tyugu and J. Penjam. VII, 452 pages. 1994.

Vol. 132: Mathematical Modelling Courses for Engineering Education. Edited by Y. Ersoy and A. O. Moscardini. X, 246 pages. 1994.

Vol. 133: Collaborative Dialogue Technologies in Distance Learning. Edited by M. F. Verdejo and S. A. Cerri. XIV, 296 pages. 1994.

Vol. 134: Computer Integrated Production Systems and Organizations. The Human-Centred Approach. Edited by F. Schmid, S. Evans, A. W. S. Ainger and R. J. Grieve. X, 347 pages. 1994.

Springer-Verlag and the Environment